ATLANTIC

ELEMENTS OF
Physical Oceanography

Dong-shan Wu
1269 Engr. Building

ELEMENTS OF
Physical Oceanography

BY

HUGH J. McLELLAN

Office of Naval Research
Washington, D. C.

PERGAMON PRESS

New York · Toronto · Oxford · London
Mexico City · Edinburgh · Sydney · Braunschweig

Pergamon Press Inc., 44-01 21st Street, Long Island City, New York 11101

Pergamon of Canada, Ltd.,
207 Queens Quay West, Toronto 1, Ontario

Pergamon Press S.A., Villalongin 32, Mexico 5, D.F.

Pergamon Press Ltd., Headington Hill Hall, Oxford
4 & 5 Fitzroy Square, London W.1

Pergamon Press (Scotland) Ltd., 2 & 3 Teviot Place, Edinburgh 1

Pergamon Press (Australia) Pty. Ltd., Rushcutters Bay, Sydney, New South Wales

Vieweg & Sohn GmbH, Burgplatz 1, Braunschweig

Reprinted 1968

Library of Congress Catalog Card No. 65-19982

Printed in the United States of America
2342

CONTENTS

PREFACE

THIS book originated in a set of lecture notes for an introductory course in Physical Oceanography given by the author in the Department of Oceanography and Meteorology at Texas A&M University. The background of the students varied greatly, some being Biologists, Chemists, or Geologists, while others had basic training in Physics and Mathematics.

The intent is to provide a broad look at most of the topics of concern to Physical Oceanography without treating any part of the subject matter completely or exhaustively. The non-physical oceanographer, it is hoped, will gain insight into the physical nature of the environment influencing his chosen studies. The physical oceanographer will be somewhat less than satisfied with the treatment and will wish to read the publications referred to and to follow the suggestions for additional reading.

An attempt has been made to keep the mathematical treatment as simple as possible. For this reason, and because of the intended audience, there are some notable omissions. The concept of vertically integrated equations of motion is introduced to show how wind driven current theory has developed, but no theory is treated in any detail. Energy spectra are introduced in the discussion of waves but nothing is said of how spectra may be obtained, nor is statistical theory covered at all. Tides are discussed only in a descriptive way. Dynamical Tidal theory is mentioned only as a field of study.

The hope is that this panoramic view will stimulate to the detailed investigation of suitably circumscribed parts of the subject matter and yet give the specialist a perspective of how his field of interest fits into the total picture.

The reader will find no new or original material in this book. What I have tried to do is to assemble and discuss the material in a way that I found satisfying. Wherever possible original sources have been quoted even though my own introduction to the material may have been second hand. I feel a great debt to those who first introduced me to the topics covered, especially R. S. Arthur, H. B. Hachey, W. H. Munk, and R. O. Reid. I feel an even greater indebtedness to the students of Oceanography at A&M who have permitted the stimulation of their company in our discussions of these matters.

The Geophysics Branch of the Office of Naval Research has provided program support over the years without which it would not have been possible for me to have the association with the teaching program at Texas A&M.

College Station, Texas HUGH J. MCLELLAN

INTRODUCTION

Although oceanography has a venerable history, it is only in recent years that the term has been widely used and that the general public has been aware that the field exists. The recent spate of publicity has brought the word into common usage but has bred wide misconceptions as to what range of activities is involved. It seems well, therefore, that we should begin by defining what, for the purpose of this book, we will take to be oceanography, and who the oceanographer.

Oceanography is the study of the real ocean, a complex, dilute, solution of extremely large volume within which a variety of chemical reactions are taking place. In response to energy received from, or through, the atmosphere, complex patterns of circulation characterize the ocean, transporting the waters with their dissolved material from place to place. An integral part of the ocean is the amazingly diverse biological community distributed throughout the sea. These life forms at once depend upon, and contribute to, the chemistry of their environment. Their distribution and productivity are determined by the circulation and physical properties. From the remains of the plants and animals are built up the sediments and sedimentary rocks.

Because of the interaction of these physical, chemical, and biological factors, there exists a body of knowledge unique to the oceans which provides a broad background against which the thorough investigator must view his observations in a suitably narrow study of ocean phenomena. Regardless of the problem being tackled it almost always turns out that something of the biology, chemistry, geology, and physics of the ocean must be known if complete understanding is to be achieved.

The people who take the effort to accumulate this broad background and then proceed to devote themselves to the study of a part of the ocean we call oceanographers, and their investigations oceanography.

To the extent to which it is possible to subdivide the field of oceanography, it is conventional to do so according to the basic scientific discipline whose techniques are mainly being exercized and the nature of the data which are being collected and analyzed. Thus we may have "Biological Oceanography," "Chemical Oceanography," "Geological Oceanography," and "Physical Oceanography."

It is with physical oceanography that we shall here be concerned and we shall understand by this the study of physical conditions and physical processes within the ocean.

PART I

DESCRIPTIVE OCEANOGRAPHY

THE primary task which faced, and to a certain extent still faces, the oceanographer, was that of observing the physical characteristics and organized motion of the waters and synthesizing a coherent picture of the nature and circulation of the oceans. It was early preoccupation with this monumental task that led to the designation of ocean studies by the term "Oceanography," which is generically correct. In the next stage, where the physical principle controlling the oceanic processes are formulated, one may argue* that the term "Oceanology" more correctly describes the endeavor.

In these first chapters we will take a look at some of the things we have learned about the ocean and introduce the terminology commonly used to describe them. We will present a grossly simplified picture with only occasional reference to localized or short term variability. At the present stage of oceanography the known complexity increases rapidly with the store of accumulated data. At a meeting held at the University of Rhode Island in September 1963 Henry Stommel made the following statement:

> We used to think of the ocean as being divided into different geographical areas and times of year. We now know that there are other dimensions, whole spectra of periods and scales; entirely different kinds of physical processes happening together. It is no wonder that we are a trifle bewildered when we contemplate future studies of the oceanic circulation.

The student should, however, first look at the ordered gross picture. The complexities will be forced upon him when first he studies a selected region or phenomenon.

* Such arguments are of course pointless since general usage rather than etymology establishes the accepted meaning of our words.

CHAPTER 1

THE OCEANS IN PERSPECTIVE

We study the oceans as a portion of the planet on which we live. As oceanographers we may be led by our very familiarity with the sea, and our tendency to examine data in convenient format, into distorted notions concerning them. We must occasionally back off and look at the whole to avoid giving ourselves and others a view that lacks the proper perspective.

1.1 The Oceans as Related to the Structure of the Earth

Water is far more typical as the exposed surface of our planet than is land, since the sea covers 70.8 per cent of the earth's surface. Kossinna (1921) has computed areas of land and water found between latitude circles that are separated by five degrees. His results are plotted in Fig. 1.1, where the heavy curve plots the land area against latitude. The curve bounding the figure on the right shows the total available area, and dashed curves representing 25 per cent and 50 per cent land are included.

In the North Polar region, we have the Arctic Ocean forming a band that is exclusively water. From 70 degrees north to 45 degrees north we have one of the two regions where land predominates. The relative amount of land decreases southward, being approximately 25 per cent from 15 degrees north to 25 degrees south. South of 40 degrees south the fraction of land becomes almost negligible, culminating in a band between 55 and 65 degrees south where the ocean is continuous around the earth. South of this the Antarctic continent presents the only region completely land covered.

Kossinna's data (which can be obtained from Gutenberg (1951) or Scheidegger (1958)) also make it possible to examine the frequency distribution of elevation of the surface of the solid earth. This is shown in Fig. 1.2 where heights and depths are referred to sea level. The frequency distribution is distinctly bimodal and this constitutes one of the more significant pieces of data in geophysics. It is apparent that deep basins and low lying land are the normal features, and since these do not grade into one another, the conclusion is forced that oceans and continents, as features of the earth's crust, differ from one another in kind rather than in degree.

Another method of presenting the data on elevations shown in Fig. 1.2 is the hypsographic curve shown in Fig. 1.3. This presentation makes the depth of the oceans quite apparent. Fifty-eight per cent of the ocean (41 per cent of the earth's surface) has depths in excess of 4000 m. Extreme elevations and depressions are found over a negligibly small portion of the earth's surface. Some interesting figures are presented below concerning elevations of the solid surface of the earth relative to sea level.

Average Crustal Level	−2440 m
Average Land Level	+245 m
Average Ocean Floor Level	−3795 m
Maximum Elevation	+8882 m
Minimum Elevation	−10,863 m

Tanner (1962), after a more refined analysis of Kossinna's data, suggests that the elevations fall in four classes with distinctive means and Gaussian distribution about the means. The means, and the percentages of the earth's surface involved are:

1. Mean −5.2 km, 50 per cent
2. Mean −4.85 km, 10 per cent
3. Mean 0.3 km, 20 per cent
4. Mean 0.35 km, 20 per cent

The classical concept to explain the bimodal distribution is that of continents, consisting of granitic blocks, which float in a material of somewhat higher density. This concept is strengthened by gravity measurements which show, in mountain regions, values attributable to a deficit of mass rather than otherwise.

Our detailed knowledge of the structure of the

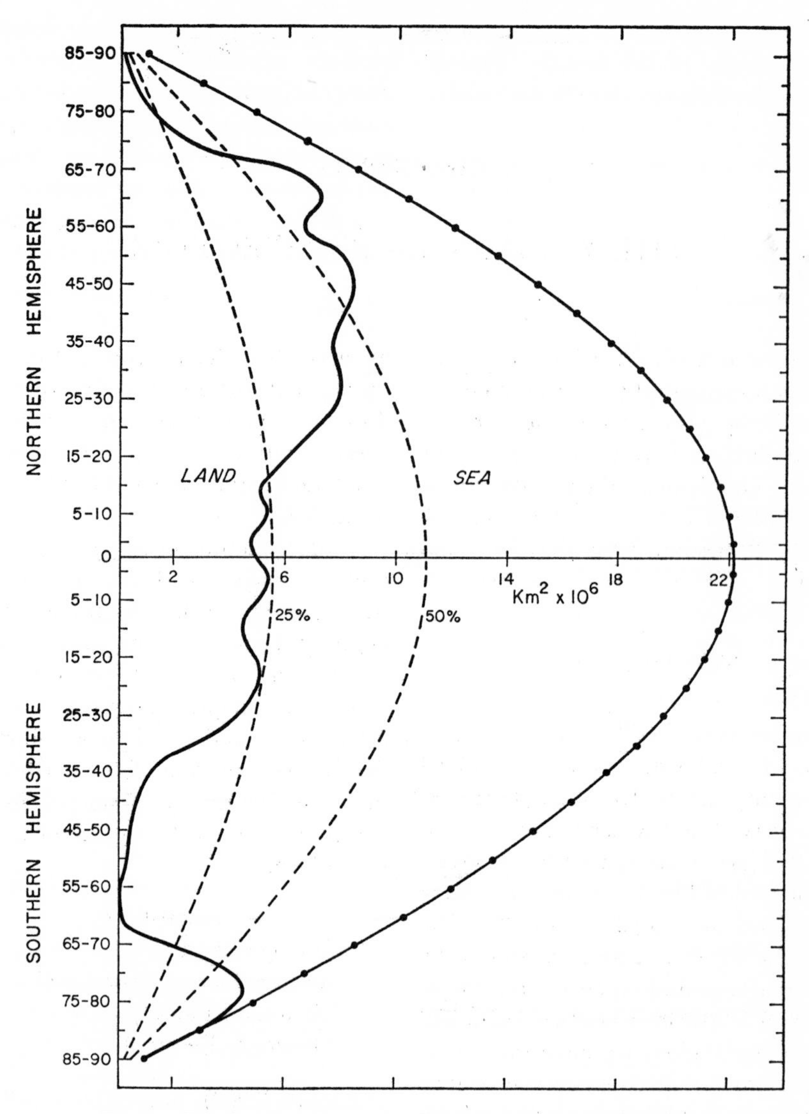

Fig. 1.1 Distribution of water and land areas in five-degree zones.

earth's crust comes mainly from seismology. Inferences can be drawn as to the densities of materials and these can be adjusted to compatibility with gravity data, but the basic observations consist of the travel times, and hence speed, of distortion waves, through the materials constituting the earth.

Figure 1.4 shows a simplified diagram of the structure of the earth's crust in continental and oceanic regions. The layering is according to the speed of propagation of pressure waves. Under the sedimentary layer on the continent, where pressure waves travel with speeds from 2 to 3 km/sec, there is a very thick layer within which speeds increase downward in the range from 4.5 to 6.0 km/sec. Certain evidence points to a distinct layer below this with speeds of 6.6 km/sec. A sharp boundary between these layers may not exist under continents but usually does in oceanic areas where three similar but much thinner layers are observed. Because of technical problems involved in making observations in the transition region, it is not known if these layers are continuous from ocean to continent. Below the 6.6 km/sec layer both in oceanic and continental regions there is an abrupt change to speeds of approximately 8.1 km/sec. This transition is known as the Mohorovicic discontinuity or "Moho" and is taken as the boundary between the crust and the mantle of the earth.

The thick continental blocks, of mainly granitic

material, float, as it were, mostly submerged, in the more dense material of the mantle. Typical mantle depths under continents are 30 km, while,

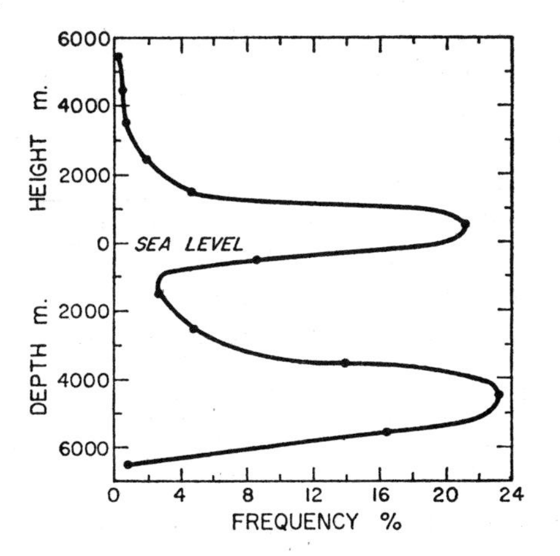

Fig. 1.2 Frequency distribution of elevation intervals of earth's surface.

under the ocean, depths of 10 to 15 km measured from sea level are the rule.

1.2 The Ocean Basins

It is usual to divide the sea into three major oceans—the Pacific, Atlantic, and Indian—in order of size. The three are freely connected at their southern extremes where a continuous band of water circles the Antarctic continent. Early writings sometimes referred to the region of interconnection as the "Antarctic Ocean" or "Southern Ocean" but this usage is now less common. The "Arctic" is sometimes classified as an ocean in its own right, and sometimes as a part of the Atlantic. In

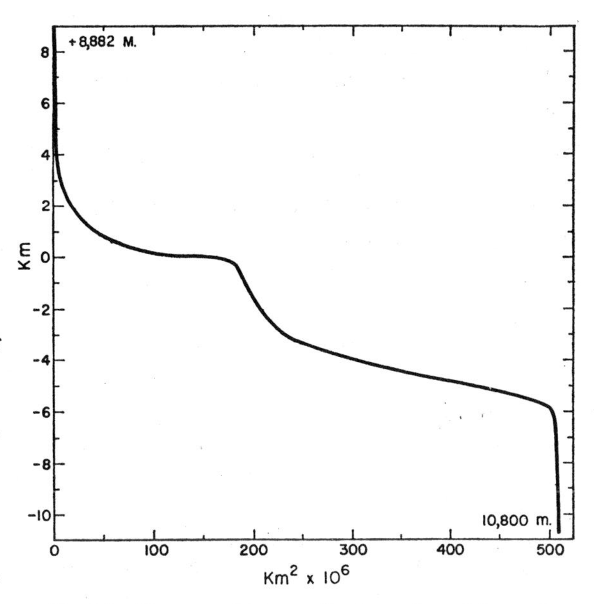

Fig. 1.3 Hypsographic curve for the surface of the earth.

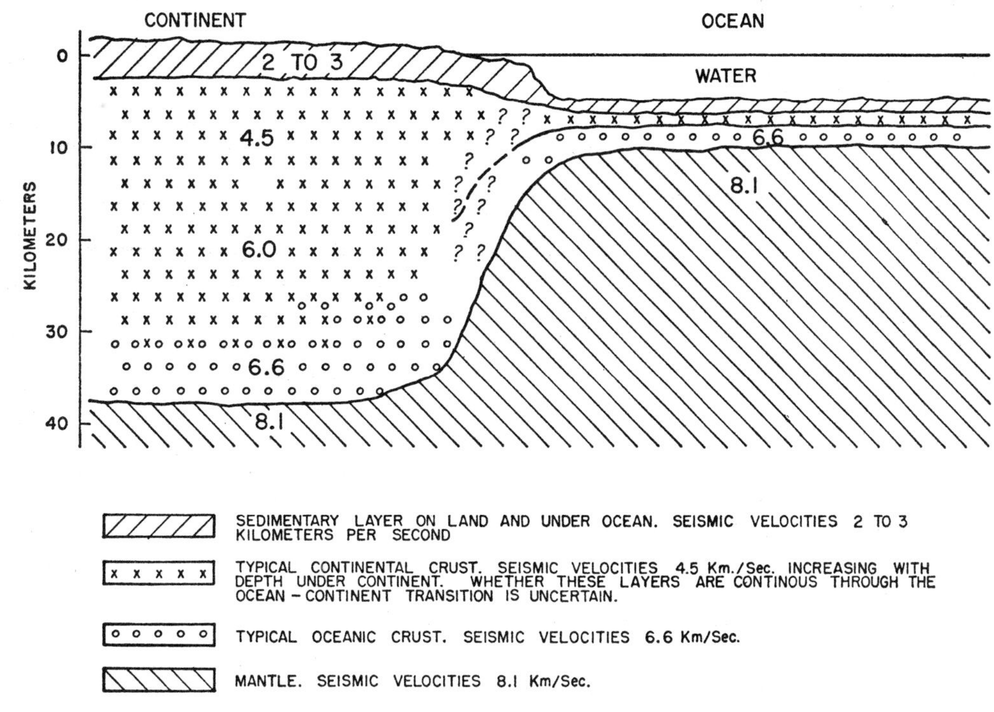

Fig. 1.4 Idealized structure of the earth's crust.

this latter system it is referred to as the "Arctic Mediterranean" and considered to be a feature analogous to the "European Mediterranean" and to the Caribbean and Gulf of Mexico or "American Mediterranean".

Table 1.1 presents some figures on the area, mean depth and volume of ocean regions. These figures originate from Kossinna's (1921) data and some modification can be expected in the light of more recent studies of submarine topography.

The Pacific is by far the largest of the oceans, being equal in area to the Atlantic and Indian together, and containing considerably more than half the total volume. The total area of all oceans, 361.06×10^6 km^2 may be compared to the total area of the planet, 510.1×10^6 km^2.

TABLE 1.1. AREA, MEAN DEPTH, AND VOLUME OF OCEANS AND SEAS

Region	Area (10^6 km^2)	Mean Depth (m)	Volume (10^6 km^3)
Pacific Ocean } Adjacent	165.25	4282	707.56
Atlantic Ocean } Seas	82.44	3926	323.61
Indian Ocean } Excluded	73.44	3963	291.03
Three Oceans Only	321.13	4117	1322.20
Arctic Mediterranean	14.09	1205	16.98
American Mediterranean	4.32	2216	9.57
Mediterranean Sea and Black Sea	2.97	1429	4.24
Asiatic Mediterranean	8.14	1212	9.87
Baltic Sea	0.42	55	0.02
Hudson Bay	1.23	128	0.16
Red Sea	0.44	491	0.21
Persian Gulf	0.24	25	0.01
Marginal Seas	8.08	874	7.06
Three Oceans plus Adjacent Seas	361.06	3795	1370.32
Pacific Ocean } Including	179.68	4028	723.70
Atlantic Ocean } Adjacent	106.46	3332	354.68
Indian Ocean } Seas	74.92	3897	291.94

Our most detailed knowledge of the topography of the ocean floor concerns the region of the "continental shelves". These shallow platforms or terraces fringe the continents and have width varying from a few miles to a few hundred miles. Most shelves display considerable topographic relief though the mean slope is small (0°07′). The outer edge of the shelf is marked by an abrupt increase in slope seaward. This outer edge or "shelf break" is often associated with the 100 fathom contour although this is clearly not definitive. Portions of the shelf terminate at much lesser and much greater depths. Shepard (1963), who gives an excellent description of the feature as a global phenomenon, assigns an average depth to the slope break of 72 fathoms. Water conditions over the continental shelf are characterized by great contrasts and regions of very great biological productivity are common.

Beyond the shelf break the "continental slope" runs down to the abyssal ocean. The slopes vary regionally but average generally between 3° and 6° from the horizontal. The slopes are characteristically cut by valleys and canyons.

About half of the slopes have deep, narrow trenches along the base. These trenches are among the most unstable portions of the earth's crust. The greatest depths in the ocean are associated with trenches at the base of the continental slope off island arcs, examples being the Puerto Rico Trench, the Aleutian Trench, the Mariana Trench, and the Tonga-Kermadec Trench.

When deep sea soundings had to be made with hemp line or wire, the general idea of the floor of the deep ocean was that it constituted a vast featureless plain. This notion has been completely reversed. There are indeed areas of "Abyssal Plain" which are exceedingly flat, but the relief features of the ocean floor are much more impressive than those on the continents. Here sharp features apparently stand without comparable errosive influences to those which work to level the land.

Figure 1.5 shows a bottom profile across the North Atlantic illustrative of the relief that is typical of much of the ocean. The prominent rise in the center is a crossing of the Mid-Atlantic Ridge. This feature runs north and south through the entire Atlantic Basin and forms part of a ridge complex that is continuous through the Indian Ocean and into the Pacific where it is manifest as the East Pacific Rise.

Sharp local elevations appear scattered throughout the ocean though for some reason much more abundant in the Pacific than in the Atlantic. These are termed "Sea Mounts". Some break the surface and constitute ocean islands like Bermuda, Madeira, and the Marquesas. In the Pacific there are a number of ridge formations with island arcs and associated trenches. Some of the sea mounts have very flat sub-surface tops that appear to have been planed off. These are referred to as "Guyots".

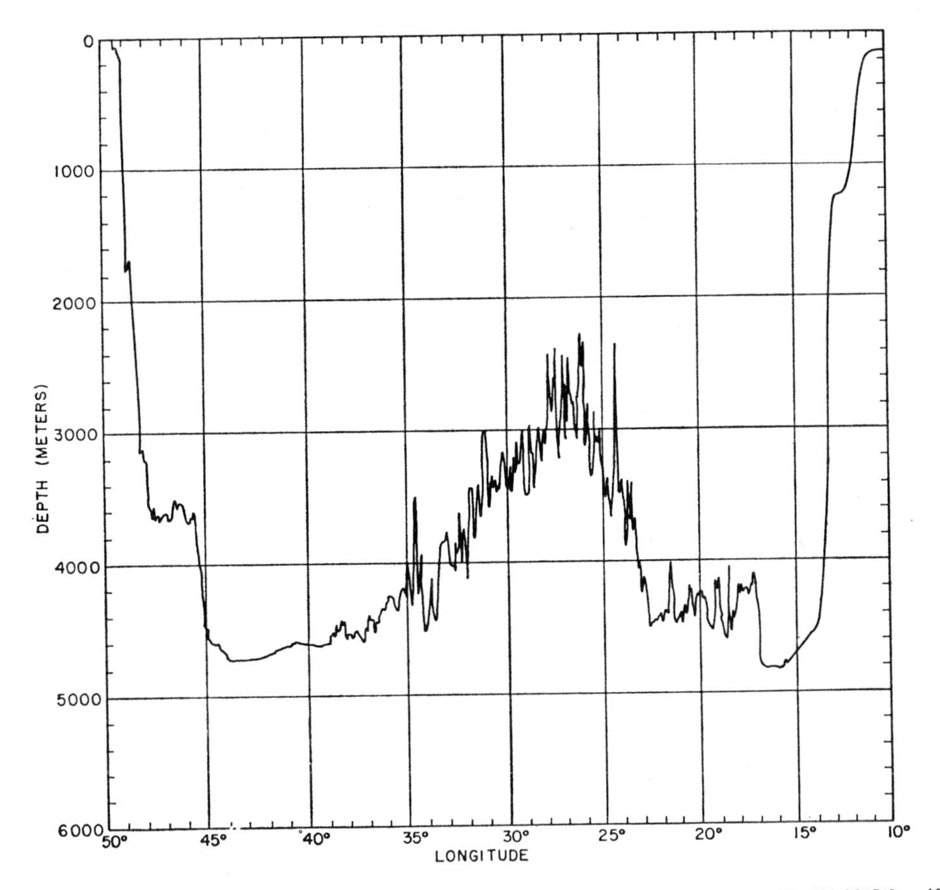

Fig. 1.5 Bottom topography, grand banks to offing of the English Channel 44° 39′ N, 49° 08′ W to 49° 40′ N, 10° 34′ W (after Fuglister, 1960).

1.3 Concerning Scales

It is well here to stop and consider the scale distortion which is usually introduced in presenting oceanographic data. It has been pointed out that the oceans have an average depth of just under four kilometers. This is indeed quite deep. We see that the more we chart the ocean depths the more relief we find there yet, on a globe of any reasonable size, the relief, accurately scaled, would be undetectable.

If one takes a rather sharp pencil in a compass and draws a circle of five inch radius, this could represent the earth with its radius of 6371 km. The pencil line is about thick enough to represent the crust of the earth (30 km) under continents but too thick for the oceanic crust (10 km). The irregularities in the line will be more than great enough to represent the range of relief found over the solid surface of the earth. There is no way of showing the oceans on such a scale but one can put them in perspective as Bascom (1961) has, by realizing that if the earth were a basketball, one would notice that much of its surface was damp.

Horizontal distances are so great over the oceans that in order to make a reasonable representation of data, it is usual to distort the scale. A given distance on a diagram will represent several hundred times as far in the horizontal as in the vertical dimension. Figure 1.5 has a scale distortion of 500:1 and the features observed may well be referred to as basins, valleys, trenches, etc. Yet, spread out as they occur over the curved surface of the earth, it is unlikely that any of these features are actually concave upward.

Figure 1.6 shows the temperature distribution in a vertical section plotted with a not unusual scale distortion. Temperature was being measured vertically every half hour from a ship travelling at 12 knots. Describing what was observed between observations 197 and 198, it is tempting to say that "The isotherms plunge precipitously downward". Yet all one really sees is that isotherms found at

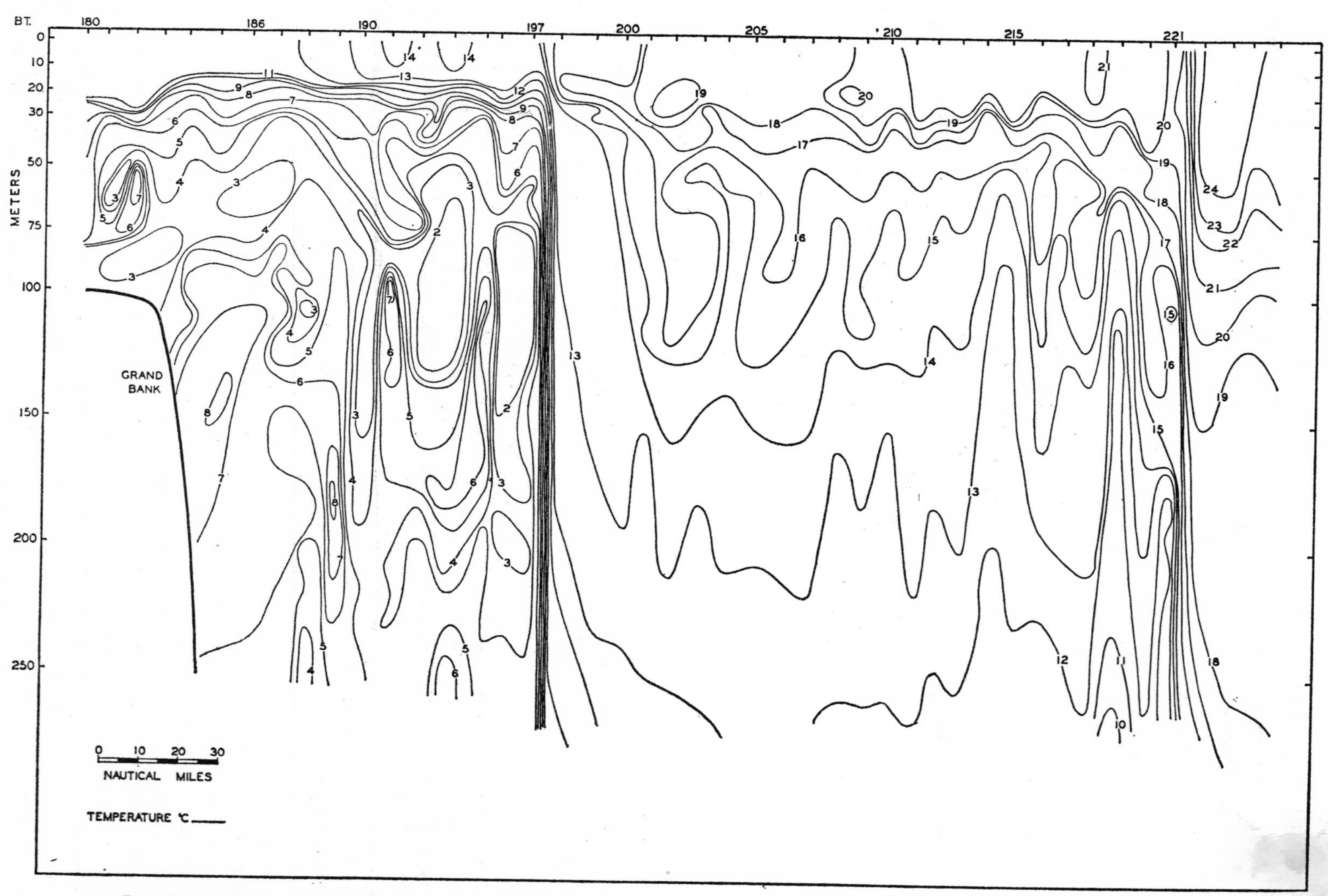

Fig. 1.6 Vertical temperature distribution from lat. 44° 25′ N, long. 52° 30′ W to lat. 39° 32′ N, long. 51° 54′ W on 25 and 27 June 1952.

20 m at 197 were deeper than 250 m at 198. The slope is at least as great as 230 m in six nautical miles or 1/48. That is, the slope represented is at least 1° 10′ from the horizontal.

Thus, the ocean is very deep if we relate it to features on land or extremely shallow if we relate it to its horizontal extent or to the planet as a whole. The problems of scale in the presentation of oceanographic data must be constantly kept under consideration or completely erroneous impressions of what the data show may be obtained.

REFERENCES

BASCOM, WILLARD. *A Hole in the Bottom of the Sea*, p. 25. Doubleday, New York. 1961.

FUGLISTER, F. C. *Atlantic Ocean Atlas*. Woods Hole Oceanographic Institution, Woods Hole, Mass. 1960.

GUTENBERG, BENO (editor). *Internal Constitution of the Earth*, (second edition), p. 314. Dover, New York. 1951.

KOSSINNA, ERWIN. *Die Tief en des Weltmeeres*. Berlin Univ., Institut F. Meereskunde, Veroff, N. F., A. Geogr. Naturwiss. Reihe, Heftg, 70 pp. 1921.

SCHEIDEGGER, ADRIAN E. *Principles of Geodynamics*, p. 10. Springer-Verlag, Berlin. 1958.

SHEPARD, FRANCIS P. *Submarine Geology* (second edition). Harper and Row, New York. 1963.

TANNER, WILLIAM F. Components of the Hypsometric Curve of the Earth. *J. Geophys. Res.* **67** (7), 2840–2843. 1962.

Sources of Additional Information

Physics and Geology. JACOBS, J. A., R. D. RUSSELL, and J. TUZO WILSON. McGraw-Hill, New York. 1959.

Submarine Geology (second edition.) SHEPARD, FRANCIS P. Harper and Row, New York. 1963.

Marine Geology. KUENEN Ph. H. Wiley, New York. 1950.

CHAPTER 2

THE NATURE OF OCEANOGRAPHIC DATA

EACH branch of man's knowledge grows in an orderly fashion. That is not to say that progress is steady and directed. On the contrary, inspiration or whim leads one individual to strike forward and bring off a significant advance in an arbitrary direction; others follow up his work as far as the limitations of the time allow, and science awaits another inspired advance which again leads in an unpredictable direction. Yet each step builds upon the past. This generation speculates from a base of solidly accepted facts that were the wild speculations of earlier generations. A single development determines how the science will progress and the result may be either stagnation or the opening up of vast new fields. Even hindsight can not always say which was the most significant discovery. It is of value, however, to know something of the history of a science, since it can make clear how much of our present posture is the result only of fortuitous events in the past. It is the investigator who frees himself of the shackles of historical thought who makes the big advances.

Each science begins with observation. After observation comes the description of what has been observed, then the correlating of observations and evaluation of patterns which permit generalizations. Next, plausible reasons are sought for the patterns being as they are, and, at the same time, the resulting generalizations are tested by further observations. After some success has been achieved, theories are developed from which phenomena not yet observed may be predicted. Then observations must be devised to check the predictions.

The facts for which we seek explanations are influenced by the kind of observations we have made. The predictions which we make are usually the type that we expect to be able to verify with existing observational techniques. Thus, a science is influenced by the nature of the pertinent data and the techniques of observation available.

2.1 OCEANOGRAPHY IN HISTORY

Man first began to study the ocean very early in history. The usefulness of the sea as a convenient trade route prompted the development of shipping, and study of the new environment was necessary for survival and for profit.

From the point of view of our western culture we look to the Greeks. They, and the Phoenecians before them, had developed a vast marine commerce in the Mediterranean and adjacent seas. They sent expeditions to the East across the northern part of the Indian Ocean. They knew, and took advantage of, the changing pattern of winds and currents, sailing east during the season of the Southwest Monsoon and returning with the advent of the Northeast Monsoon.

A Greek expedition explored the Atlantic Coast at least as far as the British Isles and encountered the large tides of the English Channel. These were properly ascribed to the influence of the moon, although no mechanism of coupling was postulated. Later we find Julius Caesar resting at the English Channel on his way to the conquest of Britain. To him the daily progression of times of high and low water was no mystery, and the secular variation in tidal range as related to the moon's phases was recognized.

The earliest seafarers had a lot of qualitative knowledge about waves. They knew them to be generated by wind either locally or at a distance. They recognized that the wind required a certain "fetch" and a certain duration in order to build up the maximum sea. The protection afforded by a windward coast was understood as was the influence of bottom topography in causing waves to build up and break over shoals and in concentrating wave energy on headlands. It was on into the eighteenth century, however, that a beginning was made on mathematical theories to explain these phenomena.

Crude magnetic compasses were brought to the West from China and served to tell the navigator his direction of travel. Chip logs of one form or another served to measure the speed through the water. It became obvious that ships did not always go in the direction in which they were pointed and that speed through the water seldom tallied with speed over the ground. Thus began the slow accumulation of knowledge concerning ocean currents. This knowledge was largely handed on through apprenticeship, as the trade secrets of navigators, and it is only with the sudden burst of enthusiasm for oceanic exploration toward the end of the fifteenth century that we first find documented accounts of currents.

Columbus discovered the Florida current and recognized it as a strong permanent feature. In 1513 Ponce de Leon wrote a description of it and Peter Martyr published a theory of the origin of the Gulf Stream System that was amazingly accurate, especially if one considers the nonsense that was to be written during the following centuries. By 1519 the Spanish, in their voyages to explore and exploit the New World, regularly made use of the equatorial current and trade winds on the outward trip and returned taking advantage of the Florida current and Gulf Stream.

In 1569 Mercator devised the nautical chart which was to be so useful for navigation, although it was not till 1759 that a suitable chronometer was devised to allow accurate determination of longitude at sea.

In 1770 Benjamin Franklin raised the objection that mail vessels from England were not taking advantage of the abundant knowledge of the Gulf Stream that New England whalers had accumulated. With Timothy Folger he produced a printed chart of the Gulf Stream. The horizontal temperature gradients associated with the edge of the stream were recognized, and Franklin in 1775 advocated the use of surface thermometers as an aid to navigation.

For the systematic treatment of the observations of mariners, we are indebted to Matthew Fontaine Maury who, as a lieutenant in the U.S. Navy, began in 1844 the study of log books from ships plying the world's ocean. He subsequently was instrumental in organizing international co-operation in this matter and in 1855 he published *The Physical Geography of the Sea* as an explanatory text to accompany the wind and current charts constructed from the log book researches. The Pilot Charts issued regularly by the U.S. Navy Hydrographic Office are an outgrowth of this early work begun by Maury.

The latter half of the nineteenth century was a particularly exciting period in oceanography. The problems of fluid dynamics were being tackled by competent mathematicians and new ways to consider oceanic phenomena were being presented. It was becoming apparent that life in the sea was not confined to a shallow surface layer but was found at all depths. Water sampling devices and reversing thermometers were developed in essentially the form used today and many expeditions set out to investigate the nature of the oceans and the life therein.

The classical expedition, which is sometimes referred to as the beginning of modern oceanography, was that of *H.M.S. Challenger*, cruising the World Ocean between 1872 and 1876 under direction of the Royal Society of London. This was preceded by a number of very significant scientific voyages and was followed by a whole series of history-making expeditions. An interesting listing of oceanographic surveys can be found in Bruns' (1958) *Ozeanologie*.

Forchhammer (1865) and Dittmar (1884) published results of chemical analysis of sea water which established the concept of constant ratios of major constituent ions.

Much of the mathematical basis for subsequent physical oceanographic work was laid at this time. The first edition of Lamb's *Hydrodynamics* was published in 1879. In 1885 Mohn developed a formula for computing ocean currents from the slope of isobaric surfaces. The same result was later obtained by Sandstrom and Helland-Hansen (1903) using Bjerknes (1898) circulation theorem. They studied the possibility of obtaining an approximation to the velocity field from an exact knowledge of the density distribution in ocean waters. Ekman's classical paper on wind driven currents appeared in 1905.

The International Council for the Exploration of the Sea was formed in 1902. This organization has been responsible for promoting international co-operation and the exchange of information among investigators concerned with the North Atlantic. It has also promoted the standardization of observational techniques.

The establishment in 1914 of the International Ice Patrol led to the regular practical application of the techniques of physical oceanography to the protection of shipping.

Significant, especially to the history of oceanography in the United States of America, is the founding in 1930 of the Woods Hole Oceanographic Institution and the launching of the research vessel *Atlantis* built for that institution.

2.2 Distribution of Available Data

Our knowledge of the ocean is largely influenced by the methods used in the collection of data. Usually a ship steers along a planned path making surface observations underway. It will stop at a "hydrographic station" and a wire will be lowered overside to which sampling devices are attached. Temperatures will be recorded at a number of depths, and simultaneously water samples will be collected at the same depths and brought on board for analysis. The ship then continues on to the next hydrographic station.

Obviously some realistic limit must be imposed upon the number of serial depths from which samples are to be collected. The distribution of sampling depths is arranged with consideration for the way in which properties being observed are expected to vary. In the upper layers, where wide variations in space and time are common, sampling depths are closely spaced. With increasing depth the waters become more nearly homogeneous and wider spacing of samples can be tolerated. Each investigator selects the depths of sampling to suit his particular need and the area in which he works. To give some uniformity to data reporting and to facilitate intercomparison, the International Association of Physical Oceanographers in 1936 set up standard depths for the reporting of data. These are, in meters: 0, 10, 20, 30, 50, 75, 100, 150, 200, 300, 400, 500, 600, 800, 1000, 1200, 1500, 2000, 2500, 3000, 4000, etc. Because of the problems involved in keeping the hydrographic wire vertical, or of knowing its exact configuration under water, samples are seldom taken at precisely these depths and values interpolated from the observations are reported. In many cases parameters are reported both at "observed" and "standard" depths.

Observations made over an oceanic area in this way must have severe limitations because of lack of detailed information. Sharp vertical gradients are not defined, and there is a practical limit to the horizontal spacing of hydrographic stations. The data also suffer by not being truly synoptic. By the time the ship stops on a station it must be assumed that conditions at the previous station may have measurably altered. In fact, where ships have been held on station for repeated sampling, this has invariably proved to be the case (Seiwell, 1937; Reid, 1956). In the very deep waters, changes, if any, defy detection by presently available methods, but, in regions of marked vertical variations, oscillations with periods less than a day can generally be detected.

It is usual, nevertheless, to treat collectively all observations taken over a region within a reasonably short period of time, and to refer to them as parts of a "quasi-synoptic" survey. In dealing with larger ocean areas it may be necessary to lump all available observations whether taken within the same year or not. The limitations imposed thus by the nature of the data must continually be kept in mind (Defant, 1950).

There have been several attempts to approach synopticity through multiple ship surveys. Notable was "Operation Cabot" (Fuglister and Worthington, 1951) where seven ships worked together to study a small part of the Gulf Stream System.

The unprecedented activity during the International Geophysical Year was an attempt to obtain data for much of the world ocean which had all been collected during one eighteen-month period.

The I.G.Y. program of the various countries making observations at sea eventually spread out over a two and one-half year period. The many ships involved turned in collectively reports from 22,600 hydrographic stations. Although this was a prodigious effort it does not represent an extremely close scrutiny of the sea. Spread out evenly over the area of the World Ocean (3.6×10^8 km^2) this would have been one station per 16,000 km^2 or one station per 4650 square miles. If one allowed 20 samples per station, this would have been a total of 452,000 observation points or one per 3000 km^3 (470 cubic miles).

2.3 Effects of Averaging

Much of the available data on the oceans has been influenced by processes of averaging, or yields desired information only in the form of some sort of average. For example, if, from observations at serial depths, one computes the vertical gradients of such properties as salinity and temperature, they appear much less steep and variable than those which continuous measuring techniques show to exist.

Again there are the data on surface currents,

which have been compiled from the logs of ships. For the most part the ships have been dependent upon astronomical navigation techniques, and were limited to three good position fixes in a day's travel. They can compute only average drift between fixes and, while broad trends are shown, it is not possible to observe narrow strong currents. Similarly when we use the results of hydrographic stations to compute ocean currents from the distribution of mass (Chapter 10), we treat the data as though the observed changes in mass distribution between two stations were spread uniformly through the horizontal separation. Thus, a Gulf Stream of 3 knots velocity might be deduced, but the narrow intense currents up to 6 knots, which may be observed by other means, are obscured by the method.

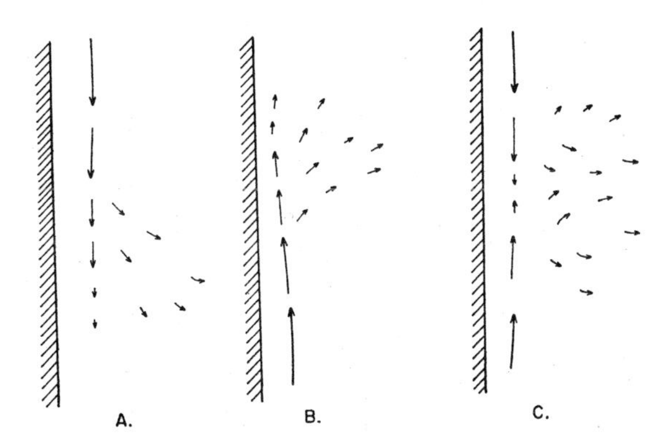

Fig. 2.1 The result (C) of time averaging surface currents where two distinct regimes (A) and (B) alternate.

Still more serious can be the effect of averaging such vector quantities as currents. This is done, for example, in preparation of certain charts which show surface currents averaged from all available observations from a certain month. While these serve a real purpose their use should be tempered by realization of how they are prepared. Take, for example, the current along a straight coast (Fig. 2.1). Suppose that in the month under considera tion two dominant regimes may alternate. In the first, a strong current parallel to the coast spreads out and diminishes with distance while turning seaward. In the second, a strong current from the opposite direction behaves in the same way. The result of averaging all observations will show a region of convergence which may never be observable.

2.4 Interpretation of Observations

Another way in which data can depart from reality is illustrated when the horizontal or vertical field of a variable is plotted on the basis of widely spaced observations. The only substitute for closely spaced observations when contouring is a concept of what the field should be like. Most workers show on such plots the locations of the observations and it is well to consider their distribution when pondering the significance of the result. Fuglister (1955) has given the classic illustration of this (Fig. 2.2) in the temperature field at 200 m depth for a part of the Gulf Stream System observed in August 1953. Here the situation was complicated by closely spaced observations along lines which were separated by great distances. There is no basis for saying any one of the presentations is "better" than the others except knowledge of what this part of the Gulf Stream is really like. Data other than those presented are necessary to provide this knowledge.

2.5 Some Recent Developments

Much of the recent effort in oceanographic instrumentation has been aimed at improving the types of data available. The bathythermograph, in use since 1938, gives a continuous record of temperature against depth for the upper nine hundred feet and can be lowered from a ship underway. The "geomagnetic electro-kinetograph" (von Arx, 1950) provides a continuous indication of surface current transverse to the direction of ship's travel, and a vector resolution can be obtained periodically by executing a jog in the ship's course. Since 1958 limited use has been made of faired chains which are towed behind a ship and have instrumentation to provide virtually continuous temperature records in the horizontal from a number of depths (Richardson, 1958).

A number of groups have been working since around 1950 with instrumented buoys, either anchored or free floating, which can record data or send it periodically to shore stations by radio telemetry (Walden and Franz, 1962). In 1961 a line of anchored buoys was set out from Cape Cod to Bermuda to record a time series of synoptic data on the Gulf Stream (Richardson, 1962). The availability of fixed platforms on the continental shelves has been exploited to maintain arrays of rather sophisticated instrumentation for continuous measurement (LaFond, 1959). Acoustic devices ballasted to a float freely at various depths

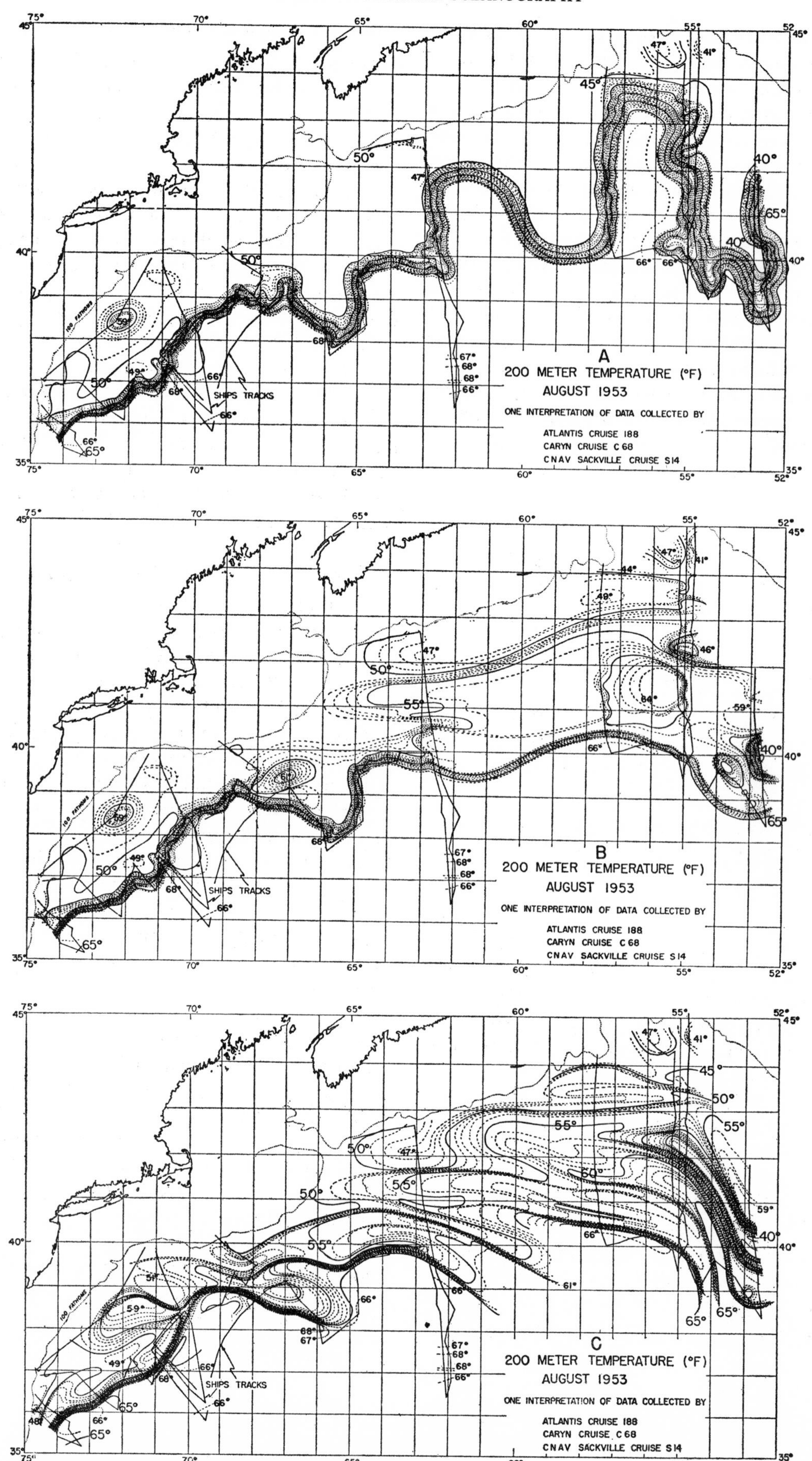

Fig. 2.2 Three alternative analyses of the temperature fields (°F), at a depth of 200 m in the Gulf Stream between 75° and 52° west long. (after Fuglister, 1955).

are being tracked to study subsurface currents (Swallow, 1955).

Ocean weather ships, maintaining station close to a fixed location, are providing time series for the study of short term variations. Notable is the series of observations from Ocean Station "P" which include observations made to and from this station in the North Pacific (Tully *et al.*, 1960). Regular reporting of data from this station constitutes one of the first approaches to synoptic oceanography.

Developments such as these promise a supply of oceanographic data of a completely different kind from those heretofore available. As the technical problems of operating instruments at sea are solved and the problems of collecting and analyzing the data are tackled, it will become possible to study the ocean in a kind of detail that has previously been impossible.

References

Bjerknes, V. (1898) Ueber einen hydrodynamichen Fundamentalsatz und seine Anwendung besonder auf die Mechanik der Atmosphare und des Weltmeeres. *Kongl. Svenska Vetenskaps-Akad. Itandl., N. F.* (4th Ser) **31** (4), 35 pp.

Bruns, E. *Ozeanologie*. Berlin. Deutscher Verloz der Wissenschaften. 1958.

Defant, A. (1950) Reality and illusion in oceanographic surveys. *J. Mar. Res.* **9**, 120–138.

Dittmar, W. (1884) Report on researches into the composition of ocean water, collected by H.M.S. *Challenger. Challenger Repts. Physics and Chem.* **1**, 1–125.

Ekman, V. W. (1905) On the influence of the earth rotation on ocean currents. *Ark. Math. Astr. och Fys.* **2**, 11, Stockholm.

Forchhammer, G. (1865) On the composition of sea water in the different parts of the ocean. *Phil. Trans. Roy. Soc. London* **155**, 203–262.

Fuglister, F. C. and L. V. Worthington. (1951) Some results of a multiple ship survey of the Gulf Stream. *Tellus* **3**, 1–14.

Fuglister, F. C. (1955) Alternative analyses of current surveys. *Deep Sea Res.* **2**, 213–229.

LaFond, E. C. (1959) How it works—the N.E.L. Oceanographic Tower. *Proc. U.S. Naval Inst.* **85** (11), 146–148.

Lamb, Sir H. *Hydrodynamics* (sixth edition). Dover (and numerous other editions), New York. 1945.

Maury, M. F. *The physical geography of the sea*. Rev. ed. Harper, New York. 1859.

Mohn, H. *Die Stromungen des europaischen Nordmeeres*. Petermanns Mitt., Erganzungshefte No. 79, 20 pp. Gotha: Justus Perthes. 1885.

Reid, J. L. Jr. (1956) Observations of internal tides in October 1950. *Trans. Amer. Geophys. Union* **37** (3), 278–286.

Richardson, W. S. (Unpublished). *Measurement of thermal microstructure*. Woods Hole Oceanog. Inst., Reference No. 58–11. 1958.

Richardson, W. S. Current measurements from moored buoys. *Marine sciences instrumentation*, Vol. 1, pp. 205–209. Plenum Press, New York. 1962.

Sandstrom, J. W. and B. Helland-Hansen. (1903) Uber die Berechnung von Meeresstromungen. *Repts. Norweg. Fish and Mar. Investigations* **2** (4), 43 pp.

Seiwell, G. E. (1937) Short period vertical oscillations in the western basin of the North Atlantic. *Papers in Phys. Oceanog. and Mar. Met.* **5**, 2.

Swallow, J. C. (1955) A neutral-buoyancy float for measuring deep currents. *Deep Sea Res.* **3**, 74–81.

Tully, J. P., A. J. Dodimead, and S. Tabata. (1960) An anomalous increase of temperature in the ocean off the Pacific coast of Canada through 1957 and 1958. *J. Fish. Res. Bd. Can.* **17** (1), 61–80.

von Arx, W. S. (1950) An electromagnetic method for measuring the velocity of ocean currents from a ship underway. *Papers in Phys. Oceanog. and Mar. Met.* **11**, 3.

Walden, R. G. and D. H. Franz. A long range oceanographic telemetering system. *Marine Sciences Instrumentation*, Vol. 1, pp. 50–54. Plenum Press, New York. 1962.

Sources of Additional Information

Founders of Oceanography and Their Work. Herdman, Sir W. A. Edward Arnold, London. 1923.

Introduction to Physical Oceanography. von Arx, W. S. Addison-Wesley. Reading. 1962. (Especially Chapter 1 and Appendix A).

CHAPTER 3

THE CHEMICAL NATURE OF THE OCEAN

THE two most remarkable things about the ocean are: first, the water, and second, the salt. The presence of water in the ocean and atmosphere of the planet earth is responsible for maintaining the small range in environmental conditions which permits life in the form we know it. Atmospheric water vapor limits the efficient radiative heat loss to a narrow band of wavelengths. Warmed by incoming solar radiation the planet must heat up to the point where it radiates strongly in these wavelengths before a heat balance can be established. The oceans store vast quantities of energy from the sun within a fairly thick surface layer, warming up in the summer season and releasing heat to the atmosphere during the winter. Thus, seasonal fluctuations in temperature are greatly reduced. The fact that most ocean water has sufficient dissolved salt that its coefficient of thermal expansion is positive at all temperatures above the freezing point makes it more efficient than fresh water in the role of global thermostat. This is especially important at high latitudes.

It is generally felt that life on earth originated in the oceans. One piece of evidence for this is a similarity in chemical composition between sea water and the body fluids of a number of life forms. The sea constitutes a suitable environment for an extremely large and diverse biological population.

3.1 Origin and Composition of the Salts

Geophysicists and geochemists are not in complete agreement concerning the early history of the earth, but every theory must explain the existence of the ocean waters and dissolved salts. One theory postulates a young earth with an atmosphere made up largely of water vapor. Shielded thus from solar radiation the earth cooled rapidly and its crust solidified. There followed a period of intense vulcanism during which further great quantities of water were released from the interior of the planet. Such juvenile water is still being produced in the regions of volcanic activity.

As the earth cooled towards present surface temperatures precipitation transferred most of the water from the atmosphere to the hydrosphere and the persistent rains weathered the surface rocks, carrying great loads of sediment and dissolved materials to the sea. This weathering is still taking place as the waters of the ocean are recycled through the atmosphere, and after precipitation, back to the sea. Analysis of the suspended and dissolved materials in river waters indicates the nature of the surface materials in the runoff area.

TABLE 3.1. PRINCIPAL IONIC CONSTITUENTS OF SEA WATER (34.4‰ SALINITY)

Species	g/kg	%S
Cations		
Sodium	10.47	30.4
Magnesium	1.28	3.7
Calcium	0.41	1.2
Potassium	0.38	1.1
Strontium	0.013	0.05
Anions		
Chloride	18.97	55.2
Sulfate	2.65	7.7
Bromide	0.065	0.2
Bicarbonate	0.14	0.4
Borate	0.027	0.08

With one notable exception, the relative abundance of ion species in sea waters is similar to that for surface rocks on a global basis. The exception is in the greater relative abundance of the halogens in sea water. The major constituent in this group is chlorine which, incidentally, is the most abundant anion in the sea. One theory has great quantities of chlorine present in the primordial atmosphere which greatly accelerated the initial weathering of the rocks. Another theory has the chlorine being added at a substantially constant rate as a result of volcanic activity.

Every element for which an adequate method of

chemical analysis has been devised has been detected in sea water. Many, of course, are present in extremely low concentration and reliable evaluations of their concentrations have not been made.

Table 3.1 lists the principal ionic species in a typical sea water of 34.4‰ salinity, expressed as grams per kilogram of sea water and as a percentage of the total salt.

The concentrations of some of the other elements in sea water are given in Table 3.2 in milligrams per cubic meter.

TABLE 3.2. CONCENTRATION OF LESS ABUNDANT ELEMENTS IN SEA WATER

Elements	Conc. (mg/m^3)
Fluorine	1400
Silica	1000
Nitrogen (NO, NO_2, NH_3)	1000
Rubidium	200
Aluminum	120
Lithium	70
Phosphorus	60
Barium	54
Iron	50
Iodine	50
Arsenic	15
Copper	5
Manganese	5
Zinc	5
Selenium	4
Uranium	2
Cesium	2
Molybdenum	0.7
Cerium	0.4
Thorium	0.4
Vanadium	0.3
Yttrium	0.3
Lanthanum	0.3
Silver	0.3
Nickel	0.1
Scandium	0.04
Mercury	0.03
Gold	0.004
Radium	0.0000001

3.2 SALINITY AND CHLORINITY

When we speak of the salinity of sea water we are referring to the quantity of salt in a given quantity of water. Ideally it is *total* salt to which we refer—yet there are serious practical problems in carrying out an analysis to determine the total salt content. For this reason, the term "salinity" as used is a defined quantity, the definition being related to the technique by which the determinations are made.

"Salinity" is the total amount of solid material in grams contained in one kilogram of sea water when all carbonate has been converted to oxide, the bromine and iodine replaced by chlorine and all organic matter oxidized.

The units used in reporting salinity are grams per kilogram or parts per thousand (‰). Table 3.3

TABLE 3.3. AVERAGE SALINITIES OF THE OCEANS

Ocean	‰
Atlantic	34.90
Pacific	34.62
Indian	34.76
World Ocean	34.72

shows average salinities for the oceans as reported by Montgomery (1958).

It is usual to quote the normal range for oceanic salinity to be from 33‰ to 37‰. This can be seen in the frequency distribution of salinities in Fig. 3.1A, after Montgomery (1958). Lower salinities, down to 28‰ or 29‰ are found in coastal waters, and some inland seas, such as the Baltic, have salinities in the low 20's. In the Gulf of Bothnia salinities are regularly less than 10‰. The peak in the frequency distribution at 38.5‰ represents waters of the Mediterranean. The Red Sea has salinities greater than 40‰, and similarly high salinities are found in places such as the Texas bays during dry seasons.

Figure 3.1B, shows, on a different frequency scale, the frequency distribution of salinity throughout the great majority of the ocean. Within this small range the larger peak is representative of the Pacific and the lesser peak of the Atlantic.

Defant (1961) points out that the ocean is really a very dilute solution, yet, even so, the salt represents 4.8×10^{16} tons and would have a dry volume of 21.8×10^6 km^3. This, spread evenly over the area of the ocean, would form a layer 60 m thick.

Early investigators found that, although the total concentration of salt varies widely, the relative proportions of the major constituents remain virtually constant. Dittmar's (1884) analysis of 77 samples from the Challenger expedition stands as the classical basis for this concept. To the extent that this is true, ocean studies are greatly simplified. It becomes possible to determine salinity by analyzing for only one of the major constituents. Chlorine, the most abundant element, has been the choice because a simple analytical technique is available.

In this determination of "chlorinity" a sea water sample is titrated with silver nitrate using a potassium chromate indicator. This titration involves all the halogens indiscriminately and so "chlorinity" has been defined for convenience in the following way.

"Chlorinity" is the total amount, in grams, of chlorine, bromine, and iodine contained in one kilogram of sea water, assuming the bromine and iodine to be replaced by chlorine.

A more recent definition aimed at being more exact and independent of re-evaluations of atomic weights is: the number giving the chlorinity in grams per kilogram of a sea water sample is identical with the number giving the mass in grams of "atomic weight silver" just necessary to precipitate the halogens in 0.32852 kg of sea water.

3.3 Determination of Salinity

The standard method for determining salinity has long been to carry out the titration with silver nitrate, known as the Knudsen Method, and, having determined chlorinity, to infer salinity from the relationship.

$$S\,‰ = 0.030 + 1.8050\ \mathrm{Cl}\ ‰,$$

which will be discussed in the following section. Special glassware is available for use in these titrations and with care a precision of $\pm$ 0.01‰ in salinity can be achieved. In routine work a precision of half this ($\pm$ 0.02‰) is usually attained.

In standardizing reagents for these titrations a sea water standard is used so as to minimize any salt errors. The standard "Eau de Mer Normal" is prepared at the Laboratoire Hydrographique in Copenhagen under the direction of the International Association of Physical Oceanographers and is delivered in sealed ampules with chlorinity stated to three decimal places and adjusted to be close to 19.400‰ (salinity 35.05‰). Each batch is closely compared to previous standards so that results from all expeditions can be readily compared.

Another method which has been widely used has been to determine the density of a sample. Knudsen's (1901) tables facilitate reduction of density observed at a measured temperature to density at a standard temperature and thence conversion to chlorinity or salinity. Density determinations are made with hydrometers usually designed

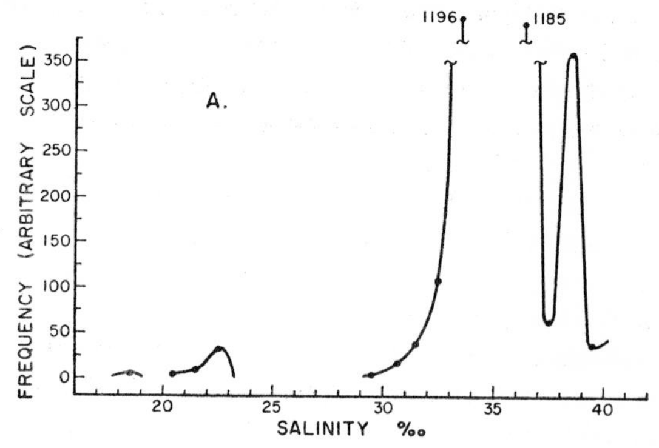

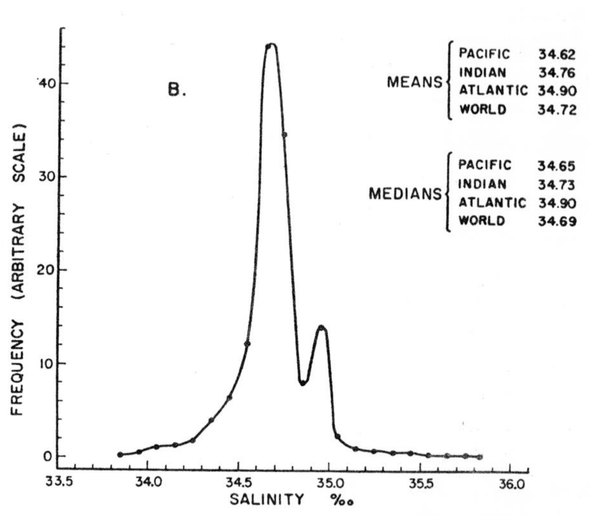

Fig. 3.1 Frequency distribution of salinity in the oceans after Montgomery (1958).
(A) By 1.0‰ intervals (data between 33 and 37‰ omitted).
(B) By 0.1‰ intervals 33.7–35.8‰.

particularly for use in the range of densities expected.

The current trend is toward determination of salinity from measurements of electrical conductivity. To avoid electrode polarization alternating current bridges are used and, because of the effect of temperature on conductivity, the measurement cells are usually immersed in a carefully controlled constant temperature bath. Most major research ships are now equipped with salinity bridges and analyses are run soon after the samples are collected. Because gas bubbles tend to form when the samples are heated, it is usual to provide refrigeration and to operate the temperature bath well below laboratory temperature.

Salinity bridges have greatly increased the precision of salinity determinations. A precision of $\pm$ 0.003‰ is generally attainable. What this means in terms of accuracy is difficult to say, since the conductivity–salinity relationship for sea water is not known with the same precision. Also there remains some uncertainty as to the effects of departures from constant composition. The same Standard Sea Water (Eau de Mer Normal) is also used for a conductivity standard and the bridges are calibrated essentially with samples diluted by weight from standard water. By international agreement subsequent batches of standard water are to be adjusted to provide continuity in conductivity as well as chlorinity calibrations.

Some recently built conductivity bridges do away with cells using electrodes by providing inductive coupling to the sea water sample. In at least one case temperature changes are compensated for in the circuitry so as to make temperature control unnecessary. The extension of this technique to precise *in situ* determination of salinity appears hopeful.

Another method which is finding some use is the measurement of refractive index (see Chapter 17). Modern differential refractometers can give precision comparable to that obtainable from conductivity bridges. These could be particularly useful in waters where the constancy of composition is violated and chlorinity is the parameter which it is desired to evaluate. The influence of the chloride ion upon the refractive index is comparatively so great that the method is virtually insensitive to changes in other ion species.

3.4 Factors Which Influence the Constancy of Composition

The relation

$$S\text{‰} = 0.030 + 1.8050\ \text{Cl}\ \text{‰}$$

was developed by an International Commission (Knudsen, 1902) from the results of determinations made on samples from the North Atlantic and the Baltic. They had nine samples with satisfactory results, whose salinity ranged from 2.6888 to 40.181. The relationship was chosen for best fit to these data points.

Knudsen pointed out that it was not to be expected that the relationship would hold for all oceans. In particular, he suggested that it might not hold for the Mediterranean. In spite of this, it has been generally taken as a universal relationship and most twentieth century oceanography makes this assumption. Several studies have been made of the sulfate : chlorinity ratio in natural waters and these have shown that measurable variations do take place. A full and careful investigation of the matter is yet to be made.

It must be expected that, in coastal areas where river runoff measurably dilutes the sea water, deviations from constancy of composition will occur. Analyses of river waters generally show the major cations in order of decreasing concentration to be: calcium, magnesium, potassium, sodium, and the major anions in similar order to be: carbonate, sulfate, chloride.

Where sea water freezes or sea ice melts significant variations in the sulfate–chlorinity ratio occur. A controversy concerning the nature of these changes existed for some time. Sverdrup (1929) determined the chlorinity of sea water and ice samples from the Siberian Shelf by titration with silver nitrate. He also determined the density by hydrometer. He found that, relative to the chloride content, the density was consistently low for the melted ice and high for the water below the ice. This he interpreted as indicating a relative excess of chloride ion in the ice, and inferred a sulfate deficit, since these are the most abundant anions. Wiese (1930) subjected surface samples from the European Arctic to analysis for chlorinity by titration and sulfate by gravimetric determination. He found, in areas where ice was melting, a sulfate : chlorinity ratio that was higher than normal. Nelson and Thompson (1954) showed conclusively that there is a selective retention of sulfate in sea ice, confirming the findings of Wiese and discounting Sverdrup's conclusions. There has as yet been no explanation for the anomalous densities observed by Sverdrup although there is reason to believe similar results can be observed in laboratory size freezing experiments. This implies more complex variations from the accepted salinity–chlorinity–density relationships.

The sulfate–chlorinity ratio is, of course, only one of many that can, and probably do, vary significantly in certain regions of the ocean.

3.5 Physical Properties Which Depend Upon Salinity

Most of the physical properties of sea water vary with salinity. In Table 3.4 some of these are listed with an indication whether the values increase or decrease with increasing salinity. The dependence upon salinity of certain properties such as the latent heats and molecular diffusivity have not yet been determined adequately.

TABLE 3.4. PHYSICAL PROPERTIES OF SEA WATER INFLUENCED BY SALINITY

A. *Increase with increasing salinity*
- Density
- Molecular viscosity
- Surface tension
- Refractive index
- Electrical conductivity
- Coefficient of thermal expansion
- Speed of sound
- Osmotic pressure

B. *Decrease with increasing salinity*
- Specific heat
- Freezing point temperature
- Temperature of maximum density
- Vapor pressure
- Thermal conductivity (molecular)

Of particular significance is the behavior of freezing point temperature and temperature of maximum density. Each decreases with increasing salinity (Fig. 3.2) but the temperature of maximum density decreases more rapidly, so that, for salinity greater than 24.69‰ (when the freezing point is − 1.33°C), the water freezes before reaching maximum density. As a result it is necessary for the cooling process to depress the temperature of a thick surface layer to the freezing point (as low as − 1.9°C for water of 34‰ *S*) before the surface freezes.

3.6 DISSOLVED GASES

When water lies at the surface, in contact with the atmosphere, there takes place across the interface an exchange of gases which will go in one direction or the other until an equilibrium is reached. Equilibrium occurs when the partial pressure of the gas in the water is equal to the partial pressure of the gas in the atmosphere. The controlling factor is the temperature of the surface water which will also be the temperature of the atmosphere at the contact surface. Each of the atmospheric gases can be found dissolved in sea water. Waters acquire their characteristics at the surface, subsequently sinking, mixing with other waters, and being subjected to biological and chemical processes. Nitrogen and the inert atmosheric gases are of little interest in the ocean. Oxygen and carbon dioxide, however, take part in biological processes and, in the case of carbon dioxide, enter into important inorganic reactions.

The equilibrium transfer of carbon dioxide is complicated by the fact that it enters into a reaction with water which can be represented by

$$CO_2 + H_2O \leftrightharpoons H_2CO_3 \leftrightharpoons H^+ + HCO_3^-$$
$$\leftrightharpoons 2H^+ + CO_3^{--}$$

Carbon dioxide, bicarbonate (HCO_3^-) ions and carbonate (CO_3^{--}) ions are all present in sea water and the relative proportions depend upon the hydrogen ion potential (pH) of the medium. Transitions from one form to the other take place in directions which tend to maintain constant pH. For a discussion of the carbonate system and the "buffering mechanism" in sea water, the reader is referred to Harvey (1960).

In the upper zone of the ocean where sufficient light penetrates to support photosynthesis, plants utilize carbon dioxide and bicarbonate in the synthesis of hydrocarbons. In the process they liberate oxygen. Where respiration takes place or organic matter is oxidized, oxygen is consumed and carbon is returned to the water.

The concentration of dissolved oxygen in sea water is usually reported in ml/l. and refers to the volume in milliliters that the oxygen dissolved in a liter of sea water would occupy at standard temperature and pressure (20°C and 760 mm of mercury). Frequently oxygen is reported as per cent saturation which refers to the equilibrium content of water at the given temperature and salinity when in contact with a standard air at normal atmospheric pressure. A tabulation of saturation values is given in Table 3.5.

Where plant growth takes place below the surface the oxygen content may exceed these values

TABLE 3.5. SATURATION VALUES OF OXYGEN IN SEA WATER (ml/l.) FROM NORMAL DRY ATMOSPHERE (FOX, 1907)

Temp. (°C)	Chlorinity‰ / Salinity ‰	15 / 27.11	16 / 28.91	17 / 30.72	18 / 32.52	19 / 34.33	20 / 36.11
−2		9.01	8.89	8.76	8.64	8.52	8.39
0		8.55	8.43	8.32	8.20	8.08	7.97
5		7.56	7.46	7.36	7.26	7.16	7.07
10		6.77	6.69	6.60	6.52	6.44	6.35
15		6.14	6.07	6.00	5.93	5.86	5.79
20		5.63	5.56	5.50	5.44	5.38	5.31
25		5.17	5.12	5.06	5.00	4.95	4.86
30		4.74	4.68	4.63	4.58	4.52	4.46

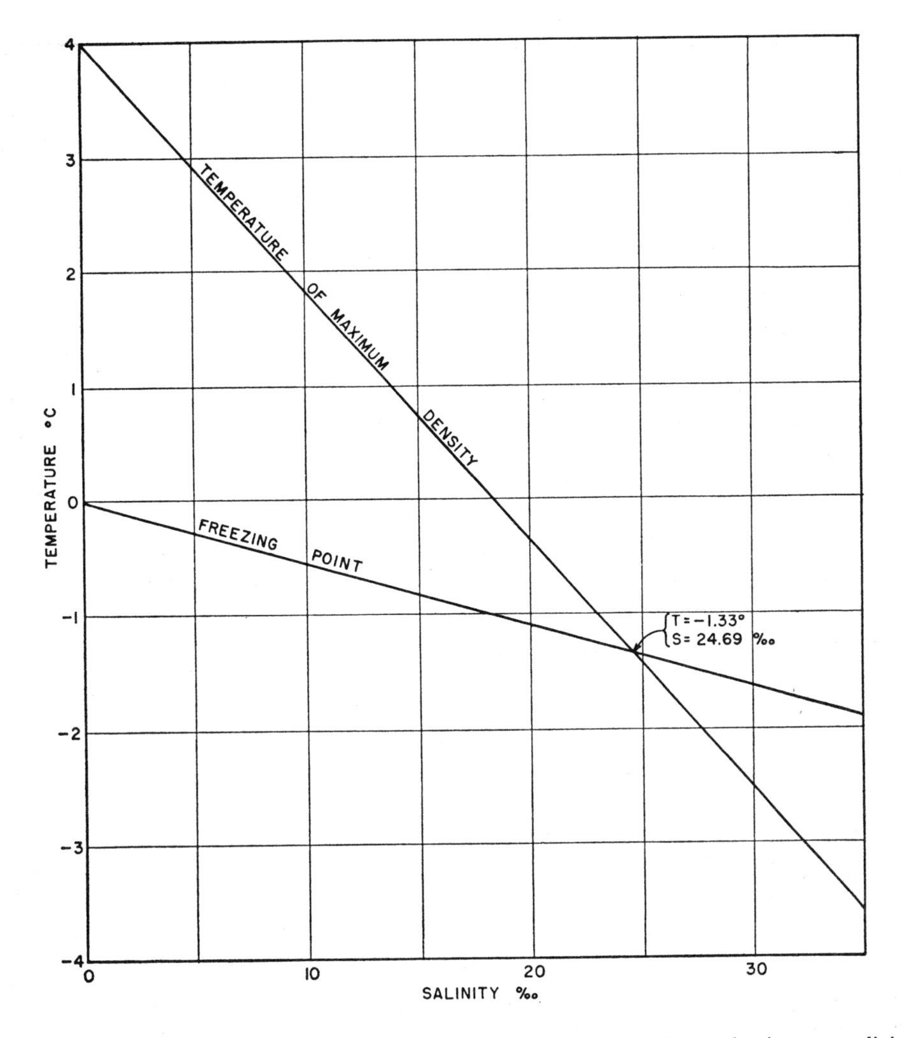

Fig. 3.2 Dependence of freezing temperature and temperature of maximum density upon salinity.

and is sometimes said to be supersaturated. It must not be inferred that under such conditions there is any tendency for oxygen to come out of solution and form bubbles, since the table applies only to saturation at atmospheric pressure.

Throughout the water column organic matter decays with the consumption of dissolved oxygen and the oxygen content of the water generally decreases with time after it leaves the surface layers. The distribution of decaying organic matter and the rate of oxidation is not uniform through a vertical column. One notable consequence of the balance between water renewal and oxygen consumption is the occurrence, in most parts of the ocean, of a distinct oxygen minimum layer at a depth of a few hundred meters.

In basins where waters are isolated from renewal all the oxygen may be used up and anerobic conditions may exist.

3.7 Non-conservative Constituents

The constancy of composition of sea water is a concept that cannot be extended to all chemical species. Since the concentration of the chemical constituents which enter into biological processes can vary greatly relative to the salinity, and not simply by mixing, these constituents are referred to as non-conservative constituents. The distributions of these constituents are of interest to the physical oceanographer because they provide clues as to the history of the water.

The dissolved gases, oxygen and carbon dioxide, are examples of non-conservative constituents as are the inorganic nutrients such as nitrate, nitrite, phosphate and silicate. Inorganic nutrients are consumed where plant growth takes place. This is limited to the upper layers where there is adequate light to support photosynthesis. They are returned to the water where plant or animal material decays.

Generally the concentration of nutrients is high in the deep water and low in the surface layers. Where deeper waters are brought to the surface by upwelling or vertical mixing the surface layer content of nutrients is increased and more vigorous growth can be supported.

Also among the non-conservative constituents must be numbered tne organic compounds. Slowey *et al.* (1962) found at least nine separate fatty acids in samples from all depths. That these fatty acids are part of the cycle of growth and decay is pointed up by the marked changes in relative amounts of the individual acids with depth of water. Deep waters showed almost no unsaturated acids and tendency toward shorter chain acids. More recently, surprisingly large quantities of organic compounds in all categories have been extracted from sea water samples (Hood, 1963). Literally hundreds of individual compounds have been evaluated by chromatographic and other techniques.

3.8 Salinity at Selected Stations

Table 3.6 gives observed temperature and salinity at serial depths for five of the stations occupied during the International Geophysical Year. They illustrate the types of salinity–depth relationships that may be observed. Salinity is plotted against depth in Fig. 3.3 for these stations.

One can note the deep, well mixed surface layer characteristic of the Sargasso Sea in (CHAIN 7-35). Contrasted to this is the comparatively shallow surface layer in the Northeast Atlantic (CHAIN 7-68). This latter station shows the subsurface influence of saline water flowing into the Atlantic from the

Table 3.6. Temperature and Salinity Observed at Five Oceanographic Stations During the I.G.Y.

Northeast Atlantic Chain-7 4-22-59 Sta. 35 36° 16′N 68° 22′W			*Northeast Atlantic* Chain-7 5-9-59 Sta. 68 36° 11′N 13° 53′W			*South Atlantic* Atlantis 5-12-59 5827 32° 31′S 8° 56′W			*Indian* Ob-2 4-26-57 Sta. 309 16° 48′S 96° 54′E			*Central Pacific* Horizon 10-31-57 "Downwind" 7 07° 08′N 129° 17′ W		
Depth (m)	Temp. (°C)	Salinity (‰)	Depth (m)	Temp. (°C)	Salinity (‰)	Depth (m)	Temp. (°C)	Salinity (‰)	Depth (m)	Temp. (°C)	Salinity (‰)	Depth (m)	Temp. (°C)	Salinity (‰)
1	21.16	36.384	1	16.78	36.378	1	19.57	35.636	0	26.32	34.57	0	28.01	34.09
24	21.09	36.404	50	16.10	36.353	45	19.60	35.640	10	36.30	34.60	8	27.99	34.09
48	19.82	36.460	99	15.59	36.217	95	16.35	35.492	25	26.27	34.66	86	16.39	34.54
97	19.56	36.474	148	15.07	36.148	190	13.81	35.303	50	25.51	34.76	174	10.94	34.75
145	19.22	36.493	197	14.22	36.004	280	12.31	35.098	75	23.00	35.00	347	9.22	34.67
194	18.97	36.508	296	12.75	35.754	375	11.16	34.966	100	21.22	35.27	525	7.55	34.67
291	18.64	36.504	396	12.05	35.664	470	9.63	34.781	150	19.51	35.54	705	6.06	34.56
390	18.11	36.491	495	11.38	35.603	565	7.41	34.530	200	18.45	35.78	885	4.92	34.57
489	17.63	36.435	595	10.98	35.632	660	5.75	34.371	250	16.80	35.74	1068	4.20	34.55
588	16.77	36.297	694	10.49	35.654	755	4.60	34.288	300	14.61	35.44	1249	3.58	34.58
688	15.35	36.039	794	10.63	35.484	945	3.66	34.300	400	11.33	35.06	1435	3.14	34.60
788	13.17	35.696	893	10.67	35.964	1135	3.17	34.386	500	9.22	34.81	1623	2.75	34.63
888	11.29	35.429	993	10.39	36.000	1330	2.89	34.502	740	6.17	34.70	1814	2.48	34.64
986	9.47	35.214	1191	10.10	36.083	1485	2.77	34.600	983	5.11	34.73	2008	2.20	34.66
1182	5.98	35.052	1389	8.51	35.832	1770	2.72	34.720	1455	3.49	34.74	2206	2.08	34.65
1303	4.90	35.014	1596	6.59	35.501	2055	2.65	34.796	1950	2.47	34.81	2368	1.94	34.68
1597	4.21	34.986	1895	4.78	35.206	2345	2.57	34.836	2440	1.92	34.79	2405	1.92	34·64
1893	3.87	34.969	2193	3.90	35.086	2635	2.51	34.856	2830	1.65	34.74	2606	1.85	34.68
2192	3.68	34.966	2491	3.37	35.022	2925	2.44	34.865	3300	1.42	34.78	2614	1.84	34.69
2491	3.48	34.975	2789	3.01	34.978	3215	2.41	34.890	3770	1.25	34.74	2862	1.76	34.69
2793	3.25	34.961	3086	2.77	34.952	3600	2.45	34.882	4240	1.14	34.77	3107	1.69	34.69
3096	2.97	34.949	3383	2.61	34.931	4075	2.27	34.870	4710	1.13	34.78	3352	1.56	34.70
3402	2.62	34.936	3680	2.50	34.921				5180	1.11	34.76	3596	1.48	34.69
3808	2.37	34.931	4075	2.47	34.910							3835	1.42	34.69
4212	2.28	34.908	4474	2.50	34.910							4079	1.42	34.70
4617	2.27	34.899	4573	2.52	34.910							4323	1.45	34.70

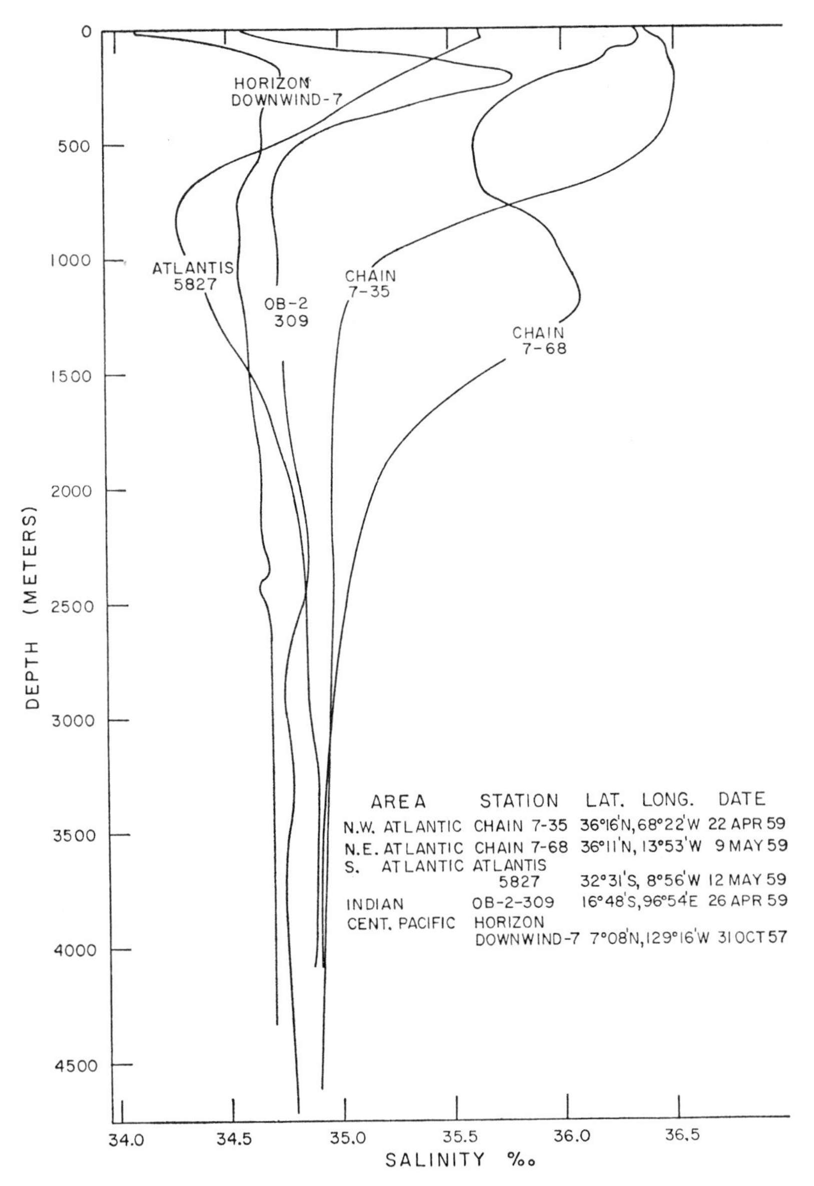

Fig. 3.3 Salinity vs. depth at selected stations.

Mediterranean, and at this station showing its maximum effect at some 1200 m depth. ATLANTIS 5827, from the South Atlantic, shows the salinity minimum at 750 m that indicates Antarctic Intermediate Water (see Chapter 7). HORIZON DOWNWIND 7 illustrates the lower salinity characterizing the deep waters of the Pacific as compared to the Atlantic. The Indian Ocean station OB 2-309 falls in an intermediate position.

REFERENCES

DEFANT, A. *Physical Oceanography*, Vol. 1, Pergamon Press, New York. 1961

DITTMAR, W. (1884) Report on researches into the composition of ocean water collected by H.M.S. *Challenger*, *Challenger Repts. Physics and Chem.* **1**, 1–251.

FOX, C. J. J. (1907) On the coefficients of absorption of the atmospheric gases in distilled water and in sea water. *Conseil Perm. Internat. p. L'Explor. de La Mer, Pub. de Circumstance* **41**, 27 pp.

HARVEY, H. W. *The Chemistry and Fertility of Sea Water* (second edition). Cambridge University Press. 1960.

HOOD, D. W. Chemical oceanography. In *Ann. Rev. of Oceanography and Marine Biology* (C. Barnes, editor). Allen and Unwin. 1963.

KNUDSEN, M. (editor). *Hydrographical tables.* Copenhagen, G.E.C. Gad. (1901) Reprinted 1962 by G. M. Manufacturing Co., New York.

KNUDSEN, M. (1902) Berichte uber die Knostantenbestimmung zur Aufstellung der Hydrographischen Tabellen von

Carl Forch, Martin Knudsen, und S. P. L. Sorensen. *D. Kgl. Dansk Vidensk. Selsk. Skrifter, and Raekke, Naturvidensk. of Mathem—Afd.* **12** (1), 155 pp.

MONTGOMERY, R. B. (1958) Water characteristics of Atlantic Ocean and of World Ocean. *Deep Sea Res.* **5**, 134–148.

NELSON, K. H. and T. G. THOMPSON. (1954) Deposition of salts from sea water by frigid concentration. *J. Mar. Res.* **13** (2), 166–182.

SLOWEY, J. F., L. M. JEFFREY and D. W. HOOD. (1962) The fatty acid content of ocean water. *Geoch. et Cosmoc. Acta* **26**, 607–616.

SVERDRUP, H. U. (1929) The waters of the North Siberian Shelf. *Norwegian North Polar Expedition with the Maud.* 1918–1925, *Scientific Results* **4**, (2), 1–206.

WIESE, W. (1930) Zur Kenntnis der salze des Meereises. *Ann. d. Hydrog. u. Meteor., Jarg.* **58**, 282–286.

Sources of Additional Information

The Oceans, Their Physics, Chemistry and General Biology. SVERDRUP, H. U., M. W. JOHNSON and R. H. FLEMMING. Prentice Hall, New York. 1946.

RUBEY, W. W. (1951) Geologic History of Sea Water. *Bull. Geol. Soc. Am.* **62** (9), 1111–1147.

Geochemistry. RANKAMA, K., and Th. G. SAHAMA. University of Chicago Press, Chicago. 1950.

Physical and Chemical Properties of Sea Water. Washington National Academy of Science, National Research Council Pub. 600. 1959.

The Sea, Vol. 1. HILL, M. N. (editor). Interscience, New York. 1962.

The Sea, Vol. II. HILL, M. N., (editor). Interscience, New York. 1963.

CHAPTER 4

THE TEMPERATURE OF THE OCEAN

TEMPERATURE is the physical variable that has been most measured in the ocean. Ocean temperatures range from a high of around 35°C to a low of − 2°C, the full range occurring at the surface. The lower limit is set by the freezing point of sea water. Most of the water in the ocean occurs at fairly low temperatures. Only a negligibly small fraction is warmer than 6°C and almost half is cooler than 2°C.

The frequency of occurrence of crude thermometers in the modern household tends to produce a false notion of the problems of temperature measurement. Extremely careful techniques are required to measure an environmental temperature with real precision.

We will discuss some of the measurement methods, the vertical variation in temperature within the oceans and the frequency distribution of potential temperature. In Chapter 7 the geographical distribution of surface temperatures will be presented and in Chapter 18 the mechanisms by which the ocean gains or looses heat will be discussed.

4.1 Surface Temperature

Surface temperature varies widely both in time and space so that for most purposes measurements accurate to ± 0.1°C are adequate. These may be obtained by dipping up a sample in a bucket and immersing a sensitive thermometer in the sample. Care must be taken to have the sample collected near the bow of the moving ship and ahead of condenser exhausts on steam ships. The bucket sample should be placed in the shade and stirred vigorously while the reading is being made. The use of wooden or canvas buckets is preferable over metallic buckets. Surface temperature as reported from hydrographic stations is usually taken with a reversing thermometer which can be from 0.5 to 3 m below the actual sea surface depending upon sea conditions.

Sometimes the temperature of cooling water drawn into the ship through intakes below the surface can be used as an indication of surface temperature.

Many ships record regularly the surface temperature at their location, and from these records charts such as Figs. 7.2 and 7.3 may be constructed.

Although either of the above methods can give good surface layer temperature, there are some problems concerning energy fluxes through the surface for which it would be desirable to have the temperature of the actual surface, say the top millimeter. Surface temperature in this sense may differ markedly from that usually recorded but no satisfactory method for measurement has been developed to the point that it can be used routinely.

One method that has been recently used is to sense the surface temperature through the infrared radiation emanating from it. This can be done from a ship or from an airplane. Surface temperatures sensed this way are generally up to 0.5°C lower than bucket temperatures. Observers have reported discrepancies as great as 7°C.

4.2 Subsurface Temperature-Reversing Thermometers

Subsurface temperatures have been measured by a number of devices. Insulated water bottles were used to bring a sample on deck where an immersion thermometer could be inserted. Since the sample would expand on decrease of the hydrostatic pressure, it was necessary to make a correction for the temperature decrease accompanying this expansion. Thermometers were lowered with their bulbs encased in a large ball of wax so as to give a long thermal time constant. After a long period at depth these were brought rapidly to the surface for reading. Both methods suffered from heat exchange with the surrounding waters during raising and this effect was difficult to evaluate.

It was the early belief that temperature decreased

monotonously with depth so that minimum recording thermometers were widely used. The Challenger expedition used this type of thermometer.

Since the firm of Negretti and Zambra produced the first reversing thermometers in 1874, these, with improvements developed by Richter of the Richter and Wiese Company, have been the standard thermometers used for subsurface temperature measurement. In the set position the reversing thermometer (Fig. 4.1) operates as a normal mercury in glass thermometer with the mercury column extending up the stem a distance dependent upon the temperature. When the thermometer is turned through 180 degrees (reversed) the mercury column breaks off at a carefully constructed constriction in the stem and the mercury which previously stood above that point is allowed to flow to the other end of the thermometer tube. A trap keeps any mercury that is subsequently extruded beyond the breakoff point from joining that originally separated.

To protect the thermometer from hydrostatic pressure, it is sealed in a glass tube (jacket). The jacket is compartmented and a large volume of mercury in the bulb end provides thermal contact between the bulb, which it surrounds, and the jacket wall. This mass of mercury gives rise to a large time constant and the instruments must be left in place for at least four minutes before reversal. Following the reversal the thermometer is brought on deck where the ambient temperature may be quite different from that where reversal took place. A change in the volume of the mercury column cut off must be expected, and, to facilitate correction for this, an auxiliary thermometer within the jacket permits recording of the ambient temperature at the time of reading.

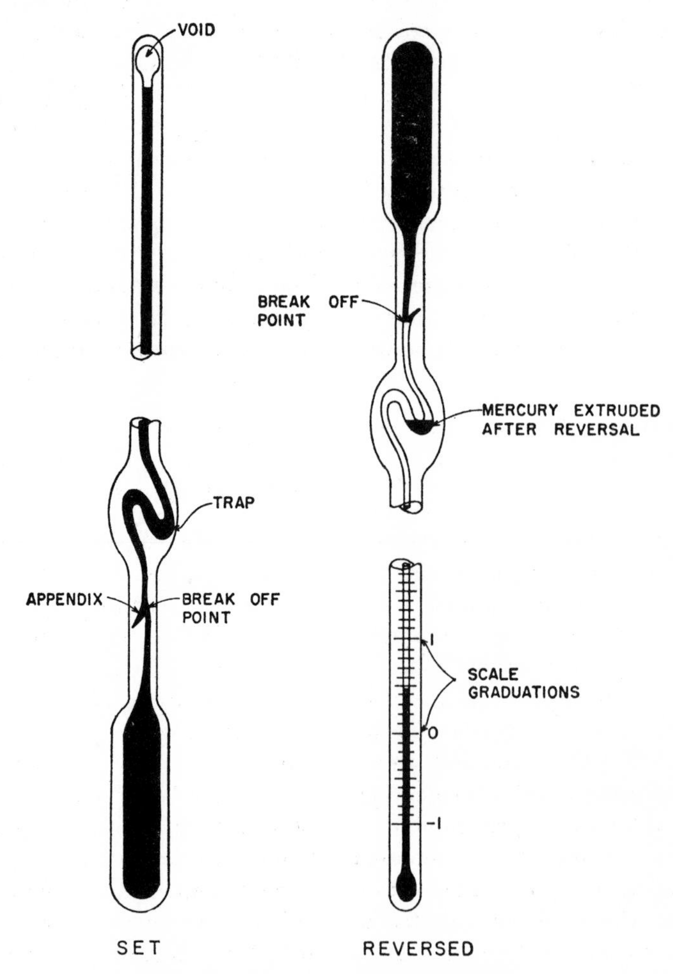

Fig. 4.1 Reversing thermometer detail.

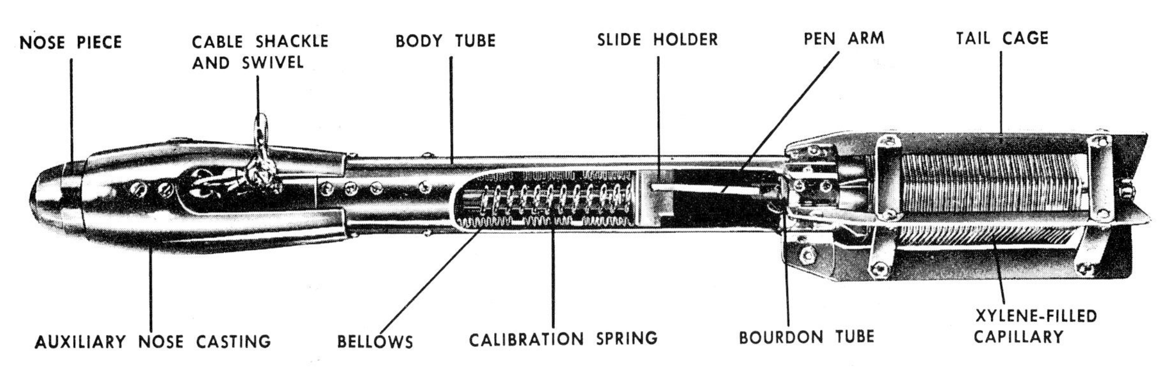

Fig. 4.2 Bathythermograph.

to face page 26

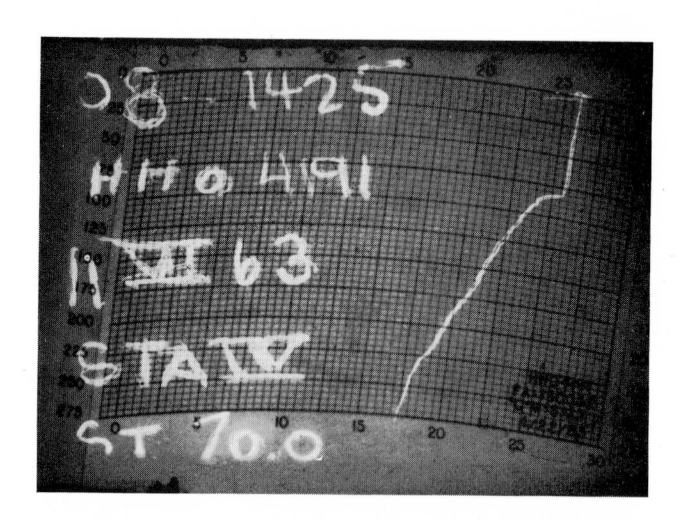

Fig. 4.3 A Bathythermograph trace photographed against the calibration grid. Horizontal scale in degrees centigrade, vertical scale in meters.

The volume change can be expressed in this way:

Volume observed = original volume (1 + $\alpha \times$ temperature change) where α is the coefficient of thermal expansion.

Now we may measure the volume of cut off mercury in units of the stem graduation (°C). Thus, if T' is the thermometer reading, the volume observed is $T' + V_0$ where V_0 is the volume (again in units of the stem graduation, i.e. °C) of mercury contained in the stem below the zero point. V_0 is of the order of 100° for most thermometers.

If a temperature T' is recorded at an ambient t, as indicated by the auxiliary thermometer, the problem is to find T, the temperature at the depth where the thermometer was reversed. We may write

$$T = T' + \Delta T, \tag{4.1}$$

and the normal equation for thermal expansion,

$$V_0 + T' = (V_0 + T)\,[1 + (t - T)/K], \tag{4.2}$$

where K is the reciprocal of the coefficient of relative thermal expansion of mercury in glass. For the most common type of glass used K has a value 6100°C.

In terms of observable quantities (4.2) may be re-written:

$$V_0 + T' = (V_0 + T' + \Delta T)\,[1 + (t - T' - \Delta T)/K],$$

which reduces to

$$\Delta T = \{(V_0 + T')\,(T' - t) + [(V_0 + T') + (T' - t)]\Delta T + \Delta T^2\}/K.$$

Neglecting ΔT^2 since $\Delta T^2 \ll (V_0 + T')\,(T' - t)$ we then have:

$$\Delta T = \frac{(V_0 + T')\,(T' - t)}{K} \times \left[1 - \frac{(T' - t) + (V_0 + T')}{K}\right]^{-1}.$$

Finally, since

$$\beta \equiv \{(T' - t) + (V_0 + T')\}/K \ll 1,$$

we may expand the factor $[1 - \beta]^{-1}$ in a binomial expansion, and, neglecting higher order terms, obtain

$$\Delta T = \left[\frac{(V_0 + T')\,(T' - t)}{K}\right] \times \left[1 + \frac{(T' + V_0) + (T' - t)}{K}\right], \tag{4.3}$$

the correction equation most often used. Except for thermometers with large V_0 and cases of large $T' - t$, the first term on the right of equation (4.3) may suffice to yield corrections to a precision of ± 0.01°C which is the desired accuracy in standard oceanographic observations. Recently some thermometers have been constructed which allow a precision of 0.002°C over their limited range.

Besides this correction for change in ambient temperature, it is necessary to apply index or stem corrections to the thermometer readings. These are obtained by careful calibration. Changes may take place in the index correction for a given thermometer especially during the first years following its manufacture. Frequent recalibration is required.

There are a number of types of malfunction which may occur in reversing thermometers. For this reason they are usually used in pairs.

4.3 Bathythermographs and Other Devices

Bathythermographs, as the name implies, are instruments which produce a graphical record of temperature versus depth. The type that has been widely used is that adapted from Spilhaus' (1938) original instrument. Xylene in a thin copper tube wound around the tail fins (Fig. 4.2) quickly takes on the temperature of the environment. A bourdon tube, sensing the pressure of the xylene, rotates a stylus which scribes a line upon a smoked glass slide. The slide in its holder is affixed to a coil spring enclosed in a sylphone bellows which collapses in response to pressure, translating the slide, as the depth varies, in a direction normal to the motion of the stylus. Units have been available with depth ranges from 0–200 feet to 0–900 feet. They may be lowered and retrieved from a ship under way and, while the accuracy obtainable is not great, have been extremely important in the study of detailed thermal structure in the surface layers.

A temperature–depth record taken with one of these instruments is reproduced in Fig. 4.3. The presentation suffers from a curvilinear calibration grid which is peculiar to each instrument. The accuracy obtainable is not great and calibration changes may result from careless handling. Yet they have given a previously unavailable record of complex thermal gradients in the surface layer, and their easy use from ships underway has resulted in the accumulation of a store of valuable data.

A number of electronic bathythermographs have been constructed though none as yet have been widely used. Typically they utilize thermistors as the temperature sensing element and present data on a rectilinear grid. They are considerably more complex than the mechanical B.T. and require conducting cable for lowering.

Richardson (1960) has introduced a system where temperature sensors at a number of depths are towed through the ocean afixed to a faired chain. With various types of recording systems these give continuous observations in the horizontal and show another degree of complexity in ocean structure. They have proved useful in the study of internal wave phenomena (LaFond, 1963).

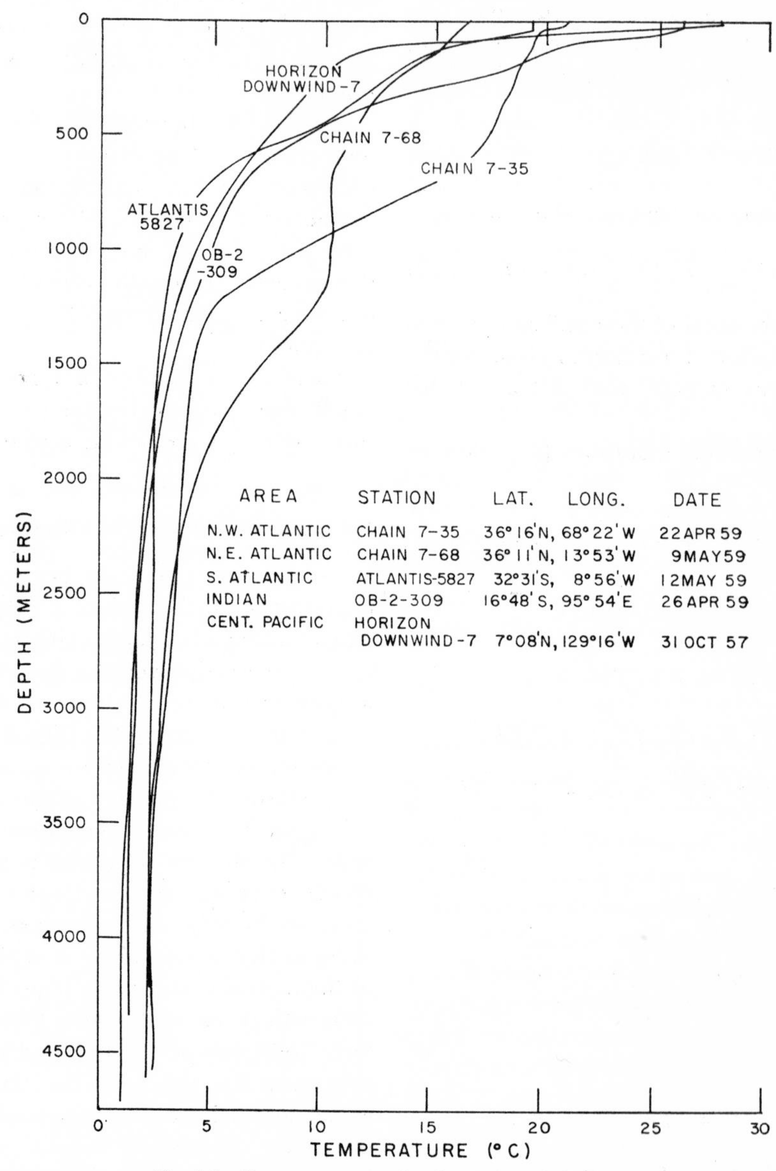

Fig. 4.4 Temperature vs. depth at selected stations.

4.4 Vertical Temperature Structure

It is convenient to divide the oceanic column into three regions when discussing its temperature.

(a) *The Surface Layer* is usually somewhat less than 200 m thick and is that portion of the column which experiences seasonal changes in response to the exchange of energy with the atmosphere and the absorption of solar radiation.

(b) *The Permanent Thermocline* is below the surface layer and is that region where, at the height of winter, the most rapid decrease in temperature with depth occurs.

(c) *The Deep Water* below the permanent thermocline usually exhibits a gradual decrease in temperature with depth to the bottom. The exception is in isolated basins or trenches where adiabatic conditions (Section 4.6) in the virtually uniform water mass below sill depth gives rise to an increase in temperature with depth.

The variation of temperature with depth is shown in Fig. 4.4 for the five selected stations in Table 3.6. Salinity at the same stations was presented in Fig. 3.3.

Chain 7-35 shows a shallow spring thermocline over a 500 m layer where temperature varies slowly with depth. Below this the deep permanent thermocline typical of the Sargasso Sea is observed. Chain 7-68 shows a layer with almost constant temperature (10.5°C) from 700 m to 1100 m where waters of the Mediterranean origin appear in the column. The very strong thermoclines near the surface in OB-2-309 and Horizon Downwind 7 coexist with low values of surface layer salinity.

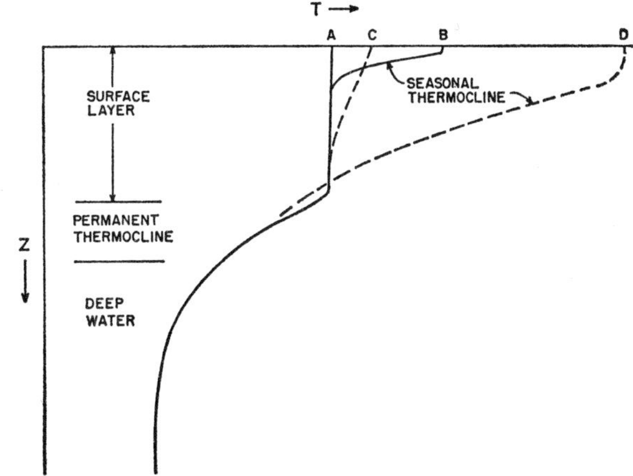

Fig. 4.5 Temperature structure in the ocean.
A. Extreme winter condition.
B. After vernal warming with light winds.
C. Condition B after vigorous wind stirring.
D. Extreme summer condition.

4.5 Seasonal Temperature Variations

The surface layer of the ocean serves for temporary storage of large quantities of thermal energy received from the sun. Heat is stored through the summer months and released to the atmosphere during the winter. Some of the mechanisms involved will be discussed in Chapter 18.

Figure 4.5A illustrates the thermal structure which might be observed in late winter. A deep mixed surface layer with almost isothermal conditions lies over the permanent thermocline. When vernal warming sets in a period of light winds may result in a shallow warmed layer with a sharp seasonal thermocline (Fig. 4.5B) that subsequent strong winds may break down as shown in Fig. 4.5C. Alterations of this nature produce a constantly changing, complex, temperature structure which culminates in a mid-summer surface layer that displays a strong thermocline throughout the stable surface layer (Fig. 4.5D). Autumnal cooling and the usually stronger winds of that season break down the stability in the surface layer and conditions gradually return to the cool, well mixed, deep surface layer of mid-winter.

In regions where a surface layer of low salinity contributes greatly to the stability of the water column seasonal thermoclines may become very intense. Changes as great as 12°C in 4 m have been observed (McLellan, 1956).

In many coastal regions of boreal or Polar Seas a cold, low salinity, layer lies over warmer oceanic water, and summer conditions feature a distinct minimum temperature within the surface layer (Fig. 4.6).

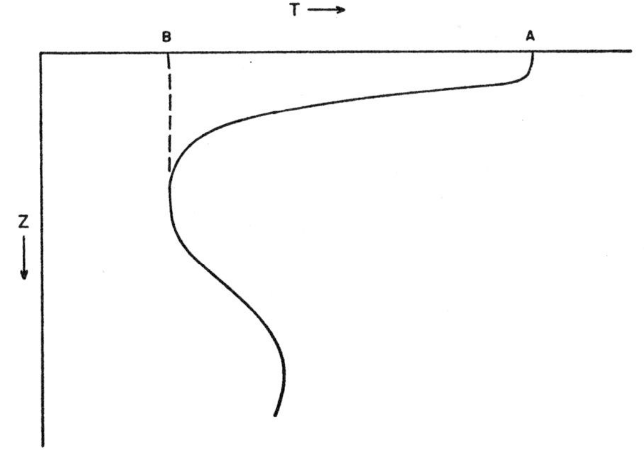

Fig. 4.6 Typical conditions in Summer (A) and Winter (B) in the upper layers of coastal regions of Boreal or Polar seas.

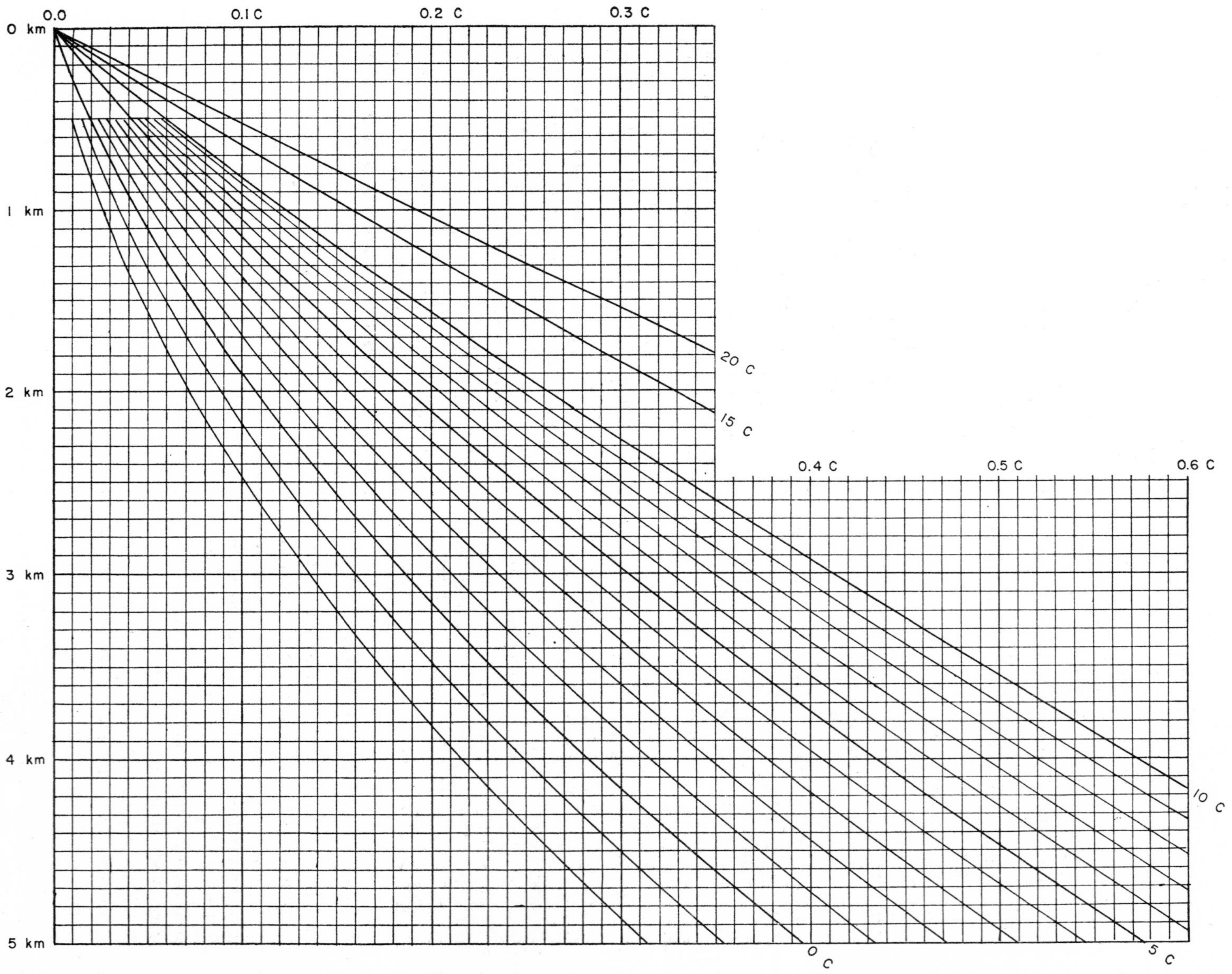

Fig. 4.7 Adiabatic cooling (abscissa) when sea water of salinity 34.85‰ (σ_0 = 28 g/l.) is raised from given depth (ordinate) and temperature (sloping isotherms) to sea surface. After Helland-Hansen, 1930 (Report of the "Michael Sars" North Atlantic Deep-Sea Expedition 1910).

With few exceptions a thermocline is also a region of rapid variation in density with depth, and a wide variety of short period fluctuations in the temperature structure can be observed and are attributed to internal waves (Section 14.13). Wherever adequate observations have been made in a time series at a fixed point such fluctuations have been observed. Very few cases are recorded, however, where sufficient data have been collected to adequately describe the wave motion involved.

4.6 Potential Temperature

If a parcel of water as observed at depth were brought to the surface without exchanging heat or mixing with its surroundings, the decrease in the hydrostatic pressure would result in an expansion and a consequent decrease in temperature. The temperature which would be attained at atmospheric pressure is referred to as the "Potential Temperature" of the water as opposed to the observed or *in situ* temperature. Helland-Hansen (1930) has given a method for computing this adiabatic cooling for a range of initial depths and temperatures (Fig. 4.7). In many deep basins and trenches conditions of constant potential temperature are observed below sill depth.

Because potential temperature is not a function of depth it is a more useful parameter than *in situ* temperature for tracing water masses in the ocean.

Montgomery (1958) has presented data on the frequency distribution of potential temperature in the world ocean and this distribution is shown in Fig. 4.8. The distribution is distinctly skewed toward the low temperatures with a mode close to 1°C representative of the so called "common water" which fills the deeper parts of the Pacific and is by far the largest water mass in the ocean.

Mean and median values of potential temperature are given in Table 4.1.

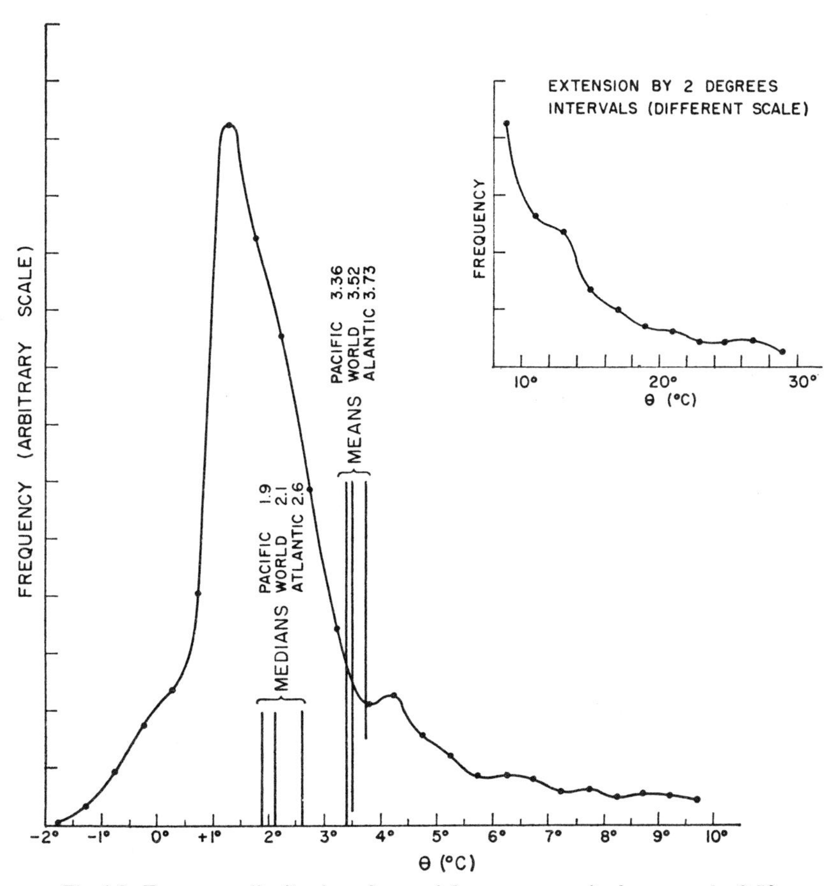

Fig. 4.8 Frequency distribution of potential temperatures in the oceans by 0.5° intervals (after Montgomery, 1958).

TABLE 4.1. POTENTIAL TEMPERATURE OF THE OCEANS

Ocean	Median	Mean
Atlantic	2.6	3.73
Pacific	1.9	3.36
World	2.1	3.52

REFERENCES

HELLAND-HANSEN, B. (1930) Physical Oceanography and Meteorology. *Michael Sars North Atlantic Deep-Sea Exped., 1910, Rept. Sci. Results,* Vol. 1, art. 2, 217 pp.

LAFOND, E. C. (1963) Detailed temperature structure of the sea off Baja California. *Limnology and Oceanography* **8** (4), 417–425.

MCLELLAN, H. J. (1956) On the sharpness of oceanographic boundaries south of Nova Scotia. *J. Fish. Res. Bd. Can.* **13** (3), 297–301.

MONTGOMERY, R. B. (1958) Water characteristics of Atlantic Ocean and of World Ocean. *Deep Sea Res.* **5**, 134–148.

RICHARDSON, W. S. and C. J. HUBBARD. (1960) The contouring temperature recorder. *Deep Sea Res.* **6** (3), 239–244.

SPILHAUS, A. F. (1938) A bathythermograph. *J. Mar. Res.* **1** (2), 95–100.

Sources of Additional Informatiom

LAFOND, E. C. (1954) Factors affecting the vertical temperature gradients in the upper layers of the sea. *Scientific Monthly* **78**, No. 4.

FOLSOM, T. R., F. D. JENNINGS and R. A. SCHWARTZLOSE. (1959) Effect of pressure upon the "protected" oceanographic reversing thermometer. *Deep Sea Res.* **5** (4), 306–309.

FOLSOM, T. R., R. A. SCHWARTZLOSE and F. D. JENNINGS. (1962) Scale errors on oceanographic mercurial thermometers. *Deep Sea Res.* **9**, 219–226.

HERDMAN, H. F. P. and L. H. PEMBERTON. (1958) The reliability of deep-sea reversing thermometers. *N.I.O. Discovery Repts.* **29**, 229–244.

REID, R. O. (unpublished). Thermal response study of the deep-sea reversing thermometer. *Scripps. Inst. Oceanog. M.L.R. Rept.*, No. 2. March 1949.

REID, R. O. (unpublished). Report on the calibration of deep-sea reversing thermometers. *Scripps Inst. Oceanog. M.L.R. Rept.*, January 1951.

SVERDRUP, H. U. (1947) Note on the correction of reversing thermometers. *J. Mar. Res.* **6** (2), 136–138.

CHAPTER 5

PRESSURE AND DENSITY

5.1 The Range of Pressure and Density Encountered

The unit most commonly used to express pressure as encountered in the ocean is the decibar, which is defined by 1 decibar = 1/10 bar = 10^5 dynes/cm^2. The bar is approximately equal to one atmosphere. It is common practice to neglect atmospheric pressure and hence the pressure referred to will be pressure above atmospheric, i.e. gage pressure. The decibar is a convenient unit since the hydrostatic pressure increases by approximately one decibar for each meter increase in depth. Thus in the deepest parts of the ocean (some 10,000 m) the pressure would be greater than atmospheric by 10,000 decibars or 10^9 dynes/cm^2 (approximately 1000 atmospheres or 15,000 lb/in^2.

Density is usually expressed in g/cm^3 or metric tons/m^3, the numerical values being identical. Density is influenced by temperature, salinity, and pressure, but never differs greatly from a value of unity. Water of salinity 30‰ at 30°C and at the surface would have a density of 1.018 g/cm^3. Water of 35‰ salinity at 0°C and 8000 m (8000 decibars pressure) would have density 1.063 g/cm^3. In computing ocean currents from the distribution of mass (Chapter 10) it is desirable to evaluate density to a precision of $\pm$ 0.00001 g/cm^3.

5.2 Thermometric Determination of Depth

Sea water samples are collected by devices which are suspended below a ship on long wires. Thermometers reversed at the time of sampling record the temperature. Since the wires do not hang vertically and their underwater configuration is not easily determinable, some method is required for determining the depth at which the samples have been collected.

The pressure above atmospheric at a depth z can be expressed by the hydrostatic equation:

$$p = \int_0^z \rho g_a dz \qquad (5.1)$$

where ρ is the density and g_a the apparent acceleration of gravity. If field variations in g_a are neglected, this can be expressed as:

$$p = g_a \rho_m z$$

where ρ_m is the mean density of the column down to the depth z. Thus, if the mean density is known, the depth z can be inferred from a measurement of pressure p. Reversing thermometers provide a means of measuring pressure, through the wide range necessary, with rather good precision.

If, instead of being sealed in a protective glass case, a reversing thermometer is left free to experience the ambient pressure, its glass bulb is compressed and an extra amount of mercury is forced up the stem. This is cut off on reversal. After correction an apparent temperature (T_u) is indicated by the unprotected thermometer which is higher than that (T) registered by a protected thermometer reversed at the same time and place.

Since the true water temperature T will already have been found from the protected thermometer the correction for change in ambient temperature may be written

$$\Delta T_u = (T'_u + V_0)\,(T - t_u)/K \qquad (5.2)$$

where t_u is the ambient temperature at the time the reading T'_u is made.

$$T_u = T'_u + \Delta T_u \text{ plus index correction.}$$

The pressure effect on thermometers is essentially linear although somewhat erratic under low pressures. The depth (z) of reversal may be written:

$$z = \frac{T_u - T}{Q \rho_m}, \qquad (5.3)$$

where Q is the pressure factor for the particular instrument used. The pressure response is such that for most instruments $T_u - T$ varies by slightly less than 1°C for a depth change of 100 m.

Thermometric depths may be determined with an accuracy of $\pm$ 5 m in the range 100–1000 m and to ± 0.5 per cent for depths greater than 1000 m (Wüst, 1933).

5.3 Density Parameters in General Use

The thermal state of any differential element of a fluid is determined uniquely and completely by $n + 1$ independent thermal variables, for a fluid mixture containing a total of n different constituents.

In a chemically pure medium ($n = 1$) two properties, say pressure (P) and specific volume (α), are sufficient to define the thermal state.

The absolute temperature (T) is defined by the equation of state for the medium with a functional form

$$T = F(P,\alpha), \tag{5.4}$$

which, for a perfect gas, is simply

$$T = P\alpha/R, \tag{5.4}$$

where R is the gas constant per unit mass for the gas. Similarly there is a functional relationship defining the entropy (η),

$$\eta = G(\alpha,P). \tag{5.5}$$

For sea water the functional relationship for temperature is somewhat more complex because of the many chemical constituents. It could be written

$$T = F(p,\alpha,Cl^-,Na^+,Mg^{++},SO_4^-,Ca^{++},K^+, Br^-,CO_3^{--}\ldots),$$

where Cl^-, Na^+, etc., refer to the ionic mass fractions, but, to the extent that the constancy of composition (see Chapter 3) holds, this may be simplified to

$$T = F(p,\alpha,S),$$

where S is the salinity as defined in Chapter 3.

More usually this is written

$$\rho = \rho_{S,\,t,\,p}, \tag{5.6}$$

where $\rho = 1/\alpha$ is the density. This says that, to a high degree of accuracy, the density of sea water is a function only of salinity (S), temperature (t), and pressure (p). $\rho_{S,\,t,\,p}$, is called the density *in situ*, that is, the density of water with the salinity and temperature observed and at the pressure appropriate to the position of observed occurrence.

Since the density of sea water is always greater than 1.0 g/cm^3 and never as great as 1.1 g/cm^3, density parameters more convenient to use are introduced such as:

$$\sigma_{S,\,t,\,p} = (\rho_{S,\,t,\,p} - 1) \times 10^3. \tag{5.7}$$

Then, instead of writing $\rho_{S,\,t,\,p} = 1.02754$, one may write $\sigma_{S,\,t,\,p} = 27.54$.

The most widely used density parameter σ_t is defined by

$$\sigma_t = (\rho_{S,\,t,\,0} - 1) \times 10^3, \tag{5.8}$$

where $\rho_{S,\,t,\,0}$ is the density of water with the indicated salinity and temperature and at atmospheric pressure. σ_t is a function of S and t only. Similarly,

$$\sigma_0 = (\rho_{S,\,0,\,0} - 1) \times 10^3 \tag{5.9}$$

is a function of salinity (chlorinity) only. This relation is

$$\sigma_0 = 0.069 + 1.4708\,Cl - 0.001570\,Cl^2 + 0.0000398\,Cl^3. \tag{5.10}$$

Knudsen's (1901) hydrographical tables give σ_0 as a function of $S‰$ and a means of evaluating an additive correction (D) to give

$$\sigma_t = \sigma_0 - D. \tag{5.11}$$

In computing the mass field for dynamic current computations (see Chapter 10) it is usual to utilize a density parameter known as the "specific volume anomaly" (δ). It is defined in the following way:

$$\delta = \alpha_{S,\,t,\,p} - \alpha_{35,\,0,\,p}, \tag{5.12}$$

where $\alpha_{S,\,t,\,p}$ is the specific volume *in situ* and $\alpha_{35,\,0,\,p}$ is the specific volume of water of 35‰ salinity at zero degrees centigrade and at the pressure (depth) p. δ can be expanded as a function of three variables giving

$$\delta = \delta_S + \delta_t + \delta_{S,\,t} + \delta_{S,\,p} + \delta_{t,\,p} + \delta_{S,\,t,\,p}. \tag{5.13}$$

It is found that the last term $\delta_{S,\,t,\,p}$ is negligible, and it is customary to lump the first three terms as $\Delta_{S,\,t}$, thus

$$\delta = \Delta_{S,\,t} + \delta_{S,\,p} + \delta_{t,\,p}. \tag{5.14}$$

Since

$$\alpha_{S,\,t,\,0} = \frac{1}{\rho_{S,\,t,\,0}} = \frac{1}{1 + 10^{-3}\,\sigma_t} = 1 - \frac{10^{-3}\,\sigma_t}{1 + 10^{-3}\,\sigma_t},$$

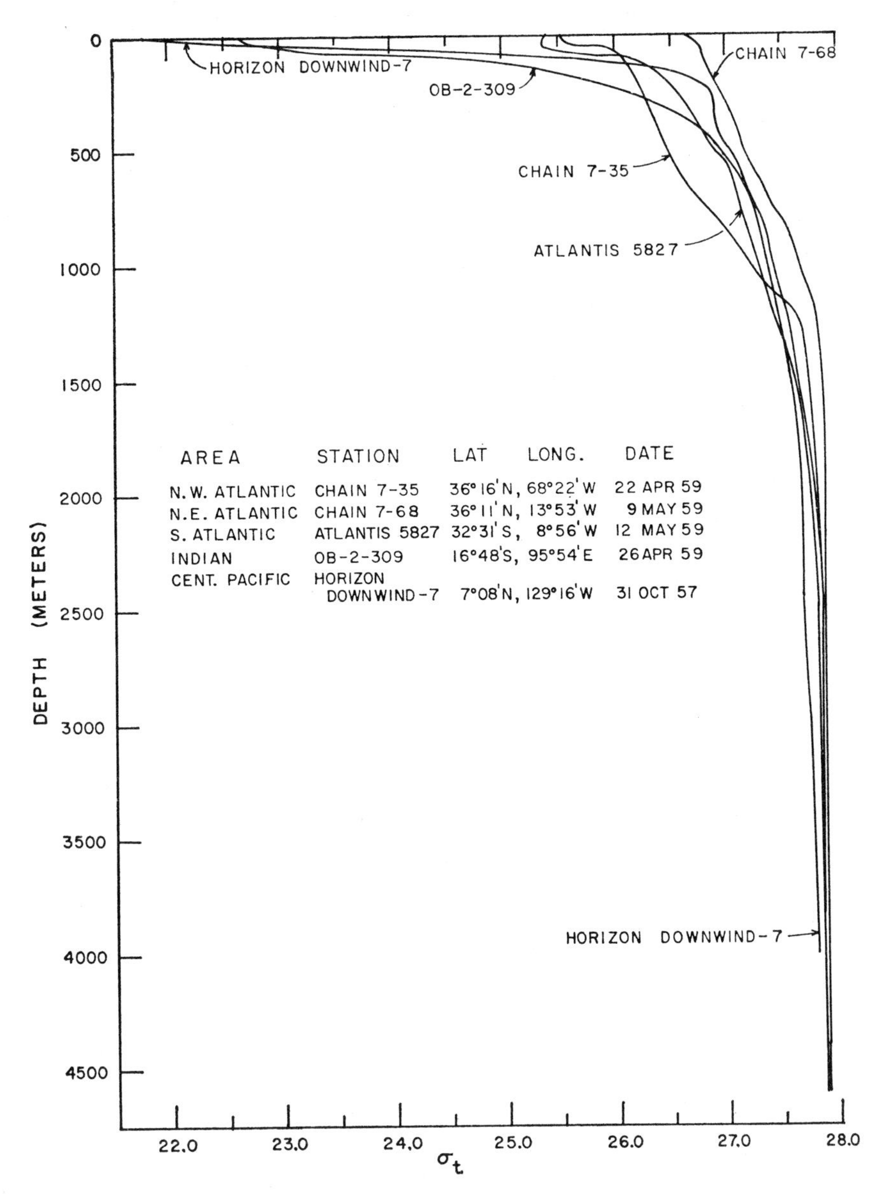

Fig. 5.1 σ_t vs. depth at selected stations.

and

$$\Delta_{S,\,t} = \alpha_{S,\,t,\,0} - \alpha_{35,\,0,\,0},$$

then

$$\Delta_{S,\,t} = 1 - \frac{10^{-3}\,\sigma_t}{1 + 10^{-3}\,\sigma_t} - \alpha_{35,\,0,\,0},$$

or, putting $\alpha_{35,\,0,\,0} = 0.97264$,

$$\Delta_{S,\,t} = 0.02736 - \frac{10^{-3}\,\sigma_t}{1 + 10^{-3}\,\sigma_t}\,. \tag{5.15}$$

$\Delta_{S,\,t}$ is thus related to σ_t.

For ease in computing δ tables are available, one which is entered with S and t and yields $\Delta_{S,\,t}$, one entered with S and p to yield $\delta_{S,\,p}$, and one entered with t and p to yield $\delta_{t,\,p}$. Both of these last are small quantities except at great depth.

Montgomery and Wooster (1954) have advocated the use of $\Delta_{S,\,t}$ as an approximate density parameter rather than the commonly used σ_t. This parameter has been given the name "thermosteric anomaly" and is quoted in units of centilitres per ton.

Another density parameter frequently referred

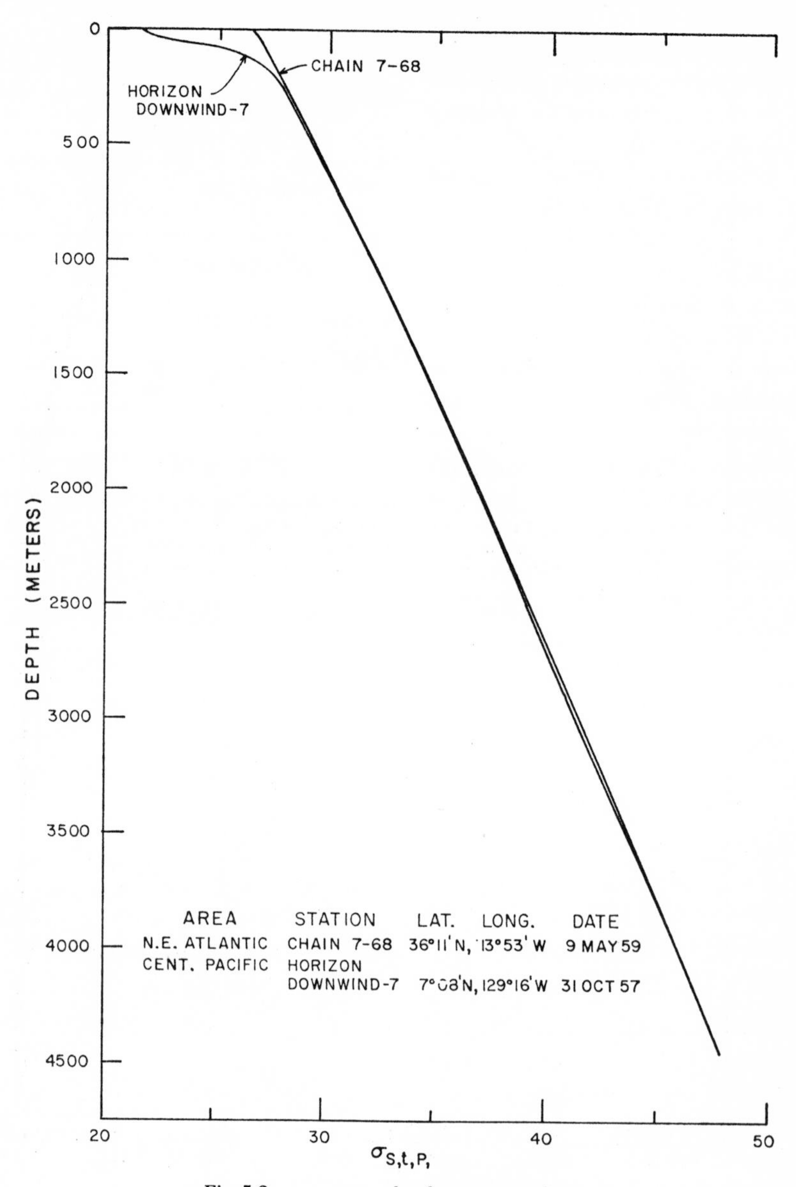

Fig. 5.2 $\sigma_{S,\,t,\,p}$ vs. depth at two stations.

to is the "potential density". This is the density a parcel of water would have if brought to the surface adiabatically. Its temperature would then be θ, the potential temperature (Section 4.6), and the potential density can be written $\rho_{S,\,\theta,\,0}$. There is the corresponding parameter

$$\sigma_\theta = (\rho_{S,\,\theta,\,0} - 1) \times 10^3. \qquad (5.16)$$

The pressure effect on density is removed in σ_t as well as in σ_θ, but σ_θ differs from σ_t by the amount that would be occasioned by the change in temperature $\theta - t$. This is seldom very great, being less than 0.2 σ_t units for a 6000 m change in depth. For this reason σ_t is sometimes rather loosely referred to as a potential density function.

5.4 Density at Selected Stations

In Fig. 5.1 σ_t vs. depth has been plotted for each of the five stations in Table 3.3. Salinity–depth and temperature–depth curves were shown in Figs. 3.3. and 4.4. Note that a rapid increase in density (pycnocline) accompanies the thermocline and that this feature is accentuated where the surface layer also exhibits low salinity values (OB-2-309 and Horizon Downwind-7). Although four of the stations showed regions where salinity decreased markedly with depth, because of the temperature structure σ_t increases with depth in all cases. This, in fact, is required for stability in the water column (Chapter 8).

For two of the stations $\sigma_{S,\ t,\ p}$ is plotted against depth in Fig. 5.2. Even with these most widely differing stations the curves are hardly separated on the scale used. Below 1000 m, $\sigma_{S,\ t,\ p}$ rarely varies from station to station by over 0.2 σ units. The variations that do take place are, however, extremely important in computing currents from the density distribution (Chapter 10). *In situ* density increases almost linearly with depth and the average $\sigma_{S,\ t,\ p}$ in the oceans is between 36 and 37. That is, the mean density of ocean water is about 1.037 g/cm^3.

References

Knudsen, M. (editor) *Hydrographical tables*. Copenhagen, G.E.C. Gad. Reprinted 1962 by G. M. Manufacturing Co., New York. 1901.

Montgomery, R. B. and W. S. Wooster. (1954) Thermosteric anomaly and the analysis of serial oceanographic data. *Deep Sea Res.* **2**, 63–70.

Wüst, G. (1933) Thermometric measurements of depth. *Hydrog. Rev.* **10** (2), 28–49.

Sources of Additional Information

Conference on Physical and Chemical Properties of Sea Water, Easton, Md. 1958. Washington, Nat. Acad. Sci., Nat. Res. Council (pub. 600). 1959.

The Oceans (Chapter III). Sverdrup, H. U., Martin W. Johnson and Richard H. Fleming. Prentice Hall, Englewood Cliffs. 1942.

Physical Oceanography, Vol. 1 (Chapters II and IV). Defant, Albert, Pergamon, New York. 1961.

CHAPTER 6

TEMPERATURE–SALINITY RELATIONSHIPS

ALTHOUGH one may characterize conditions at an ocean station by plots of temperature against depth and salinity against depth, there is generally no unique relationship which persists at one location over reasonable lengths of time or at any one time over large parts of the ocean. There do, however, exist characteristic relationships between temperature and salinity which remain virtually constant at a single location and change only very gradually in the horizontal. Temperature–salinity plots have been widely used in the analysis of oceanographic data, especially in reconstructing the history of the waters.

6.1 DEFINITIONS

If, for a station at which observations have been made at serial depths, the temperature and salinity corresponding to each depth are plotted as in Fig. 6.1, it is found that the points may be joined by a fairly simple smooth curve. This is called the "Temperature–Salinity (*T–S*) Curve" for that station.

A point on a *T–S* diagram represents water with uniform temperature and salinity—a "water type". The *T–S* curve, or a portion thereof, representing a continuum of water types describes a "water mass". Sometimes the term "water mass" is applied to a body of water throughout a region in which minor modifications of the characteristic *T–S* curve may take place.

6.2 MIXING

In the surface layer of the ocean salinity may change due to evaporation, precipitation, condensation, or runoff. Temperature may change due to absorption of solar radiation or direct exchange with the atmosphere. The initial characteristics of a water mass are achieved where it is in contact with the atmosphere. Elsewhere sea water changes its *T–S* characteristics almost exclusively by mixing with other waters of different characteristics. The form of the *T–S* curve can be considered as a clue to the mixing history.

Consider two uniform types of water referred to as water types 1 and 2, characterized by T_1, S_1, and T_2, S_2, respectively, separated by a horizontal boundary. The temperature–depth and salinity–depth relationships would be as shown by the solid lines of Fig. 6.2, and the *T–S* plot would consist of two points each representing one water type. Now consider that the waters mix across the boundary so that *T–Z* and *S–Z* relationships progress towards those shown by the broken curves of Fig. 6.2. Mixtures of water types 1 and 2 in any proportions whatsoever will result in products of mixing characterized by points on the straight line which joins the parent water types on the *T–S* diagram. Actually this is strictly so only if the specific heat has the same value for the two water types. For the normal range of temperature and salinity in the oceans the specific heat ranges from 0.945 to 0.925 cal/g, decreasing as temperature or salinity increases. Only in extreme cases would the departure from straight line mixing be greater than the uncertainty in temperature measurement.

Now consider a three-layer system as illustrated in Fig. 6.3. Initially there are three points on the *T–S* diagram, and, after mixing, two straight lines which meet at a point. Should mixing take place to the extent that there is no longer any water remaining with the original characteristics of the intermediate layer there would yet be a *T–S* curve to which the original straight lines lie tangent.

Wüst's (1935) "core method" for following the flow and mixing of an intermediate layer that is characterized by a salinity maximum or minimum utilizes *T–S* diagrams. Figure 6.4 illustrates the modification by mixing of the core of Antarctic Intermediate water as it flows northward in the Atlantic Ocean (see Chapter 7). Stockman (1946) has developed at some length a theory of *T–S*

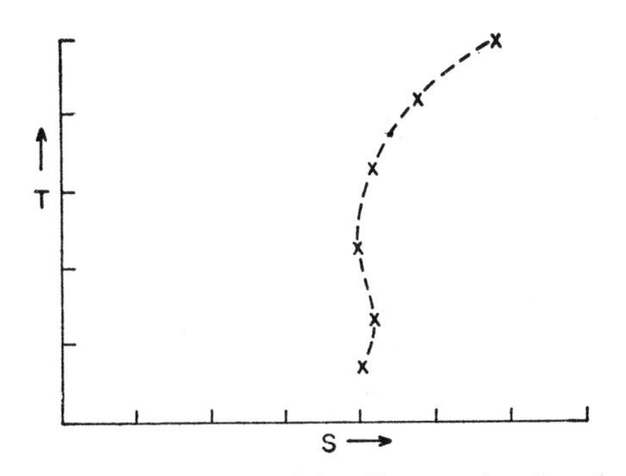

Fig. 6.1 A temperature–salinity diagram showing observed points and the *T–S* curve.

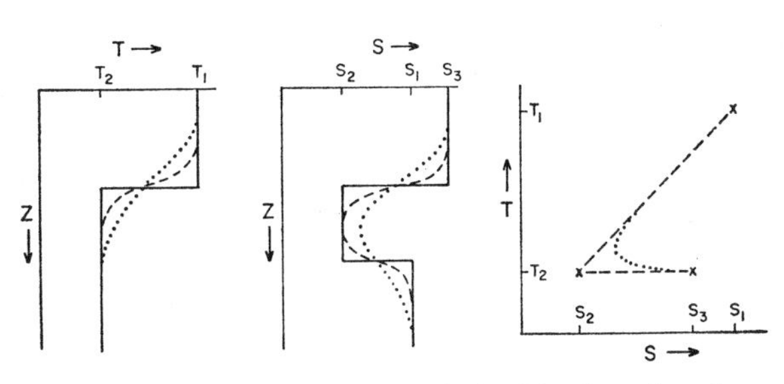

Fig. 6.3 *T–Z*, *S–Z*, and *T–S* relationships in a three-layer system.
——— and × before mixing.
– – – – – – after initial mixing.
· · · · · · · after mixing has altered all layer 2 water.

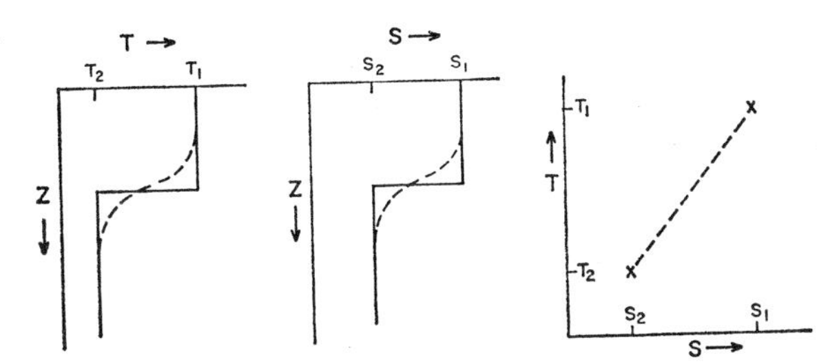

Fig. 6.2A Temperature–depth, salinity–depth and *T–S* relationships in a two-layer system.
——— and × before mixing.
– – – – – – after mixing.

curves and how they can be used to quantitatively evaluate mixing.

Since mixing tends to produce smooth *T–S* curves, the data points for a station may usually be joined up by a comparatively simple curve. This curve provides a check on interpolations to give temperature and salinity values at depths not sampled. The interpolations are carried out independently for temperature and salinity, but the results, when plotted on a *T–S* diagram, must fall on the curve through the observations.

Except for regions where major oceanic boundaries are crossed, the *T–S* curve changes only gradually from place to place. Comparison of station data on the *T–S* diagram against characteristic curves for the region can be of use in eliminating observational errors in the data.

If lines of equal σ_t are drawn on the *T–S* diagram as in Fig. 6.4 and the points are labeled as to depth, it becomes possible to estimate qualitatively the

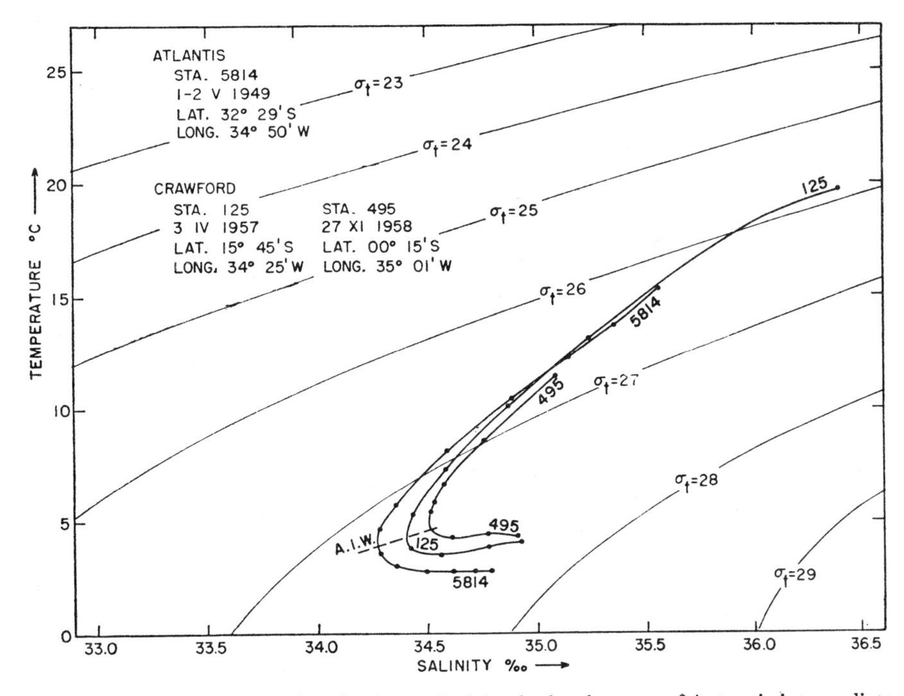

Fig. 6.4 *T–S* curves for three stations in the south Atlantic showing core of Antarctic intermediate water.

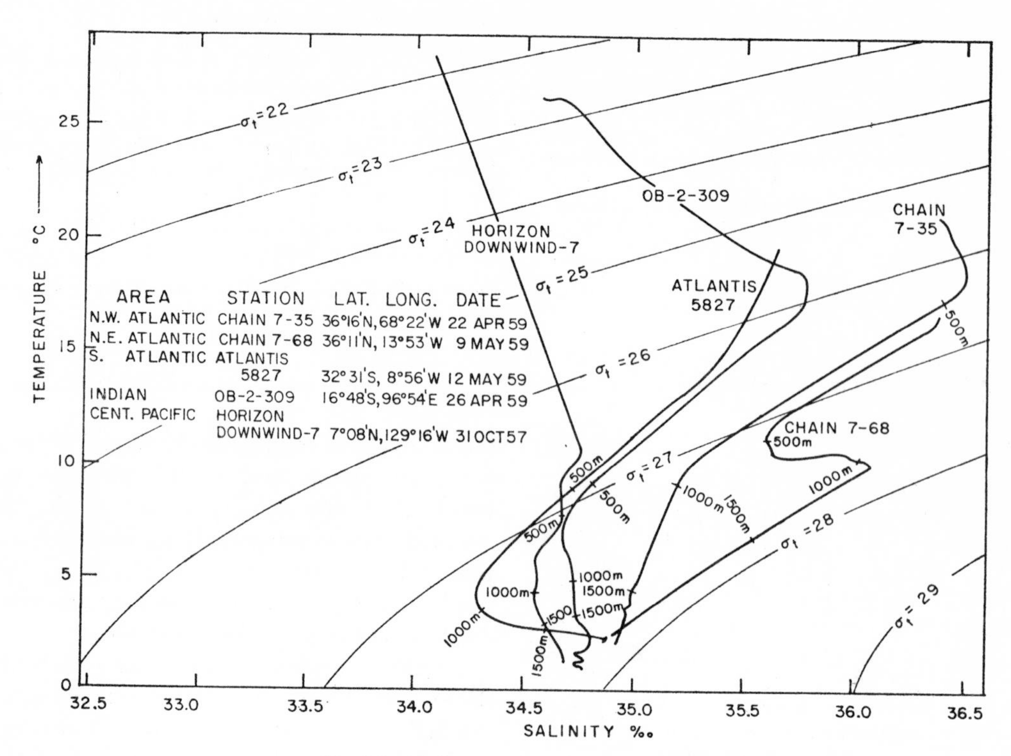

Fig. 6.5 *T–S* curves for selected stations.

vertical stability (see Section 8.3) of the water column. Plots which indicate a negative stability (σ_t decreasing with depth) must be suspect of error in observation. The recent introduction of the term "thermosteric anomaly" (Section 5.3) has led to the frequent use of this parameter in place of σ_t on *T–S* diagrams.

When horizontal mixing takes place in the ocean, there is reason to believe that it is likely to take place most effectively along surfaces of constant σ_t since buoyant forces (Section 8.6) do not inhibit exchange (Montgomery 1938). As can be seen from the curvature of the σ_t line on the *T–S* diagram (Fig. 6.4), if unlike waters with the same σ_t mix, the products of mixing, characterized by the straight line on the *T–S* diagram, will all be of greater density (σ_t) than either of the parent water types. The mixed water would then tend to sink below the unmixed waters. This process is known as cabelling. Actually *T–S* characteristics vary continuously over most of the ocean and there are very few situations where waters of similar σ_t but greatly different temperatures and salinities might mix directly. Thus, although cabelling can potentially contribute to vertical circulation, it is probably of no great significance.

6.3 *T–S* Curves for Selected Stations

In Fig. 6.5 the *T–S* curves for each of the five stations in Table 3.3 are shown. Variation of parameters with depth have been shown in Figs. 3.3, 4.4, and 5.1. Each station exhibits a curve that clearly distinguishes it from those from the other ocean areas. Each curve would be closely duplicated by other stations near by. Each curve shows regions which approximate to straight lines, indicating that a reasonably small number of parent water types need be invoked to explain the observed conditions.

Atlantis 5827 shows an inflection associated with a salinity minimum. This is indicative of the influence of Antarctic Intermediate Water as mentioned above. Chain 7-68 shows a double inflection where high salinity water of Mediterranean origin appears in the column.

Some of the more important water types and water masses will be discussed in the following chapter.

References

MONTGOMERY, R. B. (1938) Circulation in upper layers of southern North Atlantic deduced with use of isentropic analysis. *Papers in Phys. Oceanog. and Meteor.* **6** (2), 1–55.

STOCKMAN, W. B. (1946) A theory of *T–S* curves as a method of studying the mixing of water masses in the sea. *J. Mar. Res.* **6** (1), 1–24.

WÜST, G. (1935) Die Stratosphare. *Deutche Atlantische Exped. Meteor* 1925–1927, *Wiss. Erg.* Bd. 6, 1 Teil, 2 Lief, 288 pp.

Sources of Additional Information

PARR, A. E. (1938) Isopycnic analysis of current flow by means of identifying properties. *J. Mar. Res.* **1** (2), 133–154.

PARR, A. E. (1938) Analysis of current profiles by a study of pycnomeric distortion and identifying properties. *J. Mar. Res.* **1** (4), 269–290.

Dynamical Oceanography (Chapter VII). PROUDMAN, J. Methuen, London. 1953.

CHAPTER 7

CURRENTS AND WATER MASSES

It seems fitting at this point to make a cursory examination of the gross circulation patterns and the distribution of physical properties in the ocean. The conditions observed must be the result of interactions between the ocean and the atmosphere and some references will be made to the processes involved. Later, under such headings as Wind Driven Currents, The Heat Budget of the Ocean, and Thermohaline Circulation, progress towards understanding the interactions will be examined. The picture presented, however, has been pieced together from careful observations only. The test for theoretical models as they develop will be their success in explaining the existence of the observed situation.

It is not within the scope of this work to give a complete and detailed description, and this can better be done after the reader had gained some familiarity with the processes involved. The reader is referred to texts by Sverdrup *et al.* (1942, Chapter XV), Defant (1961), and Deitrich (1957 and 1963) for general descriptions with concurrent theoretical explanations. For particular regions of the oceans, monographs of Iselin (1936), Wüst (1935), Deacon (1937), Stommel (1958), may be referred to as well as papers in the scientific journals such as Munk (1950), Stommel (1957), etc.

7.1 Surface Currents in the World Ocean

Figure 7.1 depicts the gross features of the semi-permanent surface current regime in the oceans as it is currently believed to be. It is intended that this figure present only a schematic picture of the regime, and that for no particular season of the year. The circulation in the Indian Ocean is, however, perhaps applicable, as shown, only to the general period of Northern Hemisphere winter, and the equatorial counter current in the Atlantic Ocean is perhaps better developed than here shown during the Northern Hemisphere summer.

There is no single coherent set of data from which this complex circulation can be described. Rather, a synthesis of data of many types and from many sources is required. Included are historical records of ship's drift as computed by many navigators, direct measurements with current meters from anchored ships, observations of the drift of ice, and of other materials floating on or near the surface. Much of the information has been deduced from the observed distribution of temperature, salinity, and chemical characteristics of the waters and still more has been inferred from the observed distribution of mass using the methods to be discussed in Chapter 10.

The most striking feature of the circulation is the Antarctic Circumpolar Current which completely encircles the globe in a broad band centered approximately at 60° south latitude. Weak currents in an opposite direction occur close to the Antarctic Continent, though this flow does not completely encircle the continent.

The equatorial Pacific is characterized by a series of zonal flows (flow to the east or west along a parallel of latitude) in opposite directions. The equatorial currents flow westward while the equatorial counter currents, that separate them, flow eastward. Until 1961 when J. L. Reid uncovered evidence of the existence of a south equatorial counter current, it was generally believed that the equatorial current and the south equatorial current formed a continuous band of west flowing water to which the name south equatorial current was assigned. The terminology here used has not been the subject of general agreement and is used only because it appears reasonable.

The subtropical North Pacific features a huge anticyclonic (clockwise in the Northern Hemisphere) gyre, with the extremely swift and narrow Kuroshio current along the western boundary. The Kuroshio extension and the North Pacific current becomes progressively more difuse. The southward flow along the eastern boundary is in the broad slow-moving California current. Latitudinal variations in the magnitude of the acceleration associated with a rotating earth (Chapter 9) provides a theoretical explanation for the intensification of the western boundary current in oceanic gyres regardless of hemisphere or source of rotation (Stommel, 1948).

A cyclonic gyre, somewhat distorted by the interposition of the Aleutian arc, is a feature of the boreal North Pacific. Here again, the Alaskan current on the east is broad and slow while the cold Oyashio current is comparatively well defined. The subtropical gyre in the South Pacific is again anti-cyclonic but the western boundary current is not a well defined current, and the Humboldt (sometimes referred to as the Peru or Peru–Chile current) is the most distinctive part of the gyre.

There is no present evidence for a south equatorial counter current in the Atlantic. The south equatorial current bifurcates to flow southwest in the Brazil current and northwest along the north coast of South America in the Guiana current.

A narrow, swift flowing current develops at the Yucatan Straits where water flows from the Caribbean into the Gulf of Mexico. After making a wide loop this flow continues out the straits of Florida as part of the Gulf Stream System. North of the Bahamas much more water is entrained into the Gulf Stream, making it the most intense, and certainly the most studied, of the ocean currents. The North Atlantic current was formerly thought of as an extension of the Gulf Stream, but Worthington (1962) has shown that the difference in oxygen content of the waters suggests that there is a second anti-cyclonic gyre to the northeast of the subtropical gyre, somewhat as here shown.

Part of the North Atlantic current turns north into the Norwegian Sea carrying warm waters into high latitudes and supplying the main inflow into the Arctic Ocean. The compensating outflow of the colder less saline waters holds to the west side of the Greenland Sea in the East Greenland current which rounds Cape Farewell and flows north as the West Greenland current. The net flow through the various channels in the Canadian archipelago is from the Arctic. These waters join with those of the West Greenland current to form the Labrador current, thus completing a boreal cyclonic gyre as in the North Pacific.

Considerable effort has been expended upon the study of details of the Gulf Stream System and it is clear that it is a much more complex flow than is here depicted. The reader is referred to Stommel's (1958) monograph on this subject and to a recent study by Fuglister (1963). In the region down stream from Cape Hatteras, large meanders tend to form in the main stream, which in some cases serve to pass eddies of cold water to the south (Fuglister and Worthington, 1951). East of 65° west longitude, there is probably always more than one distinct filament of eastward flowing water (Fuglister, 1951). One of these filaments probably carries "slope water" which is a mixing product formed on the left side of the main stream (McLellan, 1957). The known complexity of the instantaneous Gulf Stream is probably a result only of the intensive study and it is to be expected that similar features may characterize other major currents.

At the straits of Gibraltar, surface waters flow into the Mediterranean in sufficient volume to replace the net loss by evaporation from that sea and the subsurface outflow of denser waters over the sill.

Currents in the North Indian Ocean are quite variable, with the north equatorial current subsiding and being replaced by an east flowing monsoon current in August and September. In the South Indian Ocean the subtropical anti-cyclonic gyre is a permanent feature, though of variable strength. The western boundary current, the Agulhas current, is strong and sharply defined. Most of the Agulhas current turns toward the East south of Africa but some of these waters round the Cape of Good Hope to form part of the Benguela current. Although the Benguela current is more diffuse than the Brazil current, the contrast is less striking than in the anti-cyclonic gyres of the North Pacific, North Atlantic, and South Indian Oceans.

7.2 Surface Temperature of the World Oceans

The surface temperature of the world oceans is depicted in Figs. 7.2 and 7.3 for February and August respectively. As would be expected, the waters are warmer in the tropics and cooler towards high latitudes. Likewise each hemisphere shows higher temperatures in the summer than in winter. The winter cooling is especially marked in inshore regions such as the Mediterranean, Northern Gulf of Mexico and Japan Sea. Isotherms are closely packed along the east coasts of Asia and North America where the western boundary currents of the subtropical and boreal

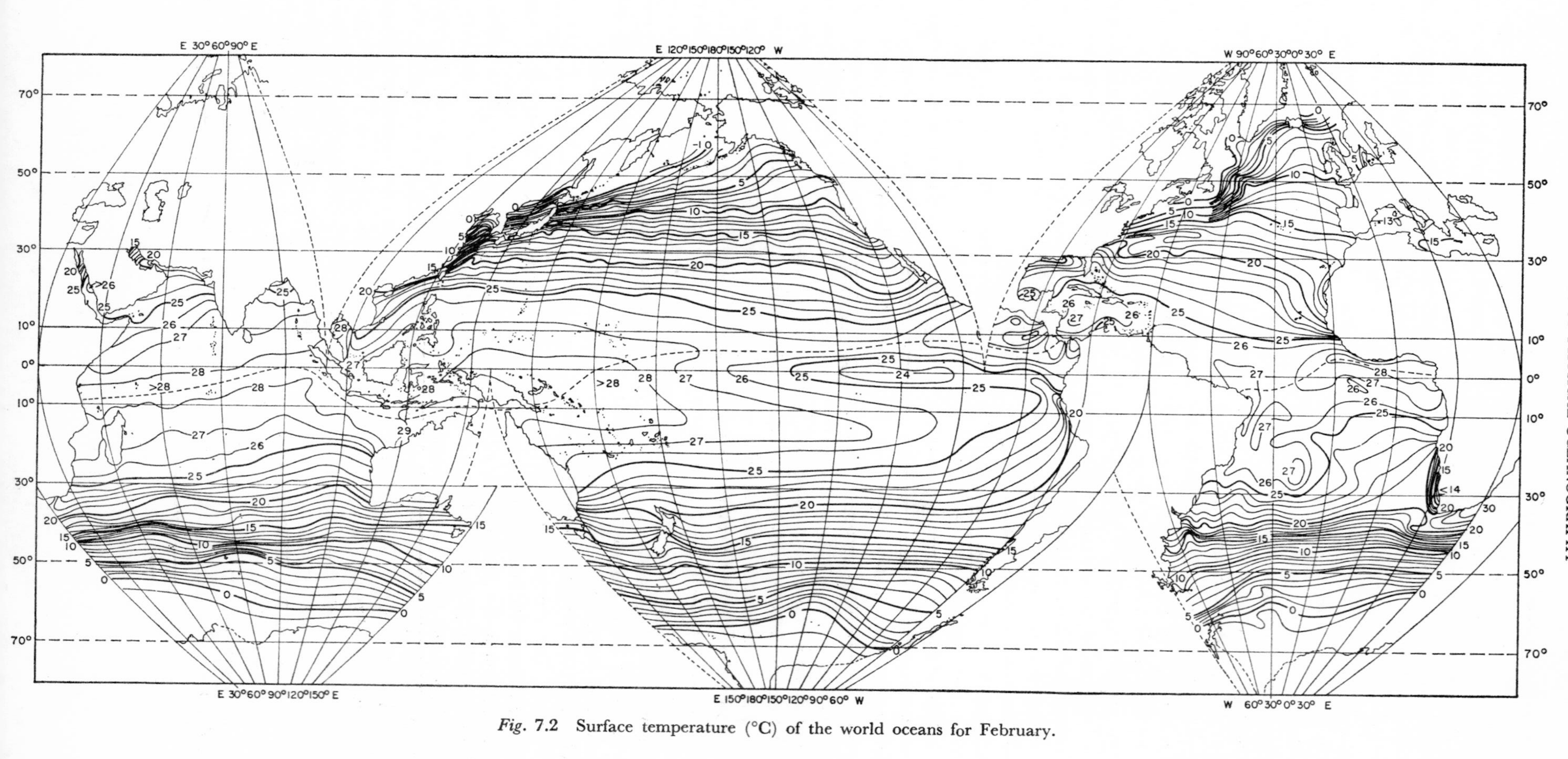

Fig. 7.2 Surface temperature (°C) of the world oceans for February.

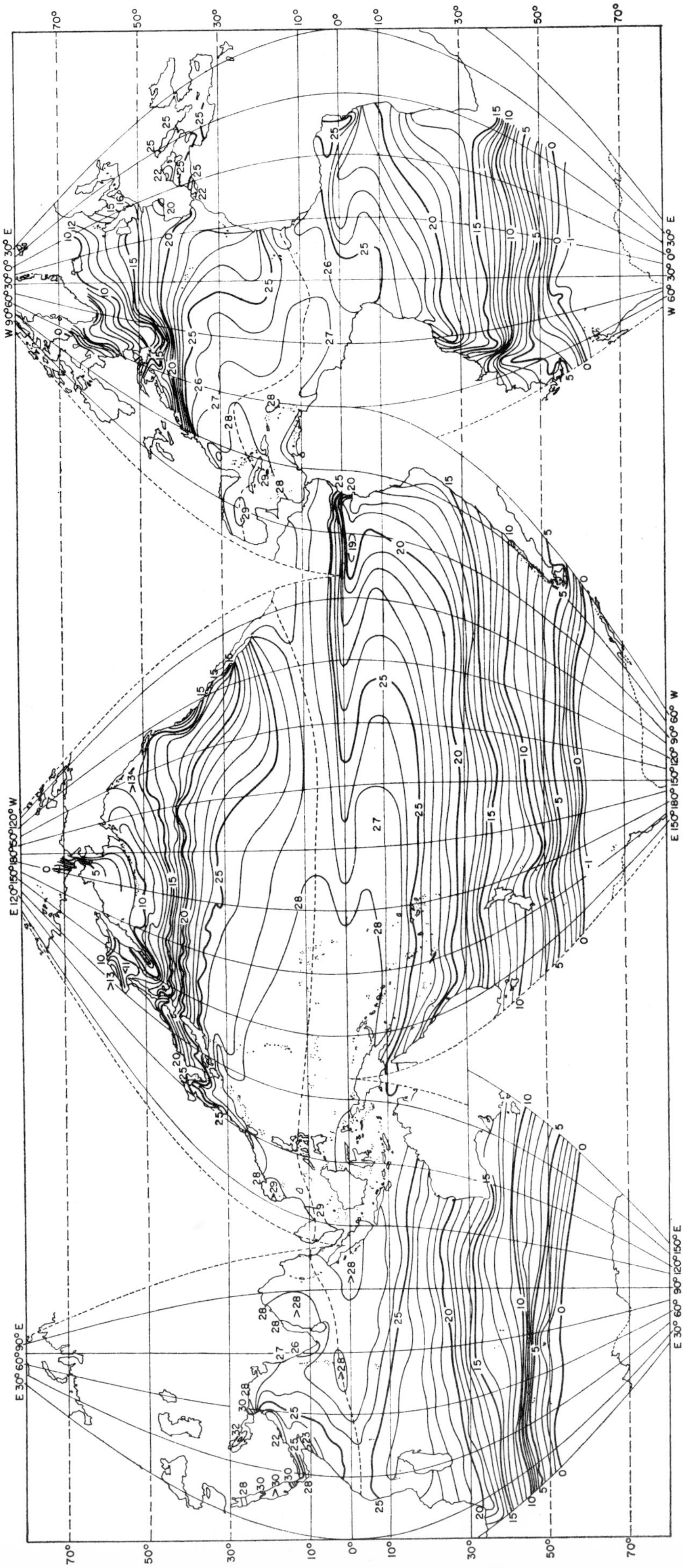

Fig. 7.3 Surface temperature (°C) of the world oceans for August.

gyres interact. To a lesser extent this effect is apparent off the Argentine Coast where the Falkland and Brazil currents flow in close proximity.

The effects of the current systems are notable along the eastern sides of the North Atlantic and North Pacific where they result in higher temperatures north of 40° north latitude and lower temperatures to the south than at similar latitudes on the western side.

Particularly noteworthy are the sharp gradients found off the Peruvian coast near the equator where the cold Humbolt current turns westward. Periodically a short term modification of the local current system will bring about an abnormal southward displacement of this feature with resultant mass mortality of marine life in the region (see Sverdrup *et al.*, 1942, p. 704).

Note the low temperatures attained south of Greenland in February and in the Weddell Sea during August. In these locations cooling and evaporation produce some of the heaviest waters that have widespread distribution in the ocean. These waters sink and spread out through the basins, the North Atlantic Deep and Bottom Water spreading southward through the Atlantic and the Antarctic Bottom Water flowing north as a wedge under the North Atlantic Deep and Bottom Water. Similarly low temperatures occur in the North Pacific and Ross Sea but, because the salinities are considerably lower (Fig. 7.4) no deep water is formed and the deep waters of the Pacific Ocean come from the Atlantic and Antarctic regions. Similarly, low salinity precludes deep water formation in the Labrador Sea.

Of meteorological interest are the regions where surface temperatures as high as 28°C occur. Tropical cyclones are generated only in regions away from the equator where the wind blows over a long stretch of water having these high temperatures. These are the regions of the Trade Winds. In late northern summer these conditions are fulfilled in the Caribbean, Gulf of Mexico, and Antilles region of the North Atlantic, in the western North Pacific, and in the northern Indian Ocean. During northern winter they are restricted to the South Indian Ocean and the region north of Australia.

7.3 Surface Salinity of the World Ocean

Figure 7.4 depicts the surface salinity of the oceans. Strong horizontal gradients occur in the regions where boundary currents of the boreal and subtropical gyres interact. In each ocean the highest values are found in the arid sub-tropical regions; the highest (> 37.25‰) in the Atlantic and the lowest value in the North Pacific (> 35.5‰).

Surface salinities are generally higher than 38‰ in the Mediterranean, and over 40‰ in the Red Sea. The inland seas of Asia, i.e. the sea of Okhotsk, Sea of Japan, Yellow Sea, and South China Sea, all have surface salinities in the low thirties. Values in the Gulf of St. Laurence, Hudson Bay, and Foxe Basin are typically 30‰ or slightly lower, while the Baltic shows values less than 20‰, and the Gulf of Bothnia 5‰ and less.

Coastal salinities are influenced by runoff and ice melting. Localized low values appear off the mouths of big river systems. Note, for example, the influence of the St. Laurence, the Mississippi, the Amazon, the La Plata, the Niger, and Congo in the Gulf of Guinea, the Ganges and, more notably, the Irrawaddy in the Bay of Bengal. Some of these river systems have marked annual variation in runoff which result in large seasonal variations in surface salinity off shore.

The low salinities in the Gulf of Panama result from high precipitation over the Isthmus of Panama and the coastal region of Columbia, west of the Andes. There are no large rivers so coastal runoff, and high precipitation rates over the ocean itself probably account for this distribution. This is a seasonal effect, the picture shown applying to northern summer. In the dry northern winter the anomaly almost disappears. The coastal effect off the southern coast of West Africa, where large rivers are absent, is also attributable to a band of heavy precipitation at the very coast.

7.4 Water Masses and Circulation of the Atlantic

Figure 7.5 shows, in vertical sections, the distributions of temperature, salinity and oxygen in the Western Atlantic according to Wüst (1935). Figure 7.6 shows schematically the major water masses involved and it is from their characteristics that the overall circulation of the Atlantic is inferred.

The west to east circulation around the Antarctic continent shown in Fig. 7.1 continues to considerable depth and involves a very uniform water mass with salinity 34.7‰, temperature 0°C

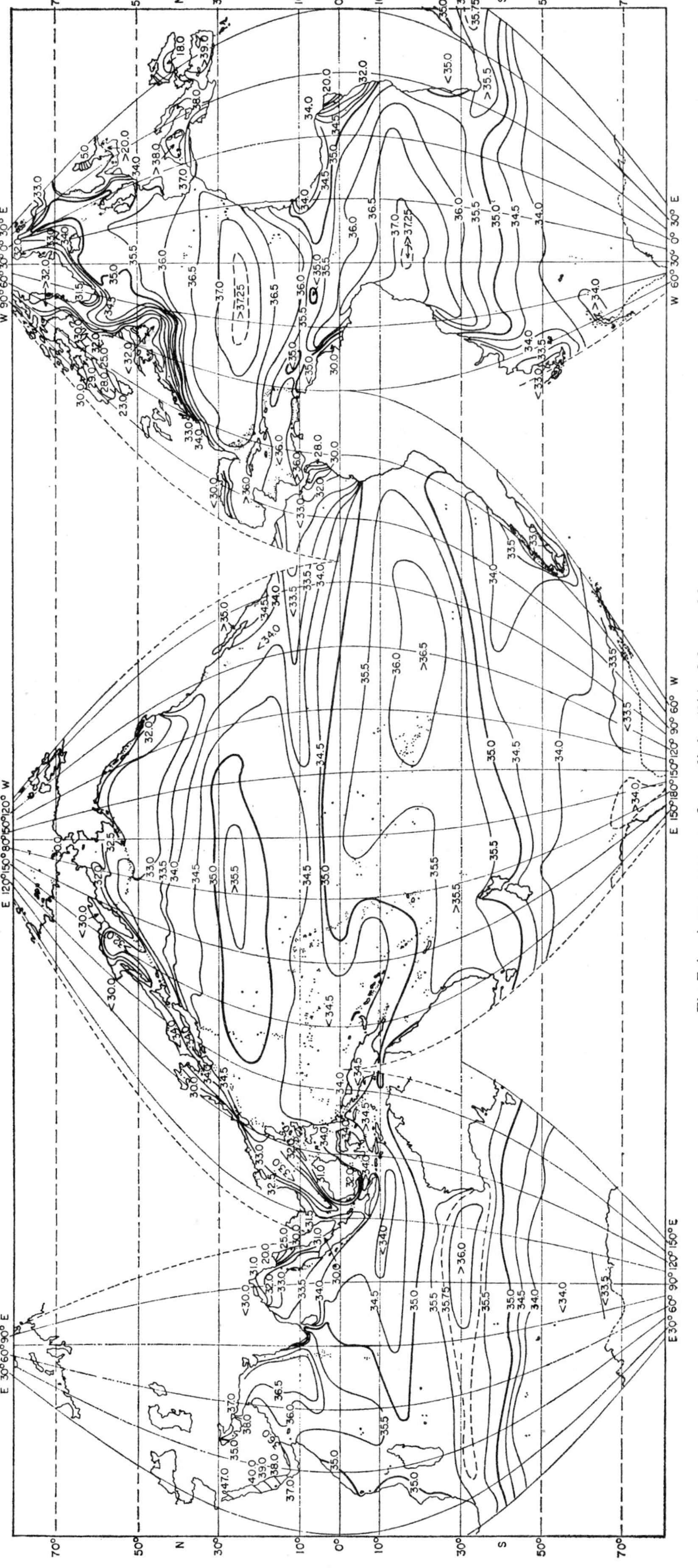

Fig. 7.4 Average sea-surface salinity (‰) of the world oceans.

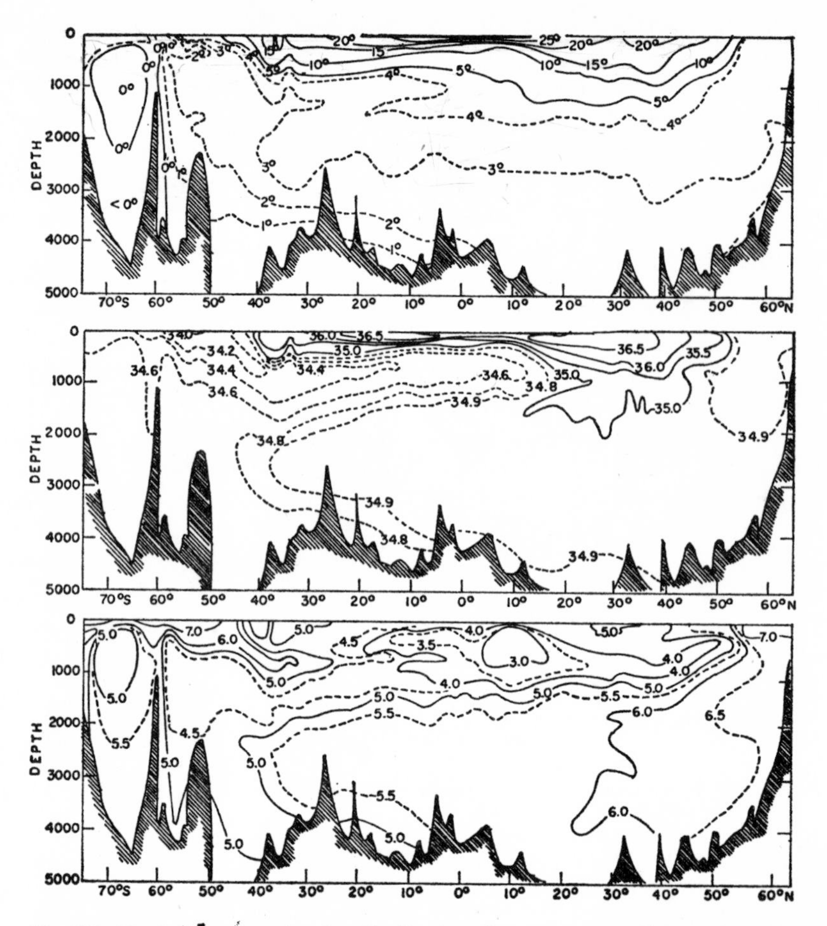

Fig. 7.5 Vertical sections showing distribution of temperature, salinity and oxygen in the western Atlantic Ocean.

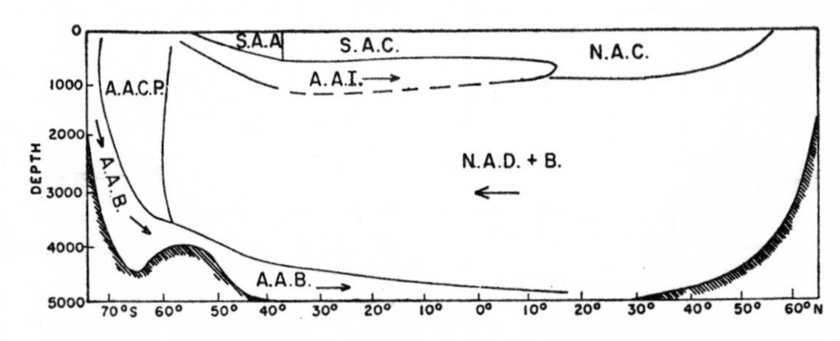

Fig. 7.6 Schematic relationships of water masses in the Atlantic.

and dissolved oxygen 5 ml/l. in the Atlantic section (we will see that these values are slightly altered in the Pacific section). This we call Antarctic Circumpolar Water (AACP).

Shelf water from the Weddell Sea at near freezing temperatures mixes with circumpolar waters to form the heaviest waters in the ocean (Fofonoff, 1956) which sink along the continental slope as Antarctic Bottom Water (AAB). Characteristics are salinity slightly over 34.6‰, temperature less than 0°C and dissolved oxygen content over 5 ml/l. This water flows into the deeper parts of the Atlantic Basin and was perhaps detected by Gerard *et al.* (1962) off the north coast of Brazil in the North Atlantic.

In the North Atlantic, around Greenland, winter cooling and evaporation produces the North Atlantic Deep and Bottom Water (NAD&B)

with salinity 34.9‰, temperatures from 2°C to 4°C and oxygen content greater than 6 ml/l. at its source.* This water mass flows south filling the greater part of the Atlantic Basin and mixes with the Circumpolar water as they flow south of Africa and through the Indian Ocean section to form the very uniform and most abundant water mass that occupies the deep Pacific (sometimes called Common Water). Although the southward flow of the Deep Water has generally been considered to be slow or "sluggish," Defant (1941) showed evidence that it was concentrated in relatively swift western boundary currents. Stommel (1957) constructed a theoretical model of ocean circulation that required just this, and Swallow and Worthington (1961) confirmed the concept by direct measurements. It is likely, then, that the horizontal circulation within this water mass is quite complex.

Between 50° and 60° south latitude, at the Antarctic Convergence, Antarctic Intermediate Water (AAI) with salinity 34.2‰, temperature 4°C, and dissolved oxygen greater than 6 ml/l. is formed. This water flows toward the north at intermediate depths (500 to 1000 m) as a core identified by a salinity minimum in the vertical profile. As such it can be detected well north of the equator and, as a last remnant, in the Gulf of Mexico. This water mass is progressively modified along its flow by vertical mixing with the waters from above and below.

In the central portion of the North Atlantic the upper 1000 m is occupied by a characteristic water mass which Iselin (1936) called Central Atlantic Water and Sverdrup refers to as North Atlantic Central Waters (NAC). The properties vary from salinity 36.5‰ and temperature 18°C to salinity 35.1‰ and temperature 8°C. This water makes up most of the circulation within the subtropical gyre of the North Atlantic. The 18°C water is a particularly stable feature that has been discussed by Worthington (1959) and others.

In the surface layer of the South Atlantic there is a corresponding water mass, the South Atlantic Central Water (SAC) ranging from 35.9‰ salinity and 18°C to 34.6‰ and 8°C.

Between this and the Antarctic Convergence lies the Sub-Antarctic Water mass (SAA) with low temperatures and variable salinity from 34.6‰ to 34.0‰.

Not depicted in Fig. 7.6 is another intermediate water mass of the Atlantic which flows out over the sill of the Mediterranean and spreads out into the Atlantic at some 1500 m depth, being modified

* A question remains as to the continuity in time of deep water formation in the North and South Atlantic. Clearly formation is restricted to the respective winter seasons, and it is possible that North Atlantic Deep Water may form only during the more severe winter seasons. Moreover, the North Atlantic Deep Water may be formed in part from waters of the Norwegian Sea which flows into the Atlantic over the Iceland–Faroe Ridge (Steele *et al.*, 1962) and through the Faroe–Faroe Bank Channel (Herman, 1959).

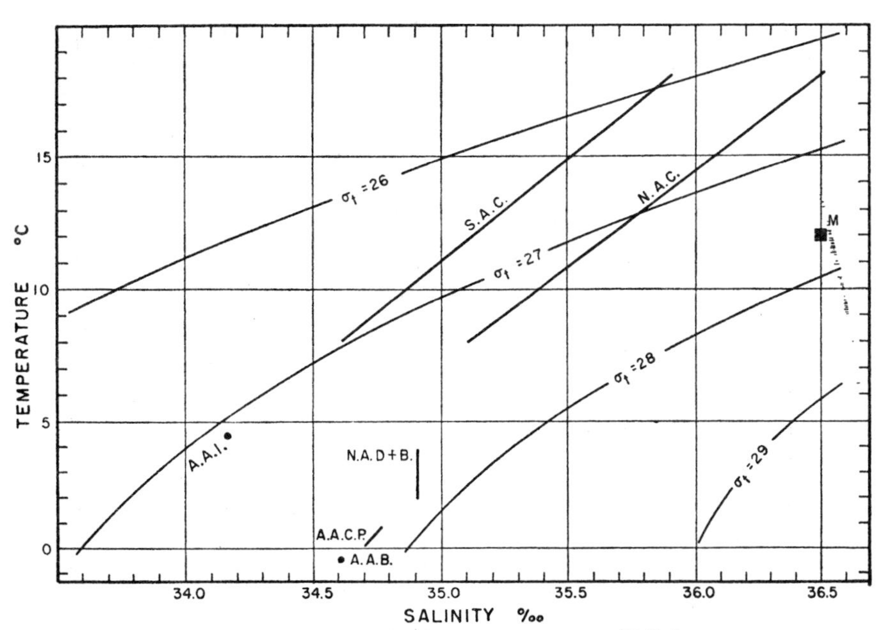

Fig. 7.7 Major Atlantic water masses on a *T–S* plot.

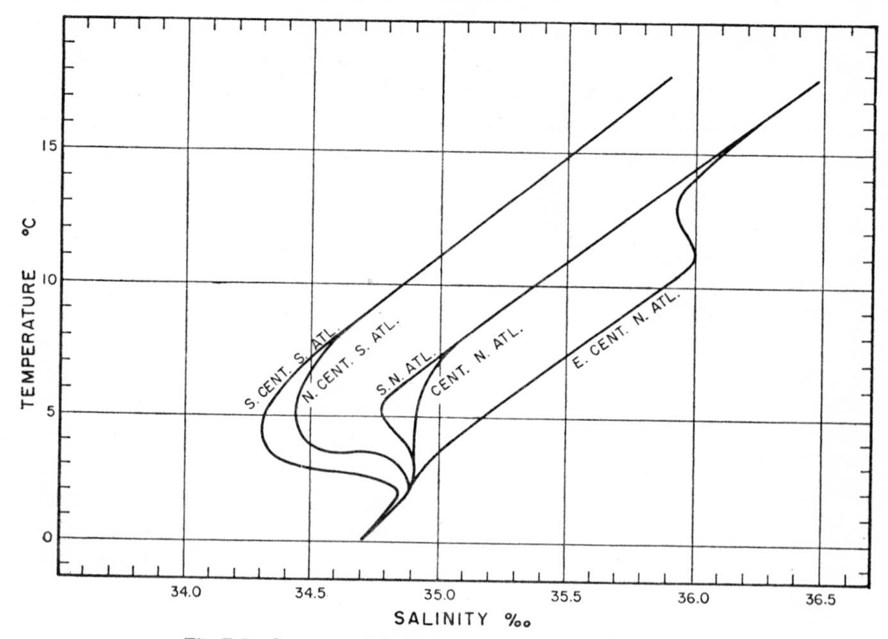

Fig. 7.8 Some possible *T–S* curves for Atlantic stations.

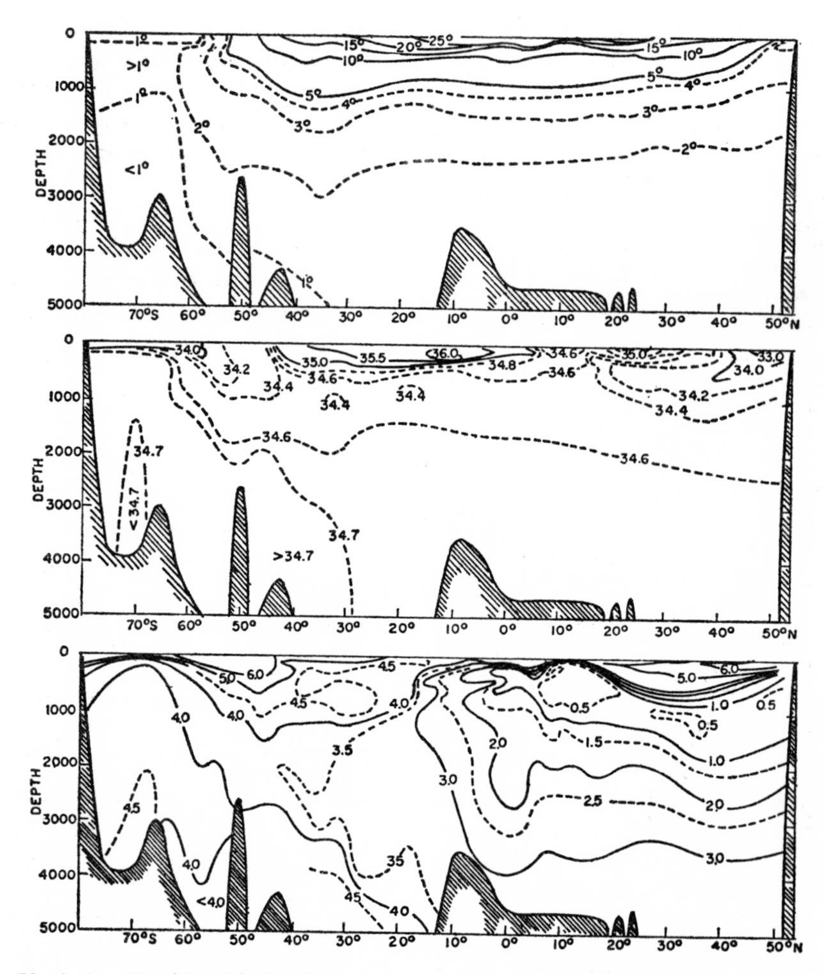

Fig. 7.9 Vertical sections showing distribution of temperature, salinity and oxygen in the Pacific Ocean.

by mixing as it proceeds. Mediterranean Water (M) is characterized by salinity 36.5‰ and temperature 12°C.

The water masses and water types here discussed are shown on a *T–S* plot in Fig. 7.7 and some of the *T–S* curves that might result at individual hydrographic stations are shown in Fig. 7.8. These may be compared to three of the curves for actual stations shown in Fig. 6.5.

7.6 Water Masses and Circulation of the Pacific

Figure 7.9 shows in vertical section the distributions of temperature, salinity and dissolved oxygen in the Pacific Ocean according to Sverdrup *et al.* (1942).

The Antarctic Circumpolar Water Mass fills the section south of 60° south latitude. The oxygen content in this water mass is slightly lower than in the Atlantic section. North of 60° south, the deeper three-fifths of the section is occupied by the Common Water with salinities between 34.6‰ and 34.7‰ and temperatures from 1°C to slightly over 2°C.

Again, at the Antarctic Convergence, Antarctic Intermediate Water is formed which sinks and flows north at some 1000 m depth. This does not appear, in the Pacific, as a distinct salinity minimum layer as it does in both the Atlantic and Indian Oceans.

In the surface layers there are a number of distinct water masses. For a description of these the reader is referred to Sverdrup *et al.* (1942), Chapter XV.

A distinctive feature of the Pacific is the low values of dissolved oxygen. This results from the fact that most of the waters are far removed from the locations where they had been in contact with the atmosphere. This is particularly true north of the equator. Here the deep waters are thought to have a clockwise circulation which is closed except for some renewal along the western edge.

Depletion of dissolved oxygen in sub-surface waters is brought about through oxidation of organic matter with the release of bound nutrient materials such as phosphate-phosphorous. The phosphate content of Pacific waters is from one and one-half to two times as great as in the Atlantic and is especially high in the North Pacific.

References

Deacon, G. E. R. (1937) The hydrology of the Southern Ocean. *Discovery Reports.* **15**, 1–125, London, Cambridge Univ. Press.

Defant, A. (1941) Die absolute Topographie des physikalischen Meeresniveaus und der Druckflachen, sowie die Wasserbewagungen im Atlantischen Ozean. *Wiss. Ergeb. Deutch. Atlant. Exped.–"Meteor"*, 1925–1927 **6**(2, 5), 191–260.

Defant, A. *Physical Oceanography*, Vol. 1. Pergamon Press, New York. 1961.

Deitrich, G. *Allgemeine Meereskunde.* Berlin, Gebruder Borntraeger. 1957.

Deitrich, G. *General Oceanography* (Translated by F. Ostapoff). Interscience, New York. 1963.

Fofonoff, N. P. (1956) Some properties of sea water influencing the formation of Antarctic Bottom Water. *Deep Sea Res.* **4**(1), 32–35.

Fuglister, F. C. (1951) Multiple currents in the Gulf Stream System. *Tellus* **3**, 230–233.

Fuglister, F. C. Gulf Stream '60. In *Progress in Oceanography*, Vol. 1. p. 263–373. Pergamon Press, New York. 1963.

Fuglister, F. C. and L. V. Worthington. (1951) Some results of a multiple ship survey of the Gulf Stream, *Tellus* **3**, 1–14.

Gerard, R., M. G. Langseth and M. Ewing. (1962) Thermal gradient measurements in the water and bottom sediment of the western Atlantic. *J. Geophys. Res.* **67**(2), 785–803.

Herman, F. (1959) Hydrographic observations in the Faroe Bank Channel and over the Faroe–Iceland Ridge, June 1959. *Cons. Int. Explor. Mer. Hydrog. Committee*, No. 118.

Iselin, C. O'D. (1936) A study of the circulation of the western North Atlantic, *Papers in Phys. Oceanog. and Meteor.* **4**(4), 1–101.

McLellan, H. J. (1957) On the distinctness and origin of slope water and its easterly flow south of the Grand Banks. *J. Fish. Res. Bd. Can.* **14**(2), 213–239.

Munk, W. H. (1950) On the wind driven ocean circulation. *J. Meteor.* **7**, 79–93.

Reid, J. L. (1961) On the geostrophic flow at the surface of the Pacific Ocean with respect to the 1000 decibar surface. *Tellus* **13**(4), 489–502.

Steele, J. H., J. R. Barrett and L. V. Worthington. (1962) Deep currents south of Iceland. *Deep Sea Res.* **9**, 465–474.

Stommel, H. (1948) The westward intensification of wind driven ocean currents. *Trans. Am. Geophys. Union* **29**, 202–206.

Stommel, H. *The Gulf Stream.* University of California Press, Berkeley. 1958.

Sverdrup, H. U., Martin W. Johnson and Richard H. Fleming. *The Oceans.* Prentice Hall, Englewood Cliffs. 1942.

Swallow, J. C. and L. V. Worthington. (1961) An observation of a deep countercurrent in the western North Atlantic. *Deep Sea Res.* **8**(1), 1–19.

Worthington, L. V. (1959) The 18°C water in the Sargasso Sea. *Deep Sea Res.* **5**(4), 297–305.

Worthington, L. V. (1962) Evidence for a two gyre circulation system in the North Atlantic. *Deep Sea Res.* **9**, 51–67.

Wüst, G. (1935) Die stratosphare. *Deutsche Atlantische Exped. Meteor* 1925–1927, *Wiss. Erg.* Bd. 6, 1 Teil Lief., 288 pp.

PART II

OCEANIC MOVEMENTS

THE waters of the ocean are in continuous motion. Many different and complex modes of motion are involved and it is necessary to study only some discrete type of motion if the problem is to be tractable. Classical hydrodynamics usually fails because of the simplifying assumptions made in order to formulate problems for which complete solutions may be generated. In particular, Coriolis acceleration is usually neglected, variation of density within the fluid is not allowed and viscosity, if not neglected, is assumed to be single valued.

We will take a stepwise approach, introducing the individual accelerative terms in the equations of motion, and investigating relationships that hold when a minimum number of these terms are considered significant. It is recognized that for some it might be preferable to first develop the equations in a complete form and to then deal with the various approximate solutions. For the intended audience, we hope that the method chosen will prove more satisfactory.

A background will be developed that should allow the reader to consider much of the recent work on theories of wind driven and inertial currents. None of these theories will, however, be presented in detail. Waves will be discussed mainly from a classical point of view and tides in a purely descriptive fashion.

CHAPTER 8

ACCELERATIONS ARISING FROM MASS DISTRIBUTION

A PARTICLE anywhere on the earth experiences an acceleration arising from the attraction of the earth's mass. It is usual to lump with this the centrifugal acceleration associated with the earth's rotation into what we call the apparent acceleration of gravity. A scalar potential function related to apparent gravity is introduced. It is found that, if pressure within a fluid is simply the hydrostatic pressure (that is pressure arising from the distribution of fluid mass in the gravity field), then increments in geopotential may be evaluated from the mass (density) distribution within the fluid. Where the fluid mass distribution is such that pressure surfaces do not coincide with geopotential surfaces the fluid will experience acceleration along the geopotential surfaces.

The acceleration resulting from the vertical perturbation of a parcel of fluid relative to its surrounding fluid is examined and the term gravitational stability is introduced.

8.1 Gravity — The Gravity Equation

The acceleration acting upon a body on or near the earth's surface, which we attribute to gravity, is the resultant of a Newtonian gravitational attraction and a component of the centrifugal acceleration associated with the earth's rotation.

The attractive force between the masses M and m whose centers are separated by a distance d is given by

$$F = \gamma Mm/d^2, \qquad (8.1)$$

where γ is the gravitational constant $= 6.664 \times 10^{-8}\ \mathrm{g^{-1}\,cm^3\,sec^{-2}}$. In the case of a small mass m at the surface of a spherically symmetric earth whose mass is M and radius a the acceleration experienced, which we call g, is given by

$$g = F/m = \gamma M/a^2. \qquad (8.2)$$

This is directed toward the center of the sphere (Fig. 8.1).

Inserting values for the mass of the earth M and its mean radius a, $M = 5.983 \times 10^{27}$ g, $a = 6.371 \times 10^8$ cm, yields a value $g = 982.3\ \mathrm{cm/sec^2}$.

A body on the surface of the rotating earth is also acted upon by a centrifugal acceleration $\Omega^2 R$ directed normally outward from the axis of rotation, where Ω is the angular velocity of rotation and R the distance from the axis of rotation (Fig. 8.1). We may write $R = a \cos\psi$ where ψ is the latitude.

The resultant or apparent acceleration g_a is directed at a small angle to g, but, since it is a very small angle, one can write to a good approximation

$$g_a = g - \Omega^2 a \cos^2\psi. \qquad (8.3)$$

At 45° latitude and at the surface (depth = 0)

$$g_{45,\,0} = g - \Omega^2 a/2. \qquad (8.4)$$

Inserting the value of g (982.3 cm/sec²) and Ω (7.292×10^{-5} radians/sec) gives $g_{45,\,0} = 980.6$ cm/sec² which is the observed value at this latitude.

Equation (8.4) can be rewritten

$$g = g_{45,\,0} + \Omega^2 a/2,$$

and

$$g_a = g_{45,\,0} - \Omega^2 a \cos^2\psi + \Omega^2 a/2$$
$$= g_{45,\,0} - (\Omega^2 a/2)(2\cos^2\psi - 1)$$
$$= g_{45,\,0} - (\Omega^2 a/2)\cos 2\psi. \qquad (8.5)$$

This is often written

$$g_a = g_{45,\,0}\,[1 - b_1 \cos 2\psi], \qquad (8.6)$$

where $b_1 = \Omega^2 a/2g_{45,\,0} = 0.00176.$

Inserting the observational value for $g_{45,\,0} = 980.6$ cm/sec² (8.6) would predict as surface values at the equator and the pole:

$$g_a\ (\text{equator}) = 978.9\ \mathrm{cm/sec^2},$$
$$g_a\ (\text{pole}) = 982.3\ \mathrm{cm/sec^2}.$$

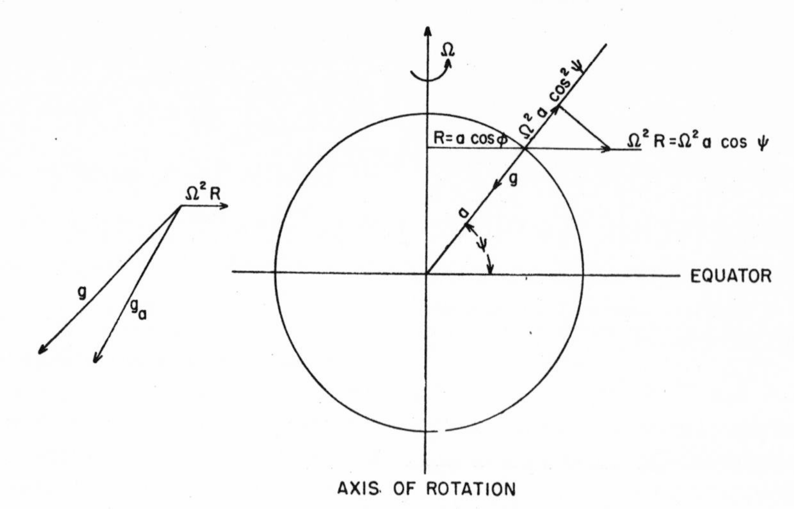

Fig. 8.1 Accelerations acting upon a body at the surface of a rotating earth.

Actual observations give:

$$g_a \text{ (equator)} = 978.0 \text{ cm/sec}^2,$$

$$\text{and } g_a \text{ (pole)} = 983.1 \text{ cm/sec}^2.$$

The departure of experimental values from the theoretical values is interpreted as arising from the fact that the earth is not a perfect sphere but more nearly an ellipsoid whose minor axis is the polar axis. The approximation (8.3) may also contribute. Irregularities in the distribution of mass may give rise to localized anomalies of gravity.

The sea-level gravity equation (8.6) is made to give a best fit to observed values by assigning an arbitrary value to b_1. Thus, we write

$$b_1 = 0.00259.$$

Equation (8.6) holds only for sea level. At a depth z in the ocean, gravity is increased by virtue of the decrease in distance from the center of the earth, and decreased because the effective mass of the earth must be decreased by the amount Δ contained in a spherical shell of thickness z. Thus

$$g_z = \gamma \frac{(M - \Delta)}{(a - z)^2} = \left(1 - \frac{\Delta}{M}\right) \frac{\gamma M}{(a - z)^2}$$

$$= g_0 \left(1 - \frac{\Delta}{M}\right) \left(\frac{a}{a - z}\right)^2, \qquad (8.7)$$

where g_z is the value at depth z and g_0 the value at sea level. Writing (8.7)

$$g_z = g_0 \left(1 - \frac{\Delta}{M}\right) \left(1 + \frac{z}{a - z}\right)^2,$$

expressing the last term in a bionomial expansion, and neglecting the terms of order $[z/(a - z)]^2$ and higher, yields:

$$g_z = g_0 \left(1 - \frac{\Delta}{M}\right) \left(1 + \frac{2z}{a - z}\right),$$

or, approximately

$$= g_0 \left(1 - \frac{\Delta}{M}\right) \left(1 + \frac{2}{a} z\right). \qquad (8.8)$$

$\Delta = 4\pi a^2 \rho z$ where ρ is the density of the shell, here taken as sea water ($\rho = 1.03$). $M = 4/3\ \pi a^3 \rho_m$ where ρ_m is the mean density of the earth taken as 5.52 g/cm³. Thus

$$\frac{\Delta}{M} = \frac{3\rho z}{\rho_m a} = \frac{0.560}{a} z,$$

and (8.8) becomes

$$g_z = g_0 \left(1 - \frac{0.560}{a} z\right) \left(1 + \frac{2}{a} z\right).$$

Performing the multiplication and neglecting the term in $(z/a)^2$ which is very much less than one, gives

$$g_z = g_0 [1 + (1.440z)/a],$$

which can be written

$$g_z = g_0 (1 + b_2 z), \qquad (8.9)$$

where $b_2 = (1.440/a) = 2.26 \times 10^{-9} \text{ cm}^{-1}$.

It should be recognized that the component due to centrifugal acceleration will also vary with distance from the surface (z) but this small change is usually neglected in the total gravity equation

$$g_a = g_{45,\,0}\,(1 - b_1 \cos 2\psi)\,(1 + b_2\,z)$$
$$= 980.6\,(1 - 0.00259 \cos 2\psi) \times$$
$$(1 + 2.26 \times 10^{-9}\,z)\ \text{cm/sec}^2 \qquad (8.10)$$

where z is in centimeters.

8.2 Geopotential

The work done in moving a unit mass a distance dz in the field of gravity, where z is measured downward (in the direction of g_a), is given by

$$\mathrm{d}W = -\,g_a\,\mathrm{d}z.$$

This is equal to the change in potential energy per unit mass associated with the change in position and we write:

$$\mathrm{d}\phi = -\,g_a\,\mathrm{d}z \qquad (8.11)$$

which defines the geopotential function ϕ.

Integrating: $$\phi = -\int g_a\,\mathrm{d}z. \qquad (8.12)$$

One of the limits of integration may be arbitrarily chosen as the reference potential. To evaluate the geopotential at a depth z referred to sea level ($z = 0$) one writes (8.12) as

$$\phi_{z,\,\text{ref }0} = -\int_0^z g_a \mathrm{d}z.$$

Using the c.g.s. system of units ϕ would be expressed in ergs/g.

In the M.T.S. (Meter, Ton, Second) system of units which is more often used in oceanography g_a would be expressed in m/sec², z in meters, and the units for ϕ would be kJ/ton $= 10^4$ ergs/g. This unit (kJ/ton) is also referred to as a dynamic decimeter.

More common still, in practical oceanographic work, is the use of a mixed set of units where geopotential is expressed in units called dynamic meters, and 1 dynamic meter $= 10^5$ ergs/g. Thus

$$\phi_{z,\,0} = -\frac{1}{10}\int_0^z g_a \mathrm{d}z \quad \text{dynamic meters} \qquad (8.13)$$

where g_a is in m/sec² and z in meters. Note that here z is measured downwards from sea level. There is no strict consistency in the sense of z within the oceanographic literature.

$\phi_{z,\,0}$ as defined by (8.13) is referred to as the "dynamic height" of a level z referred to sea level ($z = 0$). Also in common use is a geopotential unit so defined as to increase downward. This is called "dynamic depth" (D). Thus

$$D_{z,\,0} = -\,\phi_{z,\,0} = \frac{1}{10}\int_0^z g_a \mathrm{d}z. \qquad (8.14)$$

From (8.10) this may be written

$$D_{z,\,0} = \frac{1}{10}\int_0^z g_{45,\,0}\,(1 - b_1 \cos 2\psi)\,(1 + b_2 z)\,\mathrm{d}z$$

$$= (g_{45,\,0}/10)\,(1 - b_1 \cos 2\psi)\,(z + b_2 z^2/2),$$

or

$$D_{z,\,0} = 0.9806\,z\,(1 - 0.00259 \cos 2\psi) \times$$
$$(1 + 0.113 \times 10^{-6}\,z). \qquad (8.15)$$

That is, geopotential differences in dynamic meters are approximately equivalent numerically to depth intervals in meters. The dynamic depth referred to sea level would have a value of 1000 dynamic meters at a depth z equal to 1017 m at the poles or 1022 m at the equator.

8.3 Geopotential Surfaces

The apparent acceleration of gravity is the vector sum

$$\overline{g_a} = \overline{g} + \overline{g_e}, \qquad (8.16)$$

where $\overline{g}$ has a magnitude $\gamma M/r^2$, where r is distance measured outward from the center of an earth of mass M, and is directed in the $-r$ direction, and $\overline{g_e}$ has magnitude $\Omega^2 R$, where R is distance from the axis of rotation, and is directed in the R direction.

Writing these vectors as gradients of scalar potential functions:

$$\overline{\text{grad}}\,\phi_a = \overline{\text{grad}}\,\phi + \overline{\text{grad}}\,\phi_e.$$

Here

$$\overline{\text{grad}}\,\phi = -\,\mathrm{d}\phi/\mathrm{d}r = \overline{g} = -\,\gamma M/r^2$$

in the r direction, and

$$\overline{\text{grad}}\,\phi_e = -\,\mathrm{d}\phi_e/\mathrm{d}R = g_e = |\Omega^2 R|$$

in the R direction.

Now, (8.16) requires that there be a scalar potential function ϕ_a such that

$$\phi_a = \phi + \phi_e. \qquad (8.17)$$

Surfaces of constant ϕ are concentric spheres with spacing between unit values of ϕ increasing with r and numerical values increasing outward. Surfaces of constant ϕ_e are coaxial cylinders with unit spacing decreasing with R and numerical value decreasing outward. Surface of constant ϕ_a are pseudo spheres flattened at the poles as shown with great exaggeration in Fig. 8.2. These

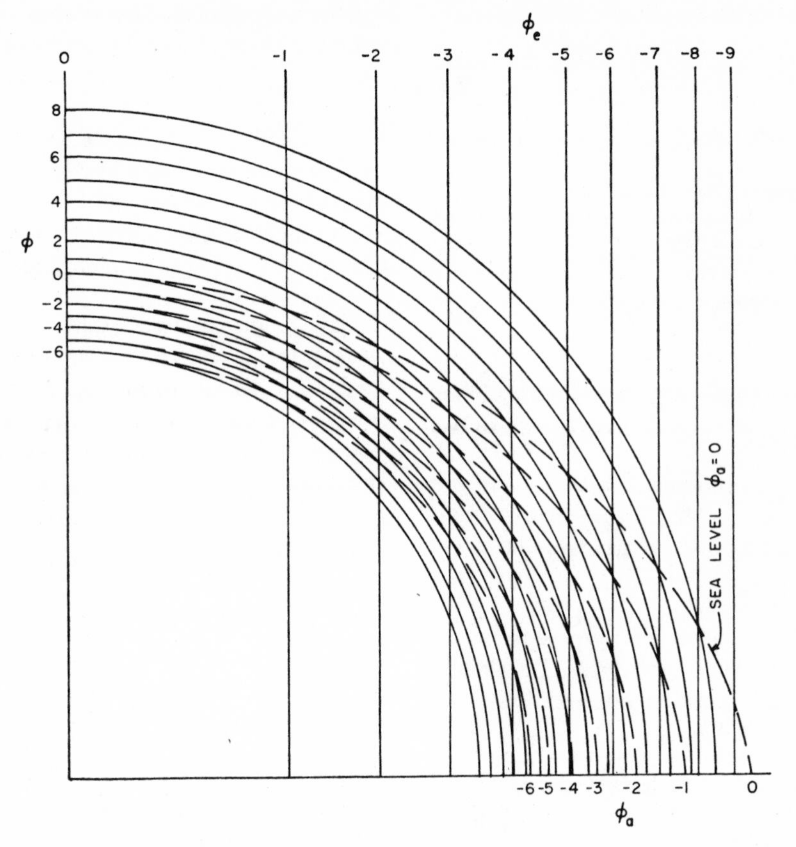

Fig. 8.2 One quadrant of a Polar section through the earth showing intersections with surfaces of constant ϕ, ϕ_a and ϕ_e. Arbitrary scales chosen to show departure from spherical shape in surfaces of ϕ_a constant.

are referred to as geopotential surfaces. The surface of the earth (mean sea level) approximates closely to a geopotential surface.

8.4 Hydrostatic Pressure

Pressure in a fluid is a single valued scalar quantity with the dimensions of energy density (ergs/cm^3 in the c.g.s. unit system). The more usual units express pressure as force per unit area (dynes/cm^2) and are also dimensionally correct. It must be remembered though that there is no preferred direction to the force.

In a fluid at rest pressure is directly related to the weight of fluid in a vertical column over a unit area normal to the direction of apparent gravity. Consider a unit area normal to the z direction (z directed with $\overline{g_a}$) in a fluid of density ρ (Fig. 8.3). If the unit area is displaced a distance Δz there is added to the fluid column above it a mass $\rho\Delta z$ and the pressure increase Δp is given by

$$\Delta p = g\rho\Delta z.$$

In the limit, as Δz approaches zero, this becomes $dp = g\rho dz$ which integrates to give $p = p_0 + \int_0^z \rho g dz$, where p_0 is the pressure at $z = 0$. In the ocean $z = 0$ usually refers to sea level, and p_0 is then atmospheric pressure. Often, although

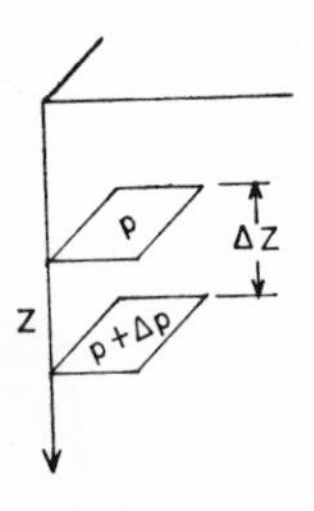

Fig. 8.3.

not specifically stated, pressure above atmospheric will be what is referred to and this will simply be written

$$p = \int_0^z \rho g dz.$$

In terms of the specific volume $\alpha (\alpha = 1/\rho)$ the differential form can be written

$$\alpha\, dp = g dz. \quad (8.18)$$

8.5 Practical Determination of Geopotential

Combining (8.11) and (8.18) yields the useful relationship

$$d\phi = -gdz = -\alpha dp, \qquad (8.19)$$

which relates the geopotential ϕ to the distribution of specific volume and pressure. Integrating from some level 1 to another level 2 yields:

$$\int_1^2 d\phi = -\int_1^2 gdz = -\int_1^2 \alpha dp,$$

or

$$\phi_2 - \phi_1 = g(z_1 - z_2) = -\int_1^2 \alpha_{35,\,0,\,p}\, dp - \int_1^2 \delta dp, \qquad (8.20)$$

where g has been considered constant over the range and α has been broken into components in accordance with (5.12).

In the so called practical units, the mixed system conventionally used by oceanographers,

$$D_2 - D_1 = (g/10)\,(z_1 - z_2) = -\int_1^2 \alpha_{35,\,0,\,p}\, dp - \int_1^2 \delta dp,$$

where D is geopotential in dynamic meters, g is in m/sec^2, z in meters, α in m^3/ton and p in decibars.

Since $\int_1^2 \alpha_{35,\,0,\,p}\, dp$ has a single value for any given range of p, this is called the standard geopotential interval, and

$$(D_2 - D_1)_{std} + \Delta D_{2,\,1} = -\int_1^2 \alpha_{35,\,0,\,p}\, dp - \int_1^2 \delta dp$$

becomes

$$\Delta D_{2,\,1} = \int_1^2 \delta dp. \qquad (8.21)$$

ΔD is called the "geopotential anomaly" and can be evaluated from the distribution of specific volume anomaly.

In practical calculations the integration process is replaced by a summation of products of mean values ($\bar{\delta}$) of δ over pressure intervals and the corresponding increments of pressure, i.e.

$$\Delta D = \sum \bar{\delta} \Delta p. \qquad (8.22)$$

It is usual to use for Δp (decibars) the number corresponding to the difference in geometric depth (meters). This introduces a small error but one that is consistent from station to station and thus has little influence on the interpretation of results. The equating of depth levels to pressure levels is justified further on the basis that pressure measurement by unprotected thermometers is the primary method of determining the depth of observation.

8.6 Stability

The gravitational stability at a point within a fluid column is a measure of the acceleration which a fluid parcel would experience if displaced a unit distance vertically from its normal position in the column without mixing. If the mass distribution is "stable" the acceleration is directed towards the initial position. Acceleration away from the initial position constitutes "instability", and when no acceleration results from displacement a condition of neutral stability is said to exist.

Consider a water column in which the density varies with depth as represented by the curve of σ_t vs. z (Fig. 8.4). If a small quantity of water from

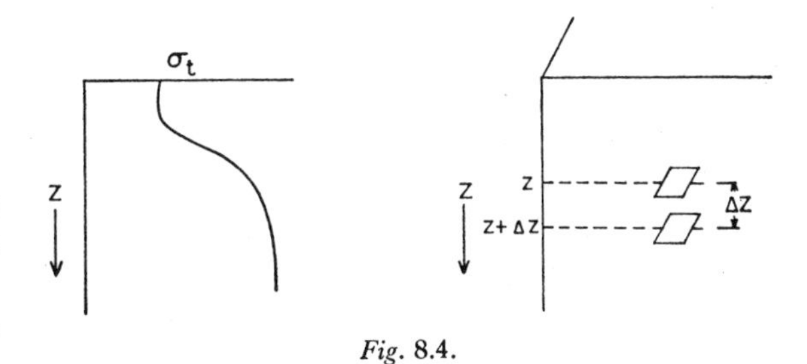

Fig. 8.4.

depth z, where σ_t has the value $(\sigma_t)_z$, is transported without mixing to a depth $z + \Delta z$ where the environment has a σ_t value $(\sigma_t)_{z+\Delta z}$, the density of the displaced parcel becomes $1 + 10^{-3}(\sigma_t)_z + \epsilon_p$ where ϵ_p is the pressure effect on density appropriate to the depth $z + \Delta z$ for the particular temperature and salinity involved. The density in the new environment is $1 + 10^{-3}\,(\sigma_t)_{z+\Delta z} + \epsilon_p'$ where ϵ_p' is appropriate to the temperature and salinity at the new depth.

For all practical purposes $\epsilon_p' = \epsilon_p$ and the difference between the density of the displaced parcel and of its environment is

$$\Delta\rho = 10^{-3}[(\sigma_t)_{z+\Delta z} - (\sigma_t)_z].$$

Because of the bouyancy effect the displaced parcel will experience an acceleration or restoring force per unit mass given by

$$\frac{d^2z}{dt^2} = -\frac{g}{\rho}\, 10^{-3}\, \frac{[(\sigma_t)_{z+\Delta z} - (\sigma_t)_z]}{\Delta z}\, \Delta z \qquad (8.23)$$

and, in the limit, as Δz approaches zero,

$$\frac{d^2z}{dt^2} = -g\frac{10^{-3}}{\rho}\frac{d\sigma_t}{dz}dz \tag{8.24}$$

$$= -gEdz \tag{8.25}$$

where
$$E \equiv \frac{10^{-3}}{\rho}\frac{d\sigma_t}{dz} \tag{8.26}$$

is called the stability.

E has dimensions 1/length and is usually reported in inverse meters.

Since the density, ρ, is seldom greatly different from unity an approximate value of stability is given by

$$E \approx 10^{-3}\, d\sigma_t/dz, \tag{8.27}$$

although this expression is not dimensionally correct.

Where

$E > 0$ that portion of the column is stable;
$E = 0$ that portion of the column is neutral;
$E < 0$ that portion of the column is unstable.

In the ocean there is a permissible range of instability limited by the condition where the density *in situ* is constant with depth $d(\rho_{S,\,t,\,p})/dz = 0$. The critical stability (E_c) for this situation is approximately

$$E_c \approx -5 \times 10^{-6}\ \mathrm{m}^{-1}.$$

For E between zero and E_c some initial disturbance is necessary to produce overturn. For E less than E_c no extraneous force is required.

Since in the real ocean there is no lack of disturbing forces, stability is almost universal. Instability may exist in the surface layers but it must indicate that processes are at work creating the instability and that vertical circulation is taking place which tends to increase the stability.

The simple equation (8.26) given for E is far from rigorous. No consideration has been given to the change in temperature which will accompany change in pressure. More accurately

$$E = \left(\frac{10^{-3}}{\rho}\frac{d\sigma_\theta}{dz}\right) \tag{8.28}$$

where σ_θ is the potential density parameter as defined by (5.16).

An exact formulation of the stability parameter can be given in the following form (Hesselberg and Sverdrup, 1915)

$$E = \frac{1}{\rho}\left[\frac{\partial\rho}{\partial S}\frac{dS}{dz} + \frac{\partial\rho}{\partial T}\left(\frac{dT}{dz} - \Gamma\right)\right], \tag{8.29}$$

where S is salinity, T temperature, dS/dz and dT/dz are the environmental gradients, $\partial\rho/\partial S$ and $\partial\rho/\partial T$ are the thermodynamic partial derivatives and Γ denotes the increase in temperature per unit increase in depth under adiabatic conditions.

The form in which stability is reported in the literature varies among authors. Sverdrup *et al.* (1942) neglect the factor $1/\rho$ which can either be considered as an approximation or as a change in basic units. Pollak (1954) prefers to define stability as gE, where E is as in (8.29). He also uses pressure (p) as a variable in place of depth (z).

Note that the differential equation (8.25) has as a solution simple harmonic oscillations in z provided the stability has a positive value. The angular frequency N is given by

$$N = \sqrt{(gE)}\ \mathrm{sec}^{-1}. \tag{8.30}$$

Because of viscous damping it is not expected that the displaced particle would oscillate at this frequency but N is significant as the limiting frequency for a free internal wave (see Chapter 14).

Eckart (1960) gives the development of a parameter, similarly related to stability, which he calls the Väisälä Frequency N.

$$N = \sqrt{\left\{g\left(\frac{1}{\rho}\frac{d\rho}{dz} - \frac{g}{c^2}\right)\right\}} \tag{8.31}$$

where c is the speed of sound in the fluid.

8.7 Pressure Gradient Accelerations

A "level surface" is defined as a surface of constant geopotential. Lines joining points of equal pressure are called "isobars" and a surface at every point of which the pressure has the same value is called an "isobaric surface".

In a fluid at rest, free from accelerations, isobaric surfaces must coincide with level surfaces. This is not necessarily true for a fluid in motion, even when the motion is steady.

Consider a fluid of constant density where an isobaric surface $p = p_0$ makes an angle θ with a level surface. In this case (Fig. 8.5) the isobaric surface would be the free surface (p_0 = atmospheric pressure). The z co-ordinate will be directed perpendicular to the level surface and to the x and y co-ordinates.

An incremental volume of the fluid $\Delta x\ \Delta y\ \Delta z$ centered on the level surface will experience a pressure force on the left-hand face equal to

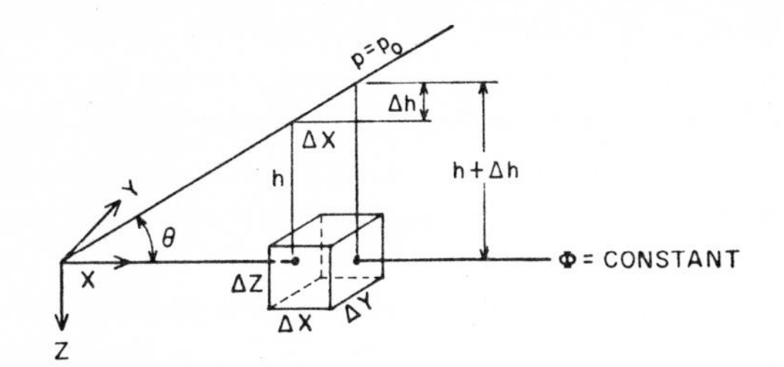

Fig. 8.5.

$(p_0 + \rho gh)\,(\Delta y\,\Delta z)$ in the positive x-direction. The right-hand face will experience a pressure force equal to $[p_0 + \rho g\,(h + \Delta h)]\,\Delta y\,\Delta z$ in the negative x-direction.

The net force in the x-direction is

$$F_x = -\,\rho g\,\Delta h\,(\Delta y\,\Delta z).$$

Dividing by the mass of the incremental volume $\rho\,\Delta x\,\Delta y\,\Delta z$ gives the acceleration in the x-direction,

$$\frac{F_x}{\rho\,\Delta x\,\Delta y\,\Delta z} = -\,g\,\frac{\Delta h}{\Delta x}.$$

In the limit, as the volume approaches zero,

$$\mathrm{d}^2x/\mathrm{d}t^2 = -\,g\,\mathrm{d}h/\mathrm{d}x = -\,g\tan\theta. \qquad (8.32)$$

This is sometimes written

$$\mathrm{d}^2x/\mathrm{d}t^2 = -\,gi$$

where $i = \tan\theta =$ the slope of the isobaric surface referred to a level surface.

Alternatively (8.32) may be written

$$\mathrm{d}^2x/\mathrm{d}t^2 = -\,g\,(\mathrm{d}z/\mathrm{d}x)_p$$

where $(\mathrm{d}z/\mathrm{d}x)_p$ is the rate of change of z with x along a surface of constant p. Neglecting small field variations in g this may be rewritten from (8.19)

$$\mathrm{d}^2x/\mathrm{d}t^2 = (\mathrm{d}\phi/\mathrm{d}x)_p \qquad (8.33)$$

relating the horizontal acceleration to the horizontal gradient of geopotential along the isobaric surface.

This pressure gradient acceleration is in such a direction as to tend to redistribute the mass until the isobaric surfaces coincide with level surfaces. If there is flow within the fluid the pressure gradient acceleration can be balanced by another acceleration related to the steady, non-accelerated, motion so that a steady state condition where isobaric surfaces and level surfaces intersect is possible. The other acceleration referred to is the "Coriolis acceleration" (see Chapter 9).

References

ECKART, C. *Hydrodynamics of Oceans and Atmospheres*. Pergamon Press, New York. 1960.

HESSELBERG, Th. and H. U. SVERDRUP. (1915) Die Stabilitätsverhältnisse des Seewassers bei vertikalen Verschiebungen. *Bergens Mus. Aarb.* **15**, 1–16.

POLLAK, M. J. (1954) Static stability parameters in oceanography. *J. Mar. Res.* **13**(1), 101–112.

SVERDRUP, H. U., M. W. JOHNSON and R. H. FLEMING. *The Oceans*. Prentice-Hall, New York. 1942.

CHAPTER 9

ACCELERATIONS ARISING FROM THE ROTATION OF THE EARTH

WE usually find it convenient to refer motion on the earth and in the ocean or atmosphere to a co-ordinate system which is fixed in the rotating earth. As a result of this choice the motion has associated with it an apparent acceleration that would not appear if a co-ordinate system fixed in space had been chosen. For many types of motion the scale and velocities are such that this acceleration can be neglected in comparison to other accelerations in the system. This is, however, seldom so in the ocean and atmosphere. We shall be mainly concerned with the representation of the acceleration in a Cartesian co-ordinate system with origin and two co-ordinates in a level (geo-potential surface and the third co-ordinate vertical.

9.1 Coriolis Acceleration

A standard exercise in vector analysis (e.g. see Page, 1935) is the transfer of the general acceleration equation in a fixed co-ordinate system,

$$\bar{f}_0 = \bar{F}/M,$$

where $\bar{f}_0$ is the vector acceleration referred to the fixed system, $\bar{F}$ is the absolute vector force and M is the mass involved, to a co-ordinate system which rotates relative to the fixed system. By a straightforward manipulation an equation similar to the following is obtained

$$\bar{f}_1 = (\bar{F}/M) - 2(\bar{\Omega} \times \bar{V}_1) - \bar{\Omega} \times (\bar{\Omega} \times \bar{r}_1), \quad (9.1)$$

where $\bar{f}_1$ is acceleration referred to the rotating co-ordinate system. $\bar{\Omega}$ is the vector angular velocity of the rotating system relative to the fixed system, directed in the sense of progression of a right-hand screw rotating with the system, $\bar{V}_1$ is the vector velocity referred to the rotating system and $\bar{r}_1$ the position vector in the rotating system. $\times$ denotes the vector cross product.

The term $-\Omega \times (\bar{\Omega} \times \bar{r}_1)$ is a familiar one. It has magnitude $\Omega^2 R$ where R is the normal distance from the axis of rotation, and is directed outward from, and perpendicular to, the axis of rotation of the co-ordinate system (Fig. 9.1). This is the centrifugal acceleration and the way in which it influences the geopotential has been discussed in Chapter 8.

The term $-2(\bar{\Omega} \times \bar{V}_1)$ is called the "Coriolis acceleration" and is quite a different sort of thing. Note that it depends upon the velocity $\bar{V}_1$ relative to the new co-ordinate system. The magnitude of this vector is $2\Omega V_1 \sin \psi$, where ψ is the angle between $\bar{\Omega}$ and $\bar{V}_1$, and its direction is that of the progress of a left-hand screw turning from $\bar{\Omega}$ to $\bar{V}_1$.

If $\bar{V}_1$ is restricted to velocities along the surface of a sphere whose center is on the axis of rotation, ψ is the latitude. In this case, the accelerations due to a northward $\bar{V}_1$ are shown in Fig. 9.2.

Since the derivation of the Coriolis acceleration term by vector algebra may seem mysterious to those unfamiliar with this mathematical tool an attempt will be made in the following section to give a simple derivation of the horizontal component which arises from horizontal flow on the surface of a rotating earth.

9.2 A Simple Derivation of Coriolis Acceleration

Consider first zonal motion (i.e. motion along a parallel of latitude) toward the east in the Northern Hemisphere (Fig. 9.3). A particle on the surface is already subject to centrifugal acceleration $C = \Omega^2 R$ due to the rotation of the earth. If an eastward velocity V_e is added, this is equivalent to adding rotation with angular velcoty $\omega = V_e/R$. Thus, the absolute rotation relative to a fixed co-ordinate system is $\omega_a = \Omega + \omega$, and the centrifugal acceleration is $C_a = \omega_a{}^2 R$.

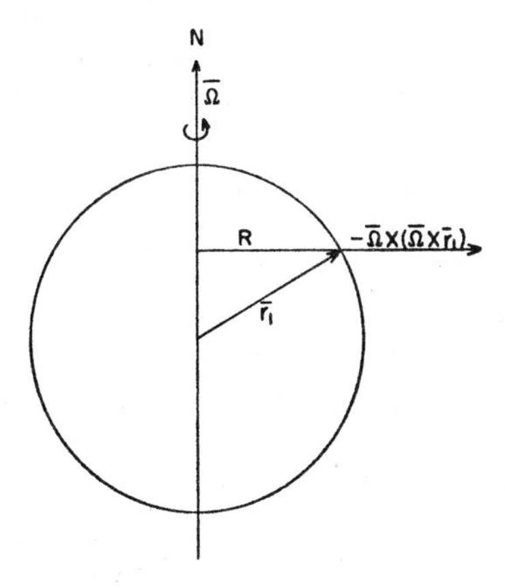

Fig. 9.1.

The centrifugal acceleration added by the velocity V_e is

$$
\begin{aligned}
C_v &= C_a - C \\
&= \omega_a{}^2R - \Omega^2R \\
&= (\Omega + \omega)^2R - \Omega^2R \\
&= \omega^2R + 2\,\omega\,\Omega R \\
&= (V_e^2/R) + 2\Omega V_e.
\end{aligned}
$$

The horizontal component (component in the tangent plane) of this acceleration is

$$C_{HV} = 2\Omega V_e \sin\psi + \frac{V_e^2 \sin\psi}{R}.$$

Then writing

$$R = a\cos\psi$$

yields

$$C_{HV} = 2\Omega V_e \sin\psi + \frac{V_e^2}{a\cot\psi} \qquad (9.2)$$

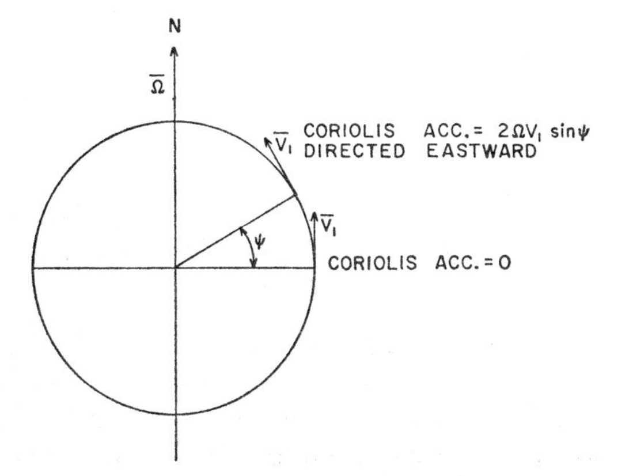

Fig. 9.2.

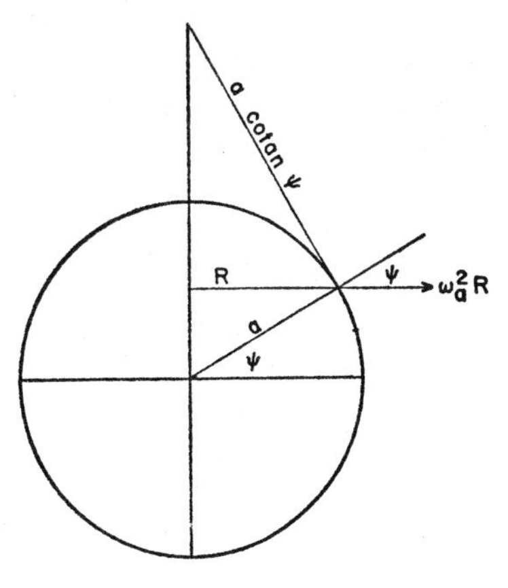

Fig. 9.3.

where $a \cot\psi$ is the distance along the tangent plane to its intersection with the axis of rotation. It is the radius of curvature of the projection of the latitude circle upon the tangent plane (Fig. 9.4).

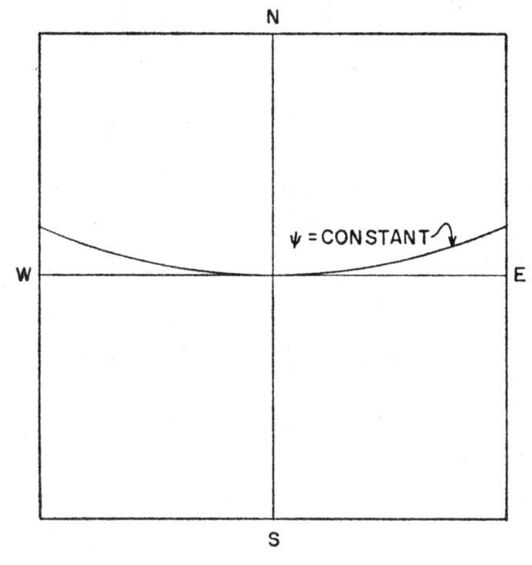

Fig. 9.4.

$V_e^2/a \cot\psi$ is, then, the horizontal component of acceleration which must be balanced out to keep the particle moving along the parallel rather than in a great circle.

The term $2\Omega V_e \sin\psi$ is the horizontal component of the Coriolis acceleration. From the construction (Fig. 9.3) it can be seen that it is directed to the south, that is to the right of the velocity. For westward motion this acceleration would be toward the north. The term $V_e^2/a \cot\psi$ is an acceleration toward the south in each case.

Next, consider horizontal meridional (along a line of constant longitude) motion directed toward the north. It is necessary here to introduce the concept that the angular momentum per unit mass ($\omega_a R^2$) about the earth's axis must be conserved, where $\omega_a = \Omega + \omega$ as before. This can be expressed by

$$d(\omega_a R^2) = 0, \qquad (9.3)$$

$$R^2 d\omega_a + 2\omega_a R dR = 0,$$

or

$$R d\omega_a + 2\omega_a dR = 0. \qquad (9.4)$$

Writing

$$R = a \cos \psi,$$

yields

$$dR = -a \sin \psi \, d\psi$$
$$= -\sin \psi \, ds,$$

where s is distance traveled northward. Thus,

$$dR = -\sin \psi \, V_N dt. \qquad (9.5)$$

Equation (9.4) can then be re-written

$$R \, d\omega_a/dt = 2\omega_a \sin \psi \, V_N$$
$$= 2(\Omega + \omega) V_N \sin \psi. \qquad (9.6)$$

The left-hand term is implicitly the horizontal acceleration toward the east, and, since we are considering motion with no east–west component, $\omega = 0$. Thus we may write

$$C_{HV} \text{ (eastward)} = 2\Omega V_N \sin \psi.$$

Again the acceleration is directed to the right of the velocity.

It can easily be shown that in the southern hemisphere the horizontal component of the Coriolis acceleration is directed toward the left of the horizontal velocity.

9.3 The Horizontal Component of Coriolis Acceleration

Poleward horizontal motion induces relative acceleration in the same direction as the earth's rotation so as to conserve angular momentum.

Zonal motion induces an additional centrifugal acceleration which has an equatorward component in the horizontal plane for motion with the earth's rotation and a poleward component for motion counter to the earth's rotation.

The following points should be remembered concerning Coriolis acceleration:

(1) The acceleration exists only when there is velocity relative to the earth's surface.
(2) The magnitude of the horizontal component is given by $2\Omega \sin \psi \, V$ where Ω is the angular velocity of the earth, ψ the latitude, and V the horizontal velocity.
(3) There is no horizontal component at the equator ($\sin \psi = 0$).
(4) The acceleration is directed normal to the velocity and to the right in the northern hemisphere, to the left in the southern hemisphere.
(5) There is no work done, since there is no component of the acceleration in the direction of the motion.

9.4 Coriolis Acceleration and Satellite Motion

Figure 9.5 depicts the projection upon the earth's surface of the paths of two satellites in polar orbits, one with a period of one day, the other with a period of one half day.

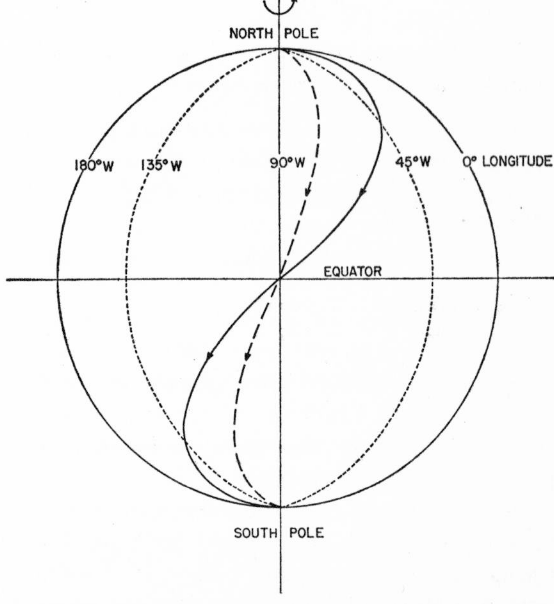

Fig. 9.5 Vertical projections upon the earth's surface of the paths of satellites in Polar orbit with periods of 1 day ——— and ½ day - - - -.

The one day satellite crosses the north pole along the 0° longitude and, since the earth turns under it, it appears to curve to the right in the northern hemisphere, crossing the equator at 90° west longitude at an angle of 45° and with no apparent curvature. Then it appears to curve more and more to the left till it approaches the south pole along the 180° longitude.

The half day satellite crosses the north pole along the 45° west meridian. Because its apparent velocity is greater its curvature is less, but is again to the right in the northern hemisphere. It also crosses the equator at 90° west on a straight path and subsequently curves to the left till it approaches the south pole along the 135° west meridian.

The satellites themselves are, of course, not accelerated but the projection of their paths upon the earth appears this way because of the earth's rotation.

Coriolis acceleration is, then, a property only of the co-ordinate system and is not related to any restraint to move along the surface of the earth.

9.5 Evaluating the Coriolis Acceleration

The angular velocity of the earth (Ω) is 7.292 × 10^{-5} radians per second, or

$$2\Omega = 1.458 \times 10^{-4}\ \text{sec}^{-1}.$$

At 45° latitude ($\sin \psi = 0.707$)

$$2\Omega \sin \psi = 1.03 \times 10^{-4}\ \text{sec}^{-1}.$$

Consider a rifle bullet discharged with a velocity of 3000 ft/sec. Coriolis acceleration = $1.03 \times 10^{-4} \times 3000 = 0.309$ ft/sec^2. In the 0.3 sec it takes to travel 300 yards (900 ft) this acceleration could produce a transverse displacement ($s = \frac{1}{2} at^2$) of 0.17 in. This displacement is probably of minor importance when related to other sources of error.

Again consider an automobile at the same latitude with velocity 60 m.p.h. (88 ft/sec). Coriolis acceleration = 0.00905 ft/sec^2. In the 60 sec that it takes to travel 1 mile the offset would be about 16 ft. Again other transverse accelerations are probably of more importance.

However, in the case of an ocean current with velocity of 1 knot (1 nautical mile per hour) Coriolis acceleration is only 2.86×10^{-8} nautical miles/sec^2, but in the hour it takes to travel 1 nautical mile the transverse displacement computed in the same way is 0.186 nautical miles or about 20 per cent of the distance traveled.

Thus for systems involving motion at low speeds the Coriolis acceleration becomes important.

9.6 The Vertical Component of Coriolis Acceleration

While only the horizontal component of Coriolis acceleration associated with horizontal motions has been considered, and while this component is the one most frequently dealt with in the oceanographic literature, it is well to remember that vertical motion is influenced by Coriolis acceleration and that there is a vertical component associated with horizontal motion.

This vertical component arises only from the east–west component of horizontal velocity. From the development in Section 9.2 it can be seen that the vertical acceleration is given by

$$2\Omega V_e \cos \psi + V_e^2/a$$

and is directed opposite to gravity (upward) for V_e positive. This component has its maximum value at the equator and is zero at the poles.

When gravity measurements are made from a moving platform this results in the necessity for the application of a correction term known as the "Eotvos correction". With an east–west velocity of 10 knots (about 500 cm/sec) this vertical component has a value of the equator of some 0.07 cm/sec^2 or 73 milligals. Hence errors in navigation, except when traveling in a north–south direction, can be a limiting factor in the accuracy of gravity measurements at sea. Surface ship gravity meters currently in use have sensitivity to less than 1 milligal.

References

Page, L. *Introduction to Theoretical Physics*, 661 pp. Van Nostrand, New York. 1935.

Sources of Additional Information

An Introduction to Physical Oceanography. von Arx. W. S. Addison-Wesley, Reading, Mass. 1962. Chapter 4 contains a simple explanation of Coriolis acceleration from a different point of view than our Section 9.2.

Dynamic Meteorology. Holboe, J., G. E. Forsythe and W. Gustin. Wiley, New York. 1945. Chapter 6 contains the vector transformation of acceleration to rotating co-ordinates referred to in Section 9.1.

CHAPTER 10

GEOSTROPHIC CURRENTS AND THEIR COMPUTATIONS

If it can be assumed that the accelerations discussed in the two previous chapters (gravity, pressure gradient, and Coriolis) are the only accelerations involved the fluid motion is said to be "geostrophic", that is "earth turned". If motion in a stratified ocean is indeed geostrophic then it becomes practical to calculate the speed and direction of flow from the observed distribution of mass. The general relationship was apparently first stated in 1885 by H. Mohn, although its use followed the independent derivation by Sandstrom and Helland-Hansen (1903) from Bjerknes (1898) circulation theorem.

Although the geostrophic assumption must be never more than approximately correct, current computations have been amazingly successful and much of our knowledge of the circulation of the oceans has been gained in this way.

We will consider first some simplified systems and then go on to outline the classical procedure for calculating currents and transport from oceanographic station data.

10.1 Currents in a Homogeneous Ocean

Consider a homogeneous fluid with an atmospheric interface ($P = P_0$) that makes an angle θ with the level surfaces (ϕ = constant) Fig. 10.1. As shown in Section 8.7, there will be a pressure gradient acceleration in the $-x$-direction given by

$$d^2x/dt^2 = -g \tan\theta \equiv -gi.$$

If the fluid is in motion with a velocity V directed into the plane of Fig. 10.1, there will also be a horizontal component of the Coriolis acceleration. In the northern hemisphere it will be directed in the $+x$-direction.

$$d^2x/dt^2 = 2\Omega \sin\psi \, V = fV,$$

where the Coriolis parameter f is written for $2\Omega \sin\psi$.

It is possible for the situation with isobaric surfaces intersecting level surfaces to exist as a steady state if these two accelerations are in balance. Then

$$ig = fV. \qquad (10.1)$$

Under the assumption that these are the only accelerations to be considered, it becomes possible to evaluate the velocity from the slope of the isobaric surface:

$$V = \frac{ig}{f} = \frac{g \tan\theta}{2\Omega \sin\psi}.$$

The assumption that there are no accelerations other than the pressure gradient acceleration and the Coriolis acceleration requires flow in a straight line (no centrifugal acceleration). It neglects friction, which may be permissible where velocity is single valued and unidirectional but certainly not at the fluid boundaries.

To evaluate the surface slopes that may be expected, assume a latitude of 45° and a velocity of 100 cm/sec (approximately 2 knots).

$$i = [(1.03 \times 10^{-4} \times 100)/980] = 1.05 \times 10^{-5},$$

or the surface slopes upward to the right (Fig. 10.1) by 1.05 cm/km.

Provided that the assumptions made here were valid, one could measure the slope of the sea surface and compute the velocity. There is, however, considerable difficulty involved in measuring such small slopes.

In such a system the velocity must be uniform throughout the fluid and isobaric surfaces will be parallel to one another. The motion is said to be "barotropic". The same conditions would hold if the fluid is permitted to have density dependent upon the (assumed hydrostatic) pressure.

10.2 Currents in a Two-Layer Ocean

In a fluid that is stratified, the measurement problem becomes considerably less difficult. Consider, for example, the hypothetical case where a fluid of density ρ_1 flows over a stationary fluid whose density, ρ_2, is greater than ρ_1 (Fig. 10.2).

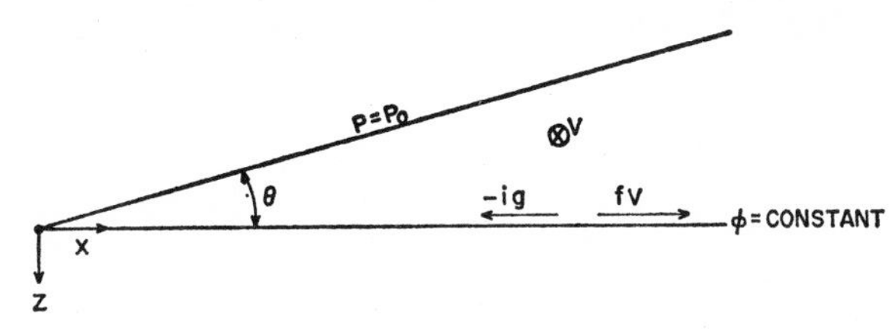

Fig. 10.1.

The free surface of fluid 2 must be a level surface since it is at rest. The free surface of fluid 1 will make an angle θ with the level surface dependent upon the velocity and latitude; the interface between the two fluids will lie at some angle θ_b to the level surfaces. Consider both these angles measured in the same sense from the level surface and write $i = \tan\theta$, $i_b = \tan\theta_b$. x will be measured towards the right from the place where the fluid–fluid interface meets the surface $Z = 0$.

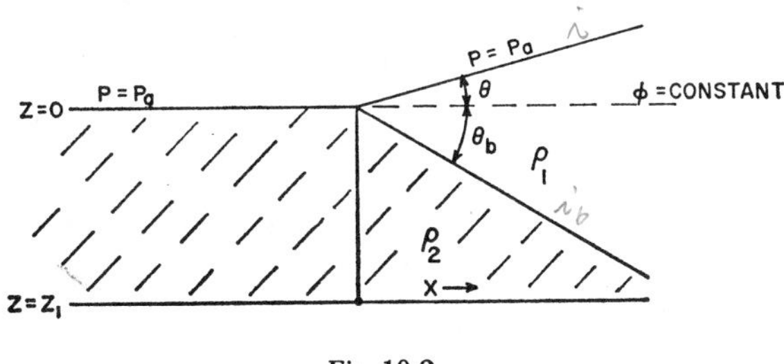

Fig. 10.2.

Throughout the motionless fluid isobaric surfaces must coincide with level surfaces so that along part of the level surface $Z = Z_1$ that lies entirely within fluid 2 pressure is single valued (p_1). Evaluating this at $x = 0$,

$$p_1 = \rho_2\, g\, Z_1 + p_a,$$

and at

$$x = x$$

$$p_1 = \rho_1\, g(ix - i_b x) + \rho_2\, g(Z_1 + i_b x) + p_a.$$

Equating these

$$\rho_2\, Z_1 = \rho_1\,(i - i_b)x + \rho_2\, Z_1 + \rho_2\, i_b x,$$

$$i_b = -\, i\, \frac{\rho_1}{\rho_2 - \rho_1}, \qquad (10.2)$$

that is, the slope of the boundary surface is opposite in sign to the surface slope, as it was drawn in Fig. 10.2, and the magnitude of the boundary slope is greater than that of the surface by the factor

$$\rho_1/(\rho_2 - \rho_1).$$

Suppose it were fresh water flowing over stationary salt water with $\rho_1 = 1.000$ and $\rho_2 = 1.025$, the boundary slope would be 40 times the surface slope.

In the case where $V = 100$ cm/sec and $\psi = 45°$, $i = 1.05$ cm/km, $i_b = 42$ cm/km.

With water of salinity 30‰ and 30°C ($\rho = 1.018$) over water of 35‰ and 30°C ($\rho = 1.022$) the factor $(\rho_1/(\rho_2 - \rho_1))$ becomes 254.5 and, for the same velocity, $i_b = 2.67$ m/km which is approaching the order of magnitude of slopes that might easily be measured. In fact, the surface slope may be neglected in measuring to obtain the boundary slope with only a small error. As the density difference becomes smaller the task of determining currents in this way becomes easier, although the precision of density determinations becomes more important.

Parts of the ocean often approximate to a two-layer system where a light surface layer is separated from the heavier deep water by a strong pycnocline (usually coinciding with the thermocline). Although the assumption that the lower layer is motionless is probably never more than a good approximation, it is sometimes possible to make a useful evaluation of the surface layer currents in this way.

At the two stations M and N (Fig. 10.3) observations are made to some depth H and it is found that

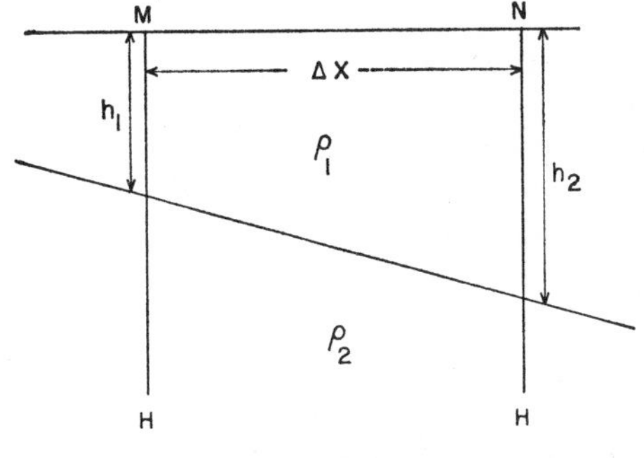

Fig. 10.3.

the situation can be approximated by two layers, with densities ρ_1 and ρ_2, separated by an interface which is found at a depth h_1 at station M and h_2 at station N. The distance between stations is written Δx, and, as before, i is the slope of the free surface and i_b the slope of the interface.

Here $i_b = -[(h_2 - h_1)/\Delta x] + i$,

and, since from (10.2)

$$i = -i_b (\rho_2 - \rho_1)/\rho_1$$

$$i = \left(\frac{\rho_2 - \rho_1}{\rho_2}\right)\left(\frac{h_2 - h_1}{\Delta x}\right). \quad (10.3)$$

The velocity in the upper layer is given (10.1) by

$$V = \frac{gi}{f} = \frac{g}{f}\left(\frac{\rho_2 - \rho_1}{\rho_2}\right)\left(\frac{h_2 - h_1}{\Delta x}\right). \quad (10.4)$$

Another way to approach the problem is to compute the gradient of geopotential at the surface. For one station the geopotential of the surface ϕ_0 refered to that at some reference level ϕ_r is given by

$$\phi_0 = \int_{p_0}^{p_r} \alpha dp + \phi_r,$$

where p_0 is the atmospheric pressure and p_r is the pressure at the reference level. We will assume that the reference level is chosen on an isobaric surface that is also a level surface.

Integrating by parts,

$$\phi_0 - \phi_r = \alpha p\Big|_{p_0}^{p_r} + \int_{\alpha_r}^{\alpha_0} p d\alpha$$

$$= \alpha_r p_r - \alpha_0 p_0 + \int_{\alpha_r}^{\alpha_0} p d\alpha.$$

In the simple two-layer case the last term above has value only at the interface, where it can be written $p_b \Delta\alpha$.

Applying this at stations M and N

$$(\phi_{0N} - \phi_{0M}) - (\phi_{rN} - \phi_{rM}) = (p_{bN} - p_{bM}) \Delta\alpha.$$

Writing $p_b = \rho_1 gh$, assuming g is constant, and recalling that $(\phi_{rN} - \phi_{rM})$ is zero by choice of reference levels,

$$\phi_{0N} - \phi_{0M} = \rho_1 g (h_N - h_M) \Delta\alpha.$$

Writing $\rho_1 \Delta\alpha = \rho_1 \left(\frac{1}{\rho_1} - \frac{1}{\rho_2}\right)$

$$= 1 - \rho_1/\rho_2 = (\rho_2 - \rho_1)/\rho_2,$$

yields

$$\phi_{0N} - \phi_{0M} = g (h_N - h_M) (\rho_2 - \rho_1)/\rho_2. \quad (10.5)$$

Then comparison to (10.4) leads to

$$V = (\phi_{0N} - \phi_{0M})/f \Delta x. \quad (10.6)$$

Equation (10.6) is valid with any self consistent system of units; for example, with V in m/sec, Δx in meters, and ϕ in dynamic decimeters.

It is more usual to write

$$V = 10 (D_{0N} - D_{0M})/\Delta x f,$$

where D is geopotential in dynamic meters. Or, more generally

$$V = C (D_{0N} - D_{0M})/\Delta x f \quad (10.7)$$

where C is a constant properly selected for whatever particular combination of units is used.

In evaluating the geopotential at the isobaric surface identified with the free surface ($p = p_0$), the assumption was made that the pressure could be evaluated from the hydrostatic equation,

$$dp = \rho \, g dz,$$

under which condition $d\phi = -gdz = -\alpha dp$.

The geopotential interval $\phi_0 - \phi_r$ under these conditions becomes the area to the left of the appropriate α vs. p plot (Fig. 10.4) and the difference in geopotential of the surface at M and N is represented by the area of the shaded rectangle. The reference level could have been chosen at any pressure p_r such that this pressure surface lay wholly within the motionless fluid.

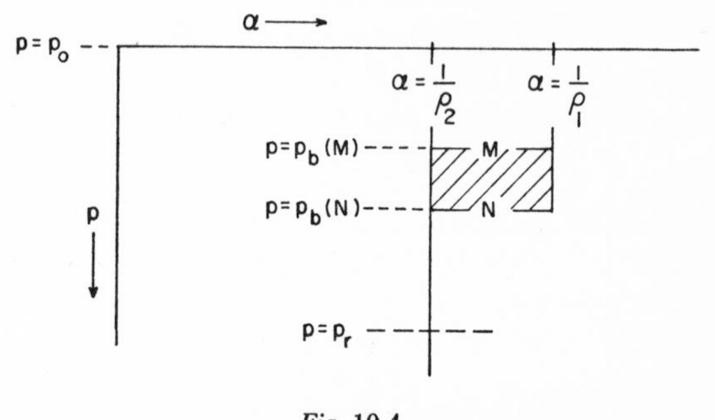

Fig. 10.4.

10.3 Currents in a Stratified Ocean

In the previous section the situation where fluid motion takes place and the pressure gradient acceleration and Coriolis acceleration are the only accelerations that need be considered, was examined for the simple case of homogeneous fluid, and for a two layer system using two methods of attack.

It was found that the velocity normal to the section could be evaluated in terms of the slope of the isobaric surface ($p = p_0$) representing the atmospheric interface, i.e.

$$V = (ig/f), \quad (10.1)$$

where

$$i = -(dz/dx)_{p = p_0}.$$

Since $d\phi = -g dz$ defines the geopotential ϕ, we have

$$i = -(dz/dx)_{p=p0} = (1/g)(d\phi/dx)_{p=p0}.$$

Thus

$$V = (1/f)(d\phi/dx)_{p=p0} \qquad (10.8)$$

relates the velocity to the rate of change in geopotential along the isobaric surface.

Although (10.8) was derived for the particular isobaric surface $p = p_0$, it can be shown to be equally valid for any isobaric surface within the moving fluid. Moreover, this relationship is not dependent upon the particular fluid model envisioned, but is equally valid for any pressure surface within a fluid system which may have both α and V as continuous functions of z (p), i.e.

$$V_p = (1/f)(d\phi/dx)_p.$$

In the situation depicted in Fig. 10.5, the

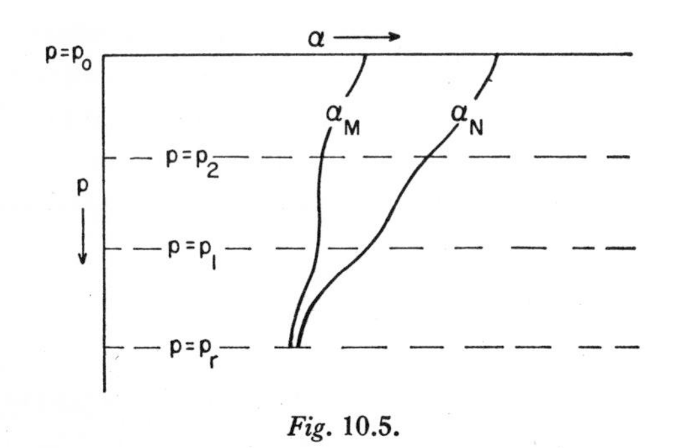

Fig. 10.5.

velocity V_1 at the pressure surface $p = p_1$ is given by

$$V_1 = \frac{1}{f}\left(\frac{d\phi}{dx}\right)_{p=p_1},$$

$$= \frac{1}{f}\frac{\phi_{N_1} - \phi_{M_1}}{\Delta x}$$

$$= \frac{1}{f\Delta x}\left[\int_{p=p_r}^{p=p_1} \alpha_N dp - \int_{p=p_r}^{p=p_1} \alpha_M dp\right],$$

$$= \frac{1}{f}\frac{\text{Area between } \alpha_N \text{ and } \alpha_M \text{ in interval } p_r \text{ to } p_1)}{\Delta x}$$

Similarly

$$V_2 = (1/f)(d\phi/dx)_{p=p_2},$$

and it can be seen that, if some reference level other than $p = p_r$ were chosen, where the velocity was not zero, then the computed velocities would be in error by the true velocity associated with the reference level picked.

In order to deal with smaller numbers and to simplify current computations, it is usual to compute geopotential anomaly (ΔD) between pressure surfaces as outlined in Section 8.5.

From calculations of geopotential at two stations one is able only to evaluate the component of horizontal velocity normal to the line joining the stations. Where observations are available for a network of stations, it is common to contour the geopotential anomaly for a pressure surface and to evaluate direction and magnitude of currents on this pressure surface in terms of the gradient of geopotential. Thus

$$V = (c/f)\ (\text{horizontal gradient of } \Delta D) \qquad (10.9)$$

where c is the correction factor for the particular set of units chosen.

It is well to remember that in the computation of geostrophic currents the assumption is made that: *There are no accelerations other than the pressure gradient acceleration and the Coriolis acceleration, and that these are in balance.* This implies that:

(a) A steady state exists.
(b) The currents flow in straight lines (curvature of the flow path must involve centrifugal acceleration).
(c) Frictional accelerations arising from current shear may be neglected.
(d) Currents are neither diminished nor augmented along the direction of flow.

In the practical computations numerical values of increments in geometric depth ΔZ are inserted for increments in pressure Δp, equating meters and decibars. This is less objectionable when one considers that pressure is the parameter actually measured with unprotected thermometers. Their calibration is, however, tied back to a depth measurement in most cases. One assumes a constant value for g. In a self-consistent survey the use of single Q factors for depth determinations tends to take care of field variations in g.

There is an uncertainty introduced in the determination of δ due to imperfect knowledge of the compressibility of sea water. The same imperfect tables are used in computing the mean density ρ_m which enters into the depth (pressure) measurements. In any case, one uses the same method for calculations at each station and the errors introduced into the differences will be small.

By far the greatest source of error (excepting possible violation of the basic assumptions) is that introduced by determination of the distance between stations. Station spacing will normally be of the order of 50 to 100 km and individual position fixes at sea may be in error by 2 km or more.

Equation (10.9) does not imply any cause and effect relationship. That is, it cannot be said that pressure surfaces slope relative to level surfaces because there is a current, or that there is a current because of the slope of isobaric surfaces. One can, of course, imagine the imposition of a current regime giving rise to a redistribution of mass or the imposition of a mass distribution giving rise to a current system.

Looking in the direction of the current in the northern hemisphere the free surface and other isobaric surfaces slope upwards to the right. Surfaces of equal density (σ_t) slope downward to the right, the lighter water at any depth being found to the right of the current. Except in regions with unusual salinity distribution, isotherms slope downward to the right with warmer waters lying to the right of the current at any depth. The slope of isotherms or σ_t lines is a good qualitative indication of the strength of the current.

10.3 Relative Currents and the Choice of a Reference Surface

Since in the real ocean it is not possible to select with complete assurance a level of no horizontal motion, the procedure is to select a pressure surface on which some valid argument suggests that horizontal velocities will be small. Geostrophic velocities are then computed as "relative" to that surface. Several methods have been used to select reference levels such that the field of relative velocity would approximate closely the field of absolute velocity.

The simplest method is to choose an isobaric surface at sufficiently great depth that any residual current could be expected to be of little magnitude. This, at least, forms a consistent basis for the presentation of relative velocities. It is known, however, that in major currents such as the Gulf Stream, velocities are significant to at least 1000 m depth. Recent observations have also shown that significant currents exist at great depths in certain regions of the ocean. On the other hand, the 1200 decibar or 1000 decibar surfaces have been widely used in the analysis of data from the North Pacific and the resultant pictures of surface layer currents have been remarkably consistent with other observations.

At one time the depth of the oxygen minimum was widely used as a reference level. More recently the theories concerning the dynamics of oxygen distribution have completely removed any validity in the choice of this reference level.

Defant (1941) introduced an objective method for determining the topography of a reference surface. For each pair of adjacent stations a level is picked such that the difference in dynamics depth anomaly, ΔD, does not vary with depth, i.e.

$$\frac{\mathrm{d}\,(\Delta D_2 - \Delta D_1)}{\mathrm{d}z} = 0.$$

This surface is then contoured and the geopotential anomalies relative to it computed for each station. Although arguments for the validity of this reference surface may appeal to physical intuition, a rigorous defense of the method is not available. It has been widely used in the analysis of data from the Atlantic.

Hidaka (1949) presented a method for selecting a depth of no horizontal motion from the observed distribution of salinity. In a layer where salinity is not varying, and where both horizontal and vertical velocities vanish, continuity of salt demands that

$$A_x \frac{\partial^2 S}{\partial x^2} + A_y \frac{\partial^2 S}{\partial y^2} + A_z \frac{\partial^2 S}{\partial z^2} = 0,$$

where S is salinity and A_x, A_y, A_z are the appropriate diffusion coefficients (see Chapter 11). These diffusion coefficients are extremely difficult to evaluate, but, if some argument can be introduced for the neglect of the first two terms, a level of no motion should exist where $\partial^2 S/\partial z^2 = 0$, and this level can be found directly from the station data. Because of the unrealistic assumptions involved, this method is perhaps of no practical value. In fact, on theoretical grounds, Stommel (1956) has called into doubt the possibility of a level where all three velocity components vanish.

10.4 Computing Volume Transport

In a section between two stations M and N (Fig. 10.6) the relative velocity V_1 at level 1 above the chosen reference level is given by (10.7)

$$V_1 = C\,\frac{(\Delta D_{N_1} - \Delta D_{M_1})}{\Delta x f}.$$

The relative volume transport ΔT_1 between this

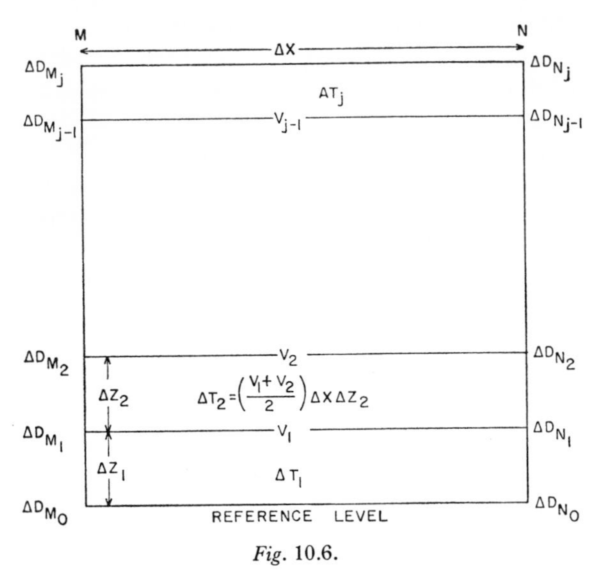

Fig. 10.6.

level and the reference level is given by

$$\Delta T_1 = \frac{\Delta x \, \Delta z \, (V_1 + V_0)}{2} \qquad (10.10)$$

if a linear variation with depth is assumed. Then

$$\Delta T_1 = \frac{(C\Delta z_1)}{f} \{(\Delta D_{N_1} - \Delta D_{M_1}) + (\Delta D_{N_0} - \Delta D_{M_0})\}/2,$$

although the term $(\Delta D_{N_0} - \Delta D_{M_0})$ is assumed zero by choice of reference level.

Similarly

$$\Delta T_2 = (C\Delta z_2/f)\{(\Delta D_{N_2} - \Delta D_{M_2}) + (\Delta D_{N_1} - \Delta D_{M_1})\}/2$$

and so on. The total volume transport through the section is given by the summation

$$T = \sum_i \Delta T_i.$$

Note that the computation of volume transport need not involve the distance Δx between stations.

For convenience one may compute a "transport function" Q for each station such that

$$Q = \sum_{i=1}^{i=j} \left(\frac{\Delta D_i + \Delta D_{i-1}}{2}\right) \Delta z_i, \qquad (10.11)$$

where ΔD_j is the dynamic height anomaly of the surface. The relative volume transport between stations M and N can then be shown to be

$$T_{M,N} = (c/f)\,(Q_N - Q_M). \qquad (10.12)$$

In many schemes for routine computation of geostrophic flow it is desirable to carry out the computations before selecting a reference depth. In such routines geopotential anomaly is computed as dynamic depth relative to the surface. A transport (Q) function may be computed by summation from the surface downward in a way analogous to (10.11). Using the Q computed in this way the transport relative to the jth level (levels numbered downward) is given by

$$(T_{M,N})_j = - (c/f)\,[(Q_{N_j} - Q_{M_j}) - (\Delta D_{N_j} - \Delta D_{M_j})\, z_r]$$

where z_r is the chosen reference depth.

Since a variety of computing schedules are currently in use one should, of course, familiarize himself with the particular manner in which terms such as the transport function have been generated before utilizing them in interpreting the data.

10.5 The Acceleration Equations for Geostrophic Flow

Although in the foregoing sections we have written the acceleration equations in a number of specialized forms pertinent to the development, it is more satisfactory for analytical purposes to state them as follows:

$$\left.\begin{aligned} \frac{1}{\rho}\frac{\partial p}{\partial x} &= fv, \\ \frac{1}{\rho}\frac{\partial p}{\partial y} &= -fu, \\ \frac{1}{\rho}\frac{\partial p}{\partial z} &= g, \end{aligned}\right\} \qquad (10.13)$$

where the x-direction points east, the y-direction points north and the z-direction is downward. v represents the y-directed component of velocity and u the x-directed component. This sort of left-handed co-ordinate system is rather generally used in the oceanographic literature. Note that the third equation in (10.13) is the hydrostatic equation.

References

Bjerknes, V. (1898) Uber einen hydrodynamischen Fundamentalsatz und seine Anwendung besonders auf die Mekanik der Atmosphäre und des Weltmeeres. *K. Svenska Vet. Acad. Handl.* **31**(4), 35 pp.

Defant, A. (1941) Die absolute Topographie des physikalischen Meersniveaus und der Druckflachen, sowie die Wasserbewegungen im Atlantischen Ozean. *Deutsch Atlantische*

Exped. Meteor. 1925–1927. Wiss. Erg., Bd. Vl, 2 Teil, 5 Lief., pp. 191–260.

HIDAKA, K. (1949) Depth of motionless layer as inferred from the distribution of salinity in the ocean. *Trans. Am. Geophys. Union* **30**(3), 346–348.

SANDSTROM, J. W. and B. HELLAND-HANSEN. (1903) Über die Berechung von Meeresström ungen. *Rep. Norweg. Fish. Invest.* **2**(4), 43 pp.

STOMMEL, H. (1956) On the determination of the depth of no meridional motion. *Deep Sea Res.* **3**(4), 273–278.

Sources of Additional Information

Physical Oceanography Vol. 1, Chapter XV. DEFANT, ALBERT. Pergamon Press, New York. 1961.

The Oceans. Chapter XIII. SVERDRUP, H. U., M. W. JOHNSON, and R. H. FLEMING. Prentice Hall, New York. 1942.

An Introduction to Physical Oceanography. (Chapter 9). VON ARX, WILLIAM S. Addison Wesley, Reading, Mass. 1962.

Processing Oceanographic Data. LAFOND. E. C. H. O. Pub. No. 614, Washington, D.C. U.S. Navy Hydrographic Office. 1951.

CHAPTER 11

TRANSFER PHENOMENA—TURBULENCE

In the consideration of geostrophic flow the accelerations that might arise from internal friction (viscosity) are specifically neglected. Although this neglect appears justified by the success of the method in the study of ocean currents, it is known that much of the ocean circulation must be driven by the winds and that the coupling mechanism must be frictional. Also current shear must always result in viscous accelerations, and geostrophic current computations really evaluate the vertical current shear.

Because of turbulent momentum exchange it is impossible to uniquely formulate viscous accelerations. The same problem occurs with respect to the transfer of heat and of dissolved materials in the ocean.

We will discuss the nature of the turbulent exchange problem and look at some of the approaches that are made to the formulation of viscous stresses in turbulent fluid media.

11.1 Viscosity

Consider a simple solid body (Fig. 11.1) constrained in some plane ($z =$ constant) against translation in the x-direction. If at some other z

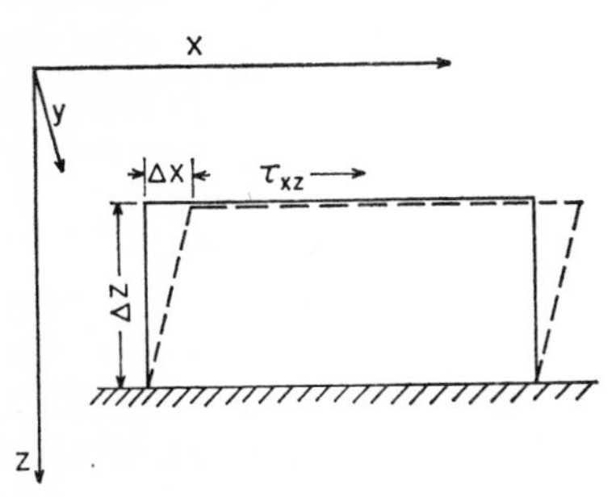

Fig. 11.1 Deformation of a constrained solid by shearing stress applied to a free face.

a force is applied in the x-direction, the body will be deformed due to the couple composed of the applied force and an equal and opposite force applied in the plane of constraint. The x-directed force per unit area in the z-plane (τ_{xz}) is spoken of as that component of the "shearing stress". The deformation consists, to a first approximation, of a differential movement of the solid at one z-level by an amount Δx relative to another level a vertical distance Δz from it. To this approximation the shearing strain can be written $\Delta x/\Delta z$. In an elastic body stress and strain are linearly related through the "modulus of shearing elasticity" or the "rigidity" as long as the elastic limits are not exceeded. If the elastic limits are exceeded flow takes place.

The property that defines a fluid is that, for a given application of shearing stress, there is no limit to the deformation. There is, however, considerable variation in the rates of deformation. Shearing stress results in velocity gradients, the exact relationship being a property of the fluid involved.

The relationship is usually written

$$\tau_{xz} = -\mu \frac{dV_x}{dz}, \qquad (11.1)$$

where V_x is the x-directed velocity and μ, as here defined, is called the dynamic viscosity. μ has dimensions $ml^{-1}t^{-1}$, or g/cm sec in c.g.s. units.

Consider flow in a channel (Fig. 11.2) of uniform depth z_m where a stress τ_{xz} is applied at the surface ($z = 0$). At the bottom $V_x = 0$ and the bottom must exert an equal and opposite stress for the system to be balanced in steady state flow.

Then, $dV_x/dz = \tau_{xz}/\mu$, and, if V_{x0} is the velocity at the surface and μ is constant throughout the fluid, $V_x = (\tau_{xz}/\mu)(z_m - z)$ describes the velocity distribution.

For steady state conditions, with constant viscosity, a constant velocity gradient is the permissible condition. This is a special type of "laminar flow" known as "Couette flow".

Consider a body of fluid to which a stress τ_{xz} is applied. This force per unit area can be equated to the time rate of change of momentum of the unit column:

$$\tau_{xz} = \int_0^\infty \frac{d(\rho V_x)}{dt}\, dz,$$

where ρ is the density. Differentiating: $d\tau_{xz}/dz = d(\rho V_x)/dt$, which, on substituting (11.1), yields

$$\frac{d}{dz}\left(-\mu\frac{dV_x}{dz}\right) = \frac{d(\rho V_x)}{dt}.$$

If μ is constant, this becomes

$$\frac{d(\rho V_x)}{dt} = -\mu\frac{d^2V_x}{dz^2}, \qquad (11.2)$$

which relates the time rate of transfer of x-directed momentum to a layer to the second derivative of x-directed velocity with depth, the proportionality constant being the coefficient of viscosity.

For the case of uniform density (11.2) becomes

$$\frac{dV}{dt} = -\frac{\mu}{\rho}\frac{d^2V}{dz^2}. \qquad (11.3)$$

The term μ/ρ is called the kinematic viscosity.

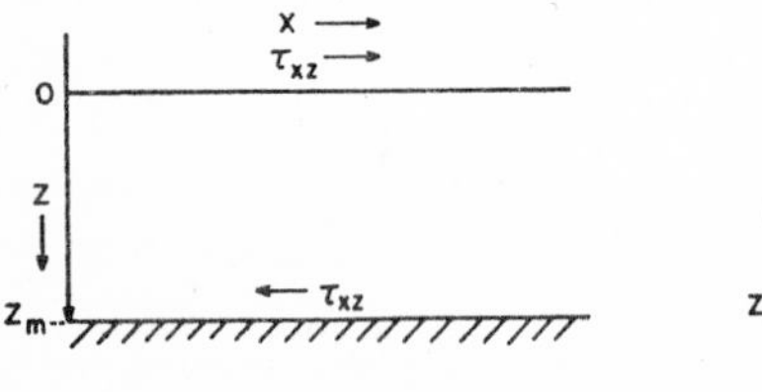

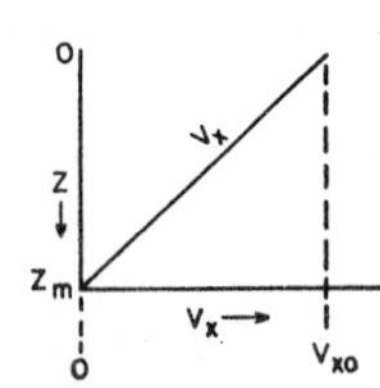

Fig. 11.2 Steady state flow in a uniform channel in response to surface stress. ρ and μ constant.

11.2 Heat Flow

The temperature of a system is a property which determines whether or not the system is in thermal equilibrium with another system. If two systems of different temperature are placed in contact, heat will flow from one to the other to equalize the temperature. We arbitrarily pick the sense of the temperature scales such that heat will flow from the system of higher temperature to that of lower temperature. Along any path, the heat flow per unit area of cross section, which tends to equalize the temperature, is proportional to the gradient of temperature.

$$\text{Heat flux} = -K\,(dT/dz) \qquad (11.4)$$

where T is temperature and the heat flux is in the z-direction. K is the coefficient of heat conduction or thermal conductivity and is a property of the material in the path.

The change in heat content (dQ) of a unit volume of substance, whose density is ρ, is given by $dQ = \rho C_p dT$, where C_p is the specific heat (e.g., calories per gram degree) at constant pressure, and dT is the change in temperature. If we consider a system uniform in x and y, the heat flow through a unit cross section normal to the z-direction can be equated to the rate of change of heat content in the column beyond.

$$\text{Heat flux} = \int_0^\infty \frac{d(\rho C_p T)}{dt}\, dz,$$

which, on differentiating, gives

$$\frac{d(\text{Heat flux})}{dz} = \frac{d(\rho C_p T)}{dt},$$

and, on substituting (11.4),

$$\frac{d[-K\,(dT/dz)]}{dz} = \frac{d(\rho C_p T)}{dt}.$$

If K, ρ, and C_p can be considered constant, this reduces to

$$\frac{dT}{dt} = \frac{-K}{\rho C_p}\frac{d^2T}{dz^2}. \qquad (11.5)$$

The time rate of change of temperature at any z is proportional to the second derivative of temperature with z.

K/C_p has units $ml^{-1}t^{-1}$ or g/cm sec, the same units as the dynamic viscosity. (The quantity $k = K/\rho C_p$ is known as the thermometric conductivity or thermal diffusivity and is analogous to the kinematic viscosity.)

11.3 Diffusion

If the concentration (C) of a substance (A) within a system varies from point to point, there is a tendency toward an equilibrium state in which the concentration is uniform. The flux of A (g/cm^2 sec) is proportional to the gradient of concentration. In the one dimensional case

$$\text{Flux of } A = -D\,(dC/dz).$$

C is non-dimensional (grams of A per gram of material) and D, the diffusion coefficient has dimensions $ml^{-1}t^{-1}$ or g/cm sec. An argument similar to that employed in the previous section yields

$$[d(\rho C)/dt] = -D\,(d^2C/dz^2) \qquad (11.6)$$

or, with constant density,

$$(dC/dt) = -(D/\rho)\,(d^2C/dz^2).$$

In the ocean A may represent the salt and C the salinity.

11.4 Kinetic Theory

In the preceeding sections it has been shown that the exchange coefficients μ, K, and D bear equivalent relationships to ρV_x, $\rho C_p T$, and ρC. That is, the transfer of momentum, heat, and salt are governed by similar laws.

We visualize these transfers taking place through random motion of the elements within the system. Small quantities of material with the characteristics of their immediate environment (velocity, temperature, or concentration) are carried to neighboring regions where these parameters have different values. Thus, on a macroscopic scale there is a net transport of momentum, heat or "salt" down gradient.

In the kinetic theory of gases the transfer is considered to result from random thermal motion of the molecules. This theory gives the following evaluation of the coefficients:

$$\mu = \rho \Omega L/3,$$

$$K = \rho \Omega L C_v/3,$$

$$D = \Omega L/3 \text{ (self diffusion)},$$

where ρ is the density of the gas, Ω is the arithmetic mean thermal speed of the molecules and C_v is the specific heat at constant volume, L is the mean free path of the molecules. Ω, K, and ρ are functions of temperature and pressure that can be evaluated for the gas.

A kinetic theory of liquids (see, for example, Frenkel, 1955) formulates equivalent relationships. Here the random motion of molecules is replaced by vibration of molecules about equilibrium positions and small random jumps in equilibrium position.

For fluids in small quantities as might be used in the laboratory, and under conditions of low flow velocities, transfer phenomena follow these classical laws in a strict sense. For given conditions of temperature, pressure and concentration one can determine unique values for μ, K, and D. These are referred to as the molecular coefficients of viscosity, heat conduction and diffusion.

11.5 The Problem in Large Quantities of Fluid

When one treats with real fluids, either liquid or gaseous, in large quantities, and attempts to formulate equations for exchange phenomena in classical form, the following difficulties are encountered:

(a) The appropriate exchange coefficients appear to be very much larger than the molecular coefficients.
(b) The exchange coefficients appear to vary with the scale of the phenomena under study.
(c) The coefficients are non-isotropic. For example, in a gravity field coefficients for vertical exchange are quite different from those for horizontal exchange. The vertical coefficients depend strongly upon the stability.
(d) The coefficients vary spatially in the neighborhood of fixed boundaries, tending to approach the values for molecular coefficients at the boundary.
(e) The presence of velocity shear within the fluid increases the apparent value of the exchange coefficients.

To explain these phenomena, it is postulated that within the fluid body there are, in addition to molecular motions, larger random motions which carry macroscopic quantities of the fluid to regions where the environment is characterized by different concentrations of the exchanged property. Thus, the rate of exchange is greatly increased ((a), above). These motions are referred to individually as eddies or collectively as turbulence.

A whole spectrum of eddy sizes is postulated to exist in a turbulent fluid regime. Clearly there is an upper limit in size imposed by the extent of the fluid body. Also very large eddies are not likely to have an effect upon exchange within a small region (b). Consider, for example, a small spot of dye in the ocean. A large scale eddy might transport the marked portion of water over large distances without changing the distribution of the dye with respect to its center of concentration. Smaller eddies, however, can cause relative separation of parts of the marked water thus contributing to its diffusion. As the dye spot spreads, more and more of the spectrum of turbulence becomes effective in its diffusion, and the applicable coefficient describing the process becomes larger.

The vertical stability of a stratified fluid in a gravity field introduces buoyant forces which inhibit the vertical components of eddy motion. Horizontal eddies will not, in general, be so inhibited (c).

In the neighborhood of a fixed boundary in the fluid the presence of the boundary inhibits the motion in large scale eddies. Immediately against the boundary only the random thermal motion of molecules remains to effect transfer (d).

One way of supplying the energy involved in eddy motion is from the organized motion of the fluid. Hence regions of velocity shear tend to be regions of enhanced turbulence (e). Modern turbulence theory formulates the cascading of energy through a spectrum to eddies of smaller and smaller size until eventually dissipated as heat (Kolmogoroff, 1941).

By analogy with the formulation of molecular exchange processes we use equations identical in form and call the larger, variable coefficients "eddy viscosity", "eddy conductivity", and "eddy diffusivity"; or "turbulent viscosity", "turbulent conductivity" and "turbulent diffusivity".

In the turbulent diffusion of momentum (viscosity effect) it can be postulated that a parcel of fluid carried to a new location must be forced quickly to come to equilibrium with its new surroundings in respect to momentum concentration because of the friction arising from differential motion. For the diffusion of other concentrations, however, the equilibration may depend only on molecular diffusion, and there is some chance of eddy motion carrying it back towards its old location before it has had its full influence on the environment. For this reason, one might expect the eddy coefficients for viscosity to be considerably greater than those for diffusion or heat transfer. This, in fact, seems to be so. For example, Suda (1936) obtains, for the region of the Kuroshio in depths 0–200 m, an eddy diffusivity of 7 to 90 g/cm sec and an eddy viscosity of 680 to 7500 g/cm sec.

11.6 Stirring and Mixing

Eckart (1948) has given a concise discussion of the role of macroscopic motion upon transfer phenomena. He distinguishes between "stirring" processes which increase the mean value of internal gradients and "mixing" processes which break down the gradients. Differential large scale motion within the fluid constitutes stirring, which, by increasing the mean value of the gradients, speeds up the mixing, which is the molecular process tending to remove the gradients. He concludes:

"(1) In all except certain very special cases, advection* alone will ultimately increase the mean value of any initial gradient.
(2) This effect of advection is appropriately called stirring.
(3) Stirring is independent of the vorticity† of the motion and can occur even if the motion is not turbulent.
(4) The effect of conduction or diffusion is to decrease the mean value of the gradient.
(5) This is appropriately called mixing.
(6) Ordinarily, the early stages of a process in which both stirring and mixing occur will be dominated by the advective processes.
(7) These may so increase the mean gradient that the mixing process will ultimately dominate over the stirring process.
(8) Viscosity, if not counteracted by other factors, tends to stop the stirring process before an appreciable amount of mixing can occur."

11.7 Statistical Consideration of Turbulent Exchange

Motion in the ocean is generally turbulent. That is, if one examines the motion of small portions of the fluid, it is found that the velocity of these portions change rapidly, both from place to place at any one time or from time to time at any one place. Generally the turbulent motions are of greater magnitude when they coexist with permanent currents or are associated with wind shear on the surface.

In the study of organized motion one is concerned with the mean values of velocity components, either at a fixed point, averaged over a suitably long time, or at a fixed time averaged over a sufficiently large region of space. The precise duration or spatial extent will depend upon the phenomena under study.

In studying a major ocean current one might

* In simple terms—differential motion within the fluid. The time differential of a quantity following the motion (d/dt) consists of the local change ($\partial/\partial t$) plus three "advective" terms related to the velocity field and spatial distribution of the quantity, $u(\partial/\partial x) + v(\partial/\partial y) + w(\partial/\partial z)$. Thus, for x-directed velocity (u)

$$\frac{du}{dt} = \frac{\partial u}{\partial t} + u\frac{\partial u}{\partial x} + v\frac{\partial u}{\partial y} + w\frac{\partial u}{\partial z}.$$

† Motion involving rotation of any small parcel of the fluid about an axis within the parcel. The vertical component of vorticity can be written $(\partial v/\partial x) - (\partial u/\partial y)$ (Section 13.2).

wish to take a time average that would eliminate the effect of tidal motion. For tidal studies, one takes time averages that eliminate motion due to wind waves—and so on. Spatially one might take averages over a few square miles in examining a major current, but this would clearly be unsuitable for observing the current pattern in a small estuary. Most of our instruments, by their nature, measure parameters averaged over real intervals of time and space.

The symbol $[A]$ is used to denote the mean value of the parameter A at a particular point x, y, z averaged over a fundamental interval of time centered on a particular instant t, or else to denote the mean value at time t through a fundamental unit of volume centered on x, y, z.

The symbols U, V, W will represent the mean values of the components of mass weighted velocity* in the x, y, and z directions, respectively, for either type of averaging process. U, V, W are functions of x, y, z, and t.

At x, y, z, t the components of total velocity will be written $(U + u)$, $(V + v)$, $(W + w)$ where u, v, w are the "components of turbulent motion". By definition

$$[U + u] = U, \quad [V + v] = V, \quad [W + w] = W,$$

and

$$[u] = [v] = [w] = 0.$$

If the density ρ is considered to be uniform, the equation of continuity† may be written,

$$\frac{\partial(U + u)}{\partial x} + \frac{\partial(V + v)}{\partial y} + \frac{\partial(W + w)}{\partial z} = 0. \qquad (11.7)$$

Now when temporal averages are taken over a fundamental interval of *time*:

$$\left[\frac{\partial U}{\partial x}\right] = \frac{\partial[U]}{\partial x} = \frac{\partial U}{\partial x}$$

while

$$\left[\frac{\partial u}{\partial x}\right] = \frac{\partial[u]}{\partial x} = 0,$$

and so on for like terms.

It follows that the application of the averaging process to (11.7) yields

$$\frac{\partial U}{\partial x} + \frac{\partial V}{\partial y} + \frac{\partial W}{\partial z} = 0, \qquad (11.8)$$

which will be called the equation of continuity for mean motion.

From (11.7) and (11.8) it follows that

$$\frac{\partial u}{\partial x} + \frac{\partial v}{\partial y} + \frac{\partial w}{\partial z} = 0, \qquad (11.9)$$

which will be called the equation of continuity for turbulent motion.

The mean value of the kinetic energy per unit volume of the fluid can be written

$$(1/2)\ [\rho\{(U + u)^2 + (V + v)^2 + (W + w)^2\}],$$

which is equal to

$$(1/2)\rho(U^2 + V^2 + W^2) + (1/2)[\rho(u^2 + v^2 + w^2)]$$

since, because U is not a function of time, $[Uu]$ can be written $U[u]$ which is by definition zero, and similarly for like terms.

The first term in the above expression can be called the mean kinetic energy per unit volume associated with mean motion, and the second term the mean kinetic energy per unit volume associated with turbulence.

Momentum Transfer — Reynolds Stresses

Consider a small area ΔS normal to the x-axis. The mass ΔM which in an interval Δt crosses ΔS in the positive x-direction is:

$$\Delta M = \rho \Delta S(U + u)\ \Delta t.$$

The momentum of this fluid has components:

$$\Delta M(U + u), \quad \Delta M(V + v), \quad \Delta M(W + w),$$

so that the x-directed momentum flux (time rate of transfer of momentum in the x-direction through unit area normal to this direction) has components:

$$\rho(U + u)^2,\ \rho(U + u)\ (V + v),\ \rho(U + u)\ (W + w)$$

per unit area per unit time. The mean values are

$$\rho U^2 + [\rho u^2], \quad \rho UV + [\rho uv], \quad \rho UW + [\rho uw].$$

These are the components of force per unit area

* By mass weighted velocity we mean the volume integral of the product of the masses of individual particles and their velocities divided by the aggregate mass of the particles within the same volume. The product of mass weighted velocity and mean density yields the momentum per unit volume.

† Consider an incremental right prism within a fluid, having dimensions Δx, Δy, Δz. Fluid mass enters through three faces at rates $\rho u \Delta y \Delta z$, $\rho v \Delta x \Delta z$ and $\rho w \Delta x \Delta y$. Mass leaves through other faces at rates $\rho\{u + (\partial u/\partial x)\Delta x\}\Delta y \Delta z$, $\rho\{v + (\partial v/\partial y)\Delta y\} \times \Delta x \Delta z$ and $\rho\{w + (\partial w/\partial z)\Delta z\}\Delta x \Delta y$. If the density is to be constant the net outflow $\rho\{(\partial u/\partial x) + (\partial v/\partial y) + (\partial w/\partial z)\}\Delta x \Delta y \Delta z$ must be zero. The outflow per unit volume $\rho\{(\partial u/\partial x) + (\partial v/\partial y) + (\partial w/\partial z)\}$ is called the divergence of mass. $(\partial u/\partial x) + (\partial v/\partial y) + (\partial w/\partial z)$ is the divergence of velocity and this must be zero in a homogeneous incompressible fluid. The relationship stating this is commonly called the equation of continuity.

that the fluid on the negative x-side of the area ΔS exerts on the fluid on the positive x-side. The part associated with the turbulence has components:

$$[\rho u^2], \quad [\rho uv], \quad [\rho uw].$$

Similar consideration of momentum flux in the other directions leads to components:

$$[\rho uv], \quad [\rho v^2], \quad [\rho vw]$$

and

$$[\rho uw], \quad [\rho vw], \quad [\rho w^2].$$

The components $[\rho u^2]$, $[\rho v^2]$, and $[\rho w^2]$ are normal to the areas across which they act and are thus pressure terms. The other terms constitute tangential forces and are of the nature of frictional stresses. This development was first presented by Reynolds (1894) in a pioneering work on turbulence. The turbulent stress terms are usually referred to as "Reynolds Stresses".

For the two-dimensional case analogous to that discussed in Section 11.1, where only stress related to variation in the z-direction of the x-directed velocity was considered,

$$\tau_{xz} = -\mu(\partial U/\partial z).$$

The pertinent component of turbulent stress is $[\rho uw]$, and, considering the stress to be entirely due to turbulence, we may write

$$\tau_{xz} = [\rho uw] = -A_z(\partial U/\partial z), \qquad (11.10)$$

where in place of μ, the molecular viscosity, we now write A_z, the turbulent or eddy coefficient of viscosity in the z-direction. Thus

$$A_z = -[\rho uw]/(\partial U/\partial z), \qquad (11.11)$$

which permits the evaluation of A_z from continuous measurements of the components of velocity at several levels in the fluid. Although the functional relationship might indicate that A_z decreases with increasing velocity shear, the converse is true because of the dependence of both u and w upon $\partial U/\partial z$.

Equation (11.11) holds only if the exchange is considered to be wholly due to turbulence. A more extract treatment (see, for example, Proudman, 1953, Chapter VI), taking into account molecular viscosity, yields:

$$A_z = -[\rho uw]/(\partial U/\partial z) + \mu. \qquad (11.12)$$

Note that the molecular viscosity may decrease the effectiveness of turbulence in the transfer of momentum.

As written above A_z has units $ml^{-1}t^{-1}$ or g/cm sec. In many treatments the so-called "kinematic coefficients" are preferred, in which case:

$$A_z = -[\rho uw]/\rho(\partial U/\partial z) + \mu/\rho,$$

and the coefficient has units l^2t^{-1} or cm²/sec.

Diffusion of Salt

By similar treatment, let S denote the mean salinity and $S + s$ the total salinity at x, y, z, t, where s is called the turbulent salinity. Then,

$$[S + s] = S \text{ and } [s] = 0.$$

The time rate of passage of mass of salt across a unit area normal to the z-direction (flux of salt in the z-direction) will be:

$\rho(W + w)(S + s)$, and the mean value will be

$\rho WS + \rho[ws]$, since

$[Ws] = [wS] = 0.$

The first term, ρWS, is the mean advection. The second term, $\rho[ws]$, is the turbulent advection or diffusion, and, by analogy to the classical form, we write

$$\rho[ws] = -D_z'(\partial S/\partial z),$$

where D_z' is the eddy diffusivity of salt in the z-direction.

This process must be thought of as acting along with molecular diffusion. Also, since parcels of water of finite size are transferred, turbulent flux will constitute stirring which, by increasing the mean value of the gradients, will promote rapid mixing.

11.8 Prandtl's Assumption — Mixing Length

Consider a homogeneous fluid lying over a plane boundary containing the origin of the co-ordinate system. Consider the mean motion to be unidirectional and two-dimensional so that it can be fully represented on an xz-plane. Take the mean motion as x-directed with a velocity gradient in the z-direction. Let the boundary surface be the xy-plane through the origin.

This is the classical boundary layer problem in its simplest form. It pertains to the atmosphere in its interaction with the earth's surface and to the flow of water over a plane bottom. Much study has gone into the formulation of models that will adequately describe the observed distribution of mean velocity in these situations. In this and the following section, we will examine certain concepts that are in common use for describing boundary layer flow.

In the model the downward (negative z-direction) flux of momentum, or eddy stress is given by

$$\tau_{xz} = -\rho[uw]. \qquad (11.13)$$

Prandtl (1925) introduced the assumption that a length (l) can be defined such that:

$$\tau_{xz} = \rho l^2 (\partial U/\partial z)^2. \qquad (11.14)$$

If one writes (11.14) in the form

$$\tau_{xz} = \rho(l) \{l(\partial U/\partial z)\} \partial U/\partial z,$$

and compares this to the expression for stress in a perfect gas:

$$\tau_{xz} = \rho L\Omega/3 (\partial U/\partial z),$$

one can see why the concept is attractive. The "mixing length" (l) corresponds to the mean free path of the molecules and the velocity $l (\partial U/\partial z)$ takes the place of Ω, the mean thermal speed of the molecules. Mixing length is thought of as being related to the statistical distribution of eddy sizes.

An attempt may be made to justify the assumption in the following way:

If a parcel of fluid comes from a level $z + l'$ (Fig. 11.3) to the level z, its x-directed velocity, if conserved, is, to a first approximation,

$$U + l' (\partial U/\partial z),$$

where by U we mean the value of U at z. Hence

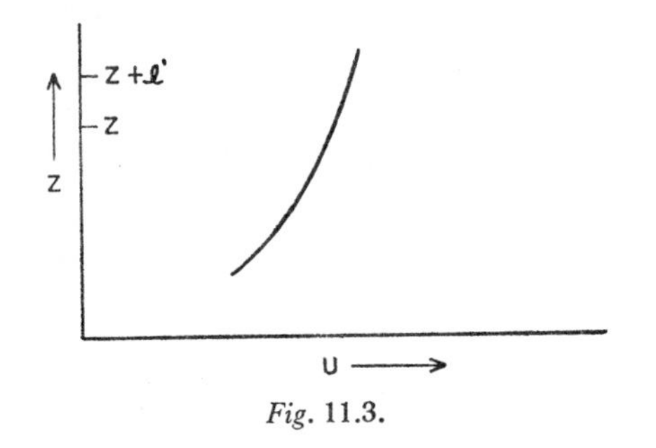

Fig. 11.3.

$u = l' (\partial U/\partial z)$ is the turbulent velocity. Substituting in (11.13)

$$\tau_{xz} = -\rho[l'w] \partial U/\partial z. \qquad (11.15)$$

It can be argued that l' and w are not independent since a parcel of fluid from above (l' positive) would cross the z-plane with negative w and one from below (l' negative) would cross with positive w. Thus,

$$-[l'w] = C_1 [|w|] [|l'|],$$

that is, since the product $l'w$ is always negative, the average value of the product can be replaced by minus the product of the averages of their magnitudes, without regard to sign, times some constant C_1. Also w and u cannot be expected to be independent. One might argue that a fluid parcel coming from a greater distance (u larger) should cross the plane with greater w. Then,

$$[|w|] = C_2 [|u|] = C_2 [|l' (\partial U/\partial z)|] =$$
$$C_2 [|l'|] (\partial U/\partial z).$$

Combining,

$$-[l'w] = C_1C_2 ([|l'|])^2 (\partial U/\partial z),$$

and by replacing $C_1C_2 ([|l'|])^2$ by l^2, equation (11.15) becomes

$$\tau_{xz} = \rho l^2(\partial U/\partial z)^2, \qquad (11.14)$$

as assumed. The eddy viscosity A_z is given by:

$$A_z = \rho l^2 (\partial U/\partial z).$$

Since the justification is far from rigorous the mixing length assumption must be considered simply as an assumption. Its value lies in the fact that it has led to a model of boundary layer flow that has had some success in explaining observations.

11.9 The Prandtl–von Kármán Boundary Layer Theory

A model of the boundary layer due to von Kármán (1930) starts with the following assumptions:

(1) Prandtl's assumption concerning mixing length is applied to a layer of fluid adjacent to the boundary surface.
(2) The layer is assumed to be sufficiently thin so that its motion is determined by the stresses on its two horizontal boundaries. One boundary is arbitrarily selected.
(3) The horizontal pressure gradients and Coriolis accelerations can be neglected.
(4) Mean motion is steady.

Because of the assumptions, stress is, to a first approximation, constant throughout the layer. The direction of mean motion is constant and must coincide with the direction of the stress at the boundaries.

Two further assumptions are made:

(5) The mixing length (l) is proportional to the height (z) above the lower fixed boundary.
(6) l has a finite value at the lower boundary that depends upon the "roughness" of the boundary surface.

From assumptions (5) and (6), we write

$$l = k_0 \, (z + z_0),$$

where k_0 is called the "universal turbulence constant" and is found experimentally to have a value of approximately 0.40; z_0 is called the roughness length and is related to the surface roughness; $k_0 \, z_0$ is the mixing length at $z = 0$ (assumption (6)).

It follows that the stress equation (11.14) becomes:

$$\tau_{xz} = \rho k_0^2 \, (z + z_0)^2 \, (\partial U/\partial z)^2. \qquad (11.16)$$

Now for convenience, a term u_* is defined such that

$$u_* = \sqrt{(\tau_{xz}/\rho)}$$

and (11.16) becomes

$$\partial U/\partial z = u_*/k_0(z + z_0). \qquad (11.17)$$

u_* is called the friction velocity. Since τ_{xz} and ρ are assumed constant, u_* is constant through the boundary layer, and (11.17) can be integrated to give

$$U_2 - U_1 = \frac{u_*}{k_0} \ln \left(\frac{z_2 + z_0}{z_1 + z_0}\right). \qquad (11.18)$$

Although this development may appear rather artificial, the results do fit the experimental observations in boundary layer flow. That is, in the boundary layer, the mean velocity is found to vary logarithmically with distance from the boundary.

To fit all the observations, it is necessary to recognize two types of flow, one for which the boundary surface is hydrodynamically smooth and one for which the boundary surface is hydrodynamically rough. Whether a given surface will be rough or smooth will depend partly upon the physical configuration of the surface and partly upon the flow velocities involved.

For a smooth surface the variation of U with z is as shown in Fig. 11.4. It is postulated that the turbulent eddies do not exist continuously down to the surface but that there exists a thin "laminar sub-layer" within which the stress is purely viscous. In the sub-layer

$$\partial U/\partial z = \tau_{xz}/\mu = \tau_{xz}\rho/\rho\mu = \frac{u_*^2}{\nu}, \qquad (11.19)$$

where $\nu = \mu/\rho$ is the kinematic molecular viscosity. Equation (11.18) holds outside the laminar sub-layer.

Over a rough surface turbulence persists to the very surface where the velocity is zero. Putting

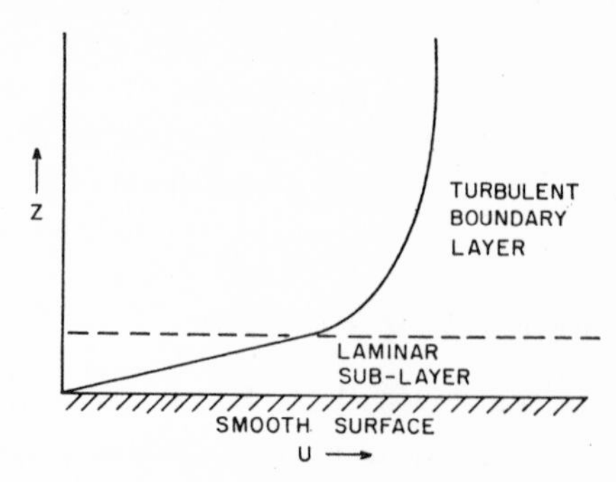

Fig. 11.4 Variation of mean velocity U in turbulent boundary layer flow over a hydrodynamically smooth surface.

$U_1 = 0$ at $z_1 = 0$ in (11.18), and omitting the subscript 2,

$$U = \frac{u_*}{k_0} \ln \left(\frac{z + z_0}{z_0}\right), \qquad (11.20)$$

describes the velocity profile as shown in Fig. 11.5.

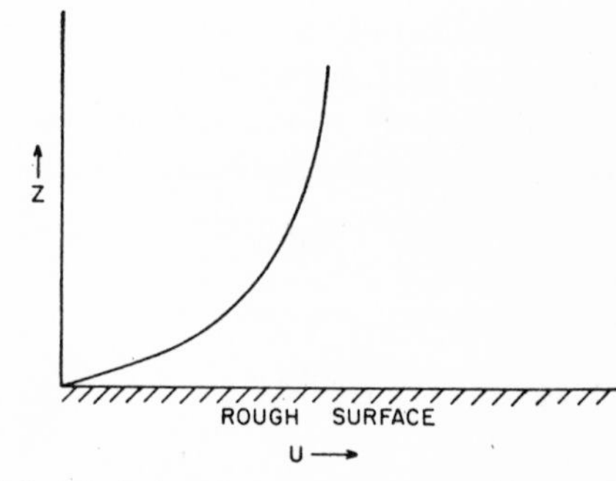

Fig. 11.5 Variation of mean velocity U in turbulent boundary layer flow over a hydrodynamically rough surface.

Here

$$\tau_{xz} = \rho u_*^2 = \rho \left(\frac{k_0}{\ln \{(z + z_0)/z_0\}}\right)^2 U^2,$$

which is often written

$$\tau_{xz} = \rho \gamma_z^2 U_z^2, \qquad (11.21)$$

where $\gamma_z^2 = (k_0/\ln\{(z + z_0)/z_0\})^2$ is called the resistance coefficient. (This is written C_d in many treatments and referred to as the "drag coefficient".) γ_z^2 is a non-dimensional parameter which relates stress in the boundary layer to the velocity at a chosen level.

In the study of wind stress on the ocean surface,

it is customary to relate the stress to wind speed measured either at 10 m or 15 m and to write for the surface stress

$$\tau_0 = \gamma_{10}^2 \, \rho_a \, U_{10}^2$$

where ρ_a is the density of the air and γ_{10}^2 is the value for measurement at the 10 m level.

Wilson (1960) has summarized all the reliable observations available to him, reducing them to standard 10 m values for the purpose of comparison. The average value of γ_{10}^2 for light winds he found to be 1.5×10^{-3}, and for strong winds 2.4×10^{-3}. Between the two ranges he concludes that γ_{10}^2 increases from 1.5×10^{-3} to 2.4×10^{-3} in a manner which is probably nonlinear. This represents a modification of the view (Munk, 1947) long generally held that there was an abrupt (if not discontinuous) jump in γ^2 at some "critical wind speed" around 6 m/sec or 13 m.p.h. At this critical wind speed, it was postulated that the nature of the boundary layer flow changed from the equivalent of flow over a smooth surface to flow over a rough surface. It is still generally held that the nature of the interface changes from light to strong winds but there is no general agreement on the concept of a critical wind speed.

The treatment in this section has assumed constant density and no Coriolis acceleration. In the atmospheric boundary layer, and for boundary layer flow in the ocean, both stratification and Coriolis acceleration will modify the flow. The reader is directed to more complete treatments in recommended sources of additional information below.

References

Eckart, C. (1948) An analysis of the stirring and mixing processes in incompressible fluids. *J. Mar. Res.* **7**(3), 265–275.

Frenkel, J. *Kinetic Theory of Liquids*. Dover, New York. 1955 (reprint).

Kolmogoroff, A. (1941) The local structure of turbulence in incompressible viscous fluid for very large Reynolds numbers. *Comptes. Rend. Acad. Sci., U.S.S.R.* **30**, 301.

von Kármán, Th. (1930) Meckanische Ahnlichkeit und Turbulenz. *Nachr. Ges. Wiss. Göttingen, Math-Phys. Kl.* 58.

Munk, W. H. (1947) A critical wind speed for air–sea boundary processes. *J. Mar. Res.* **6**(3), 203–218.

Prandtl, L. (1925) Bericht über Untersuchungen zur ausgebildeten Turbulenz. *Zeitschr. agnew. Math. Mech.* **5**, 136.

Proudman, J. *Dynamical Oceanography*. Methuen, London. 1953.

Reynolds, O. (1894) On the dynamical theory of incompressible viscous fluids and the determination of the criterion. *Phil. Trans. Royal Soc.* **A 186**, 123.

Suda, K. (1936) On the dissipation of energy in the density current. *Geophys. Mag.* **10**, 131–243, Tokyo.

Wilson, B. W. (1960) Note on surface wind stress over water at low and high speed. *J. Geophys. Res.* **65**(10), 3377–3382.

Sources of Additional Information

Dynamical Oceanography. Proudman, J. Methuen, London. 1953.

Micrometeorology. Sutton, O. G. McGraw-Hill, New York. 1953.

Turbulent Transfer in the Lower Atmosphere. Priestley, C. H. B. The University of Chicago Press. Chicago, 1959.

Cousin, S. (1961) Turbulent Flow. *Am. Scientist* **39**(3), 300–325.

CHAPTER 12

WIND DRIVEN CURRENTS

We will examine first Ekman's classical solution for wind driven currents. Here pressure gradient accelerations are neglected and Coriolis and frictional accelerations considered in balance. If one makes a rather severe simplification regarding the vertical eddy viscosity coefficient, an elegant solution is obtained. The solution is qualitatively informative in spite of the assumptions and, moreover, vertical integration yields an evaluation of transport that is independent of the actual form of the coefficient.

Next, acceleration equations containing the Coriolis, pressure gradient and viscous terms are presented and an indication is given of how they are made to yield acceptable models of wind driven ocean circulation.

12.1 Wind Drift and the Ekman Spiral

During the historic drift of the vessel *Fram* across the North Polar Sea, Nansen observed that the drift of the ice floes was not generally in the direction of the wind, but deviated to the right some 20 to 40°. He devised a qualitative explanation which involved a balance between the Coriolis acceleration and viscous accelerations. Ekman (1902), in a classical paper on the subject, formalized this explanation.

Take a rectilinear co-ordinate system such as that in Fig. 12.1, with its origin in the water surface and z-directed vertically downward. Consider the wind (W) to blow in the y-direction so that the wind stress on the surface consists wholly of the component τ_{yz}.

Assume a homogeneous unbounded ocean without pressure gradient accelerations and in the northern hemisphere. Further, assume unaccelerated horizontal flow, i.e.

$$(\mathrm{d}U/\mathrm{d}t) = (\mathrm{d}V/\mathrm{d}t) = 0,$$

where U is the x-directed velocity and V the y-directed velocity.

The acceleration equations under these conditions can be written:

$$\rho f V + \frac{\partial}{\partial z}\left(A_z \frac{\partial U}{\partial z}\right) = 0,$$

$$- \rho f U + \frac{\partial}{\partial z}\left(A_z \frac{\partial V}{\partial z}\right) = 0, \qquad (12.1)$$

where ρ is the density, f the Coriolis parameter ($2\Omega \sin \psi$) and A_z the vertical eddy coefficient of viscosity. If the further assumption is made that A_z is independent of depth (12.1) can be written

$$\rho f V + A_z \frac{\partial^2 U}{\partial z^2} = 0,$$

$$- \rho f U + A_z \frac{\partial^2 V}{\partial z^2} = 0,$$

for which there exists the solution:

$$U = C_1 \exp \left(\frac{\rho f}{2A_z}\right)^{1/2} Z \ \cos \left[\sqrt{\left(\frac{\rho f}{2A_z}\right)}\, z + b\right] + C_2 \exp - \left(\frac{\rho f}{2A_z}\right)^{1/2} Z \ \cos \left[\sqrt{\left(\frac{\rho f}{2A_z}\right)}\, z + d\right],$$

$$V = C_1 \exp \left(\frac{\rho f}{2A_z}\right)^{1/2} Z \ \sin \left[\sqrt{\left(\frac{\rho f}{2A_z}\right)}\, z + b\right] - C_2 \exp - \left(\frac{\rho f}{2A_z}\right)^{1/2} Z \ \sin \left[\sqrt{\left(\frac{\rho f}{2A_z}\right)}\, z + d\right]. \qquad (12.3)$$

Writing $D = \pi\sqrt{(2A_z/\rho f)}$, (12.3) becomes:

$$U = C_1\, e^{(\pi z/D)} \cos\left(\frac{\pi z}{D} + b\right) + C_2\, e^{-(\pi z/D)} \cos\left(\frac{\pi z}{D} + d\right),$$

$$V = C_1\, e^{(\pi z/D)} \sin\left(\frac{\pi z}{D} + b\right) - C_2\, e^{-(\pi z/D)} \sin\left(\frac{\pi z}{D} + d\right). \qquad (12.4)$$

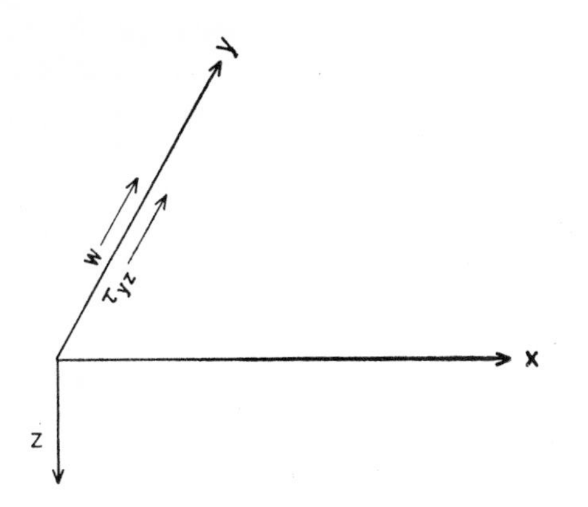

Fig. 12.1.

The solution takes its simplest form if the water is sufficiently deep and U and V approach zero near the bottom. This requires that C_1 be zero and (12.4) becomes

$$U = C_2\, e^{-(\pi z/D)} \cos\left(\frac{\pi z}{D} + d\right),$$
$$V = -\, C_2\, e^{-(\pi z/D)} \sin\left(\frac{\pi z}{D} + d\right). \tag{12.5}$$

Because of the assumed direction of wind stress we may write

$$(\tau_{yz})_0 = -\, A_z\, (dV/dz)_0,$$

and

$$(\tau_{xz})_0 = -\, A_z\, (dU/dz)_0 = 0,$$

where the subscripts, 0, indicate the values at the surface ($z = 0$). Applying these boundary conditions to (12.5) allows the evaluation of C_2 and d, and one obtains

$$U = S_0\, e^{-(\pi z/D)} \cos\left(\frac{\pi}{4} - \frac{\pi z}{D}\right),$$
$$V = S_0\, e^{-(\pi z/D)} \sin\left(\frac{\pi}{4} - \frac{\pi z}{D}\right), \tag{12.6}$$

where

$$S_0 = (\tau_{yz})_0\, D/\pi A_z\sqrt{2} = (\tau_{yz})_0/\sqrt{(\rho f A_z)}. \tag{12.7}$$

S_0 is the magnitude of the surface water velocity. This velocity ($z = 0$) is directed 45° to the right of the y-axis, that is 45° to the right of the surface wind stress.

The magnitude of the velocity falls off exponentially with depth $e^{-(\pi z/D)}$, falling at a depth $z = D$ to $e^{-\pi} S_0$, or about $S_0/23$. At such depths this velocity will be so small that it may be neglected with respect to the surface velocity. D, then, is a measure of the depth of penetration of wind driven currents on a rotating earth. Ekman called it the "frictional depth". It is sometimes referred to as the "depth of the Ekman layer".

The angle that the velocity vector makes with the y-axis increases linearly with depth ($\pi z/D$) such that it is entirely in the x-direction at $z = (D/4)$, is directed opposite to the wind stress at $z = (3D/4)$, and has turned 180° from the surface current direction at $z = D$. Figure 12.2 illustrates the vertical structure of horizontal velocity in a pure wind drift current under the assumptions here made.

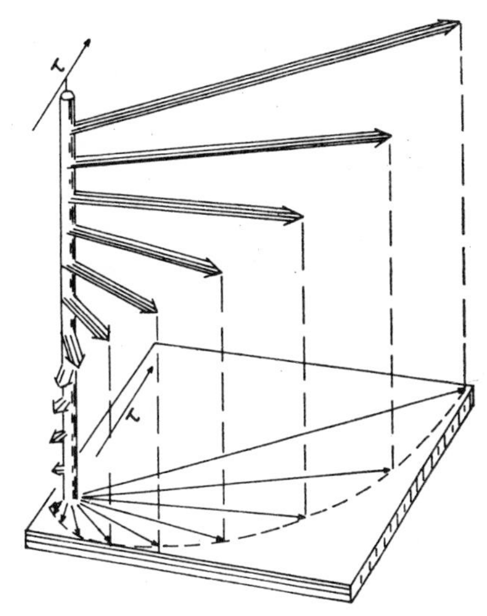

Fig. 12.2 Vertical structure of horizontal velocity in pure wind drift current according to Ekman.

It should be noted that D is a function of A_z, ρ, and f while S_0 depends upon τ_{yz} as well. However, D may depend upon the wind stress since A_z in general will be a function of the velocity shear, although the simple solution does not allow for variation of A_z with depth.

Ekman derived, from existing data available to him, the following empirical relationship between D in meters and W, the wind speed in meters per second:

$$D = 7.6\, W/\sqrt{(\sin\psi)}. \tag{12.8}$$

Thorade (1914) suggested that, at wind speeds below 6 m/sec (12.8) should be replaced by

$$D = 3.67\, W^{3/2}/\sqrt{(\sin\psi)}. \tag{12.9}$$

Equations (12.8) and (12.9) imply that A_z, if single

valued through the water column as assumed, should have the values

$$A_z = 1.02\ W^3 \text{ g/cm sec for } W < 6 \text{ m/sec}, \quad (12.10)$$

and

$$A_z = 4.3\ W^2 \text{ g/cm sec for } W > 6 \text{ m/sec}. \quad (12.11)$$

Neither the assumption of A_z constant with depth nor the assumption of unlimited depth can be accepted lightly. Ekman examined the case of shallow water, assuming the velocity to be zero at the bottom and re-evaluating the constants in (12.4). The analysis showed that the deflection of the surface current from the wind would be less than 45° and the turning with depth slower. Rossby (1932) and Rossby and Montgomery (1935) allowed for the sort of variations in A_z that the mixing length theory would suggest. They also arrive at deflections of the surface current less than 45° and dependent upon wind speed. Sverdrup *et al.* (1942, p. 497) point out that variation of density with depth will both modify the assumption of homogeneous water mass and introduce stability which will force variations in A_z with depth.

12.2 Ekman Transport and Some Consequences

Integration of (12.1) can yield expressions for the components of mass transport in the wind drift current:

$$M_x = \int_{\infty}^{0} \rho U dz = \frac{(\tau_{yz})_0}{f}, \quad (12.12)$$

and

$$M_y = \int_{\infty}^{0} \rho V dz = \frac{(\tau_{xz})_0}{f} = 0, \quad (12.13)$$

where M_x is the mass transport in the x-direction (per unit distance in y).

The integrated mass transport is entirely perpendicular to the wind stress and to the right in the northern hemisphere. M_x is not dependent upon the assumptions regarding the nature of A_z.

It should be noted at the equator ($f = 0$) the mass transport becomes infinite according to (12.12) so that the solution cannot be valid in this region. In fact, S_0 and D also become infinite for $f = 0$, so that (12.6) cannot be valid in this region either.

The wind drift theory as developed by Ekman assumes no boundaries and no horizontal pressure gradients. In the real ocean it may be argued that the mass transport in the x-direction will eventually pile up water against some boundary and thus set up pressure gradients in the negative x-direction which will oppose further transport. This could lead eventually to a situation in which the flow is essentially in the direction of the wind stress, and Coriolis acceleration and pressure gradient acceleration tend to balance one another. In many parts of the ocean the major currents appear just this way, i.e. they flow in the direction of wind stress and the geostrophic relationship (which neglects frictional accelerations) appears to describe the velocity field quite well.

This apparent inconsistency arises because of the finite response time of the ocean to impressed forces, being vastly different for differing modes of response. Ekman (1905) investigated the transient response to a suddenly imposed wind system and showed that it might be several days before his steady state solution (12.5) was fully applicable. Veronis and Stommel (1956) investigated in some detail the response of a stratified ocean to variable wind stress and indicate that a purely geostrophic flow regime may only be set up after a period of years. We think of the major ocean circulations as resulting from the climatological mean wind stress with perturbations induced by short period stress variations and brought about, at least in part, by Ekman type transport.

One value of the Ekman solution is that it permits a simple visualization of how the mass distribution associated with permanent circulation might arise. One can imagine the imposition of an atmospheric high over an ocean at rest. The circular wind pattern would result in transport of mass within the water towards the center of the high until, eventually, the currents flow in essentially the same direction as the wind and pressure gradient accelerations are in approximate balance with the Coriolis acceleration.

One may also visualize how, in the Northern Hemisphere, a wind from the north blowing along the west coast of a land mass might transport surface water westward (offshore) with resulting upwelling of deeper waters along the coast. Upwelling of this type occurs in many locations, for example, off the California coast in response to prevailing northwesterly winds (Sverdrup *et al.*, 1942, p. 500).

12.3 Vertically Integrated Equations of Motion

Because of the many modes of internal motion possible, and the complexities introduced by vertical stratification, detailed formulation of wind driven currents involves mathematical equations that are in general intractable. Considerable success has been achieved in formulating mathematical models of the permanent horizontal circulation by dealing with the vertically integrated equations in some form or other. Thus, mass transport rather than velocity becomes the variable under consideration. Some of the most important recent advances in ocean current theory have resulted from this approach.

A co-ordinate system is picked with origin in the surface. The x-axis points to the east, the y-axis points northward and the z-axis points vertically downward. Vertical motion is considered unimportant and the inertial terms (Chapter 13) neglected, so that the equations for horizontal acceleration may be written:

$$\frac{\partial U}{\partial t} = fV - \frac{1}{\rho}\frac{\partial p}{\partial x} + \frac{1}{\rho}\frac{\partial}{\partial z}\left(A_z \frac{\partial U}{\partial z}\right) + \frac{1}{\rho}\left\{\frac{\partial}{\partial y}\left(A_y \frac{\partial U}{\partial y}\right) + \frac{\partial}{\partial x}\left(A_x \frac{\partial U}{\partial x}\right)\right\},$$

$$\frac{\partial V}{\partial t} = -fU - \frac{1}{\rho}\frac{\partial p}{\partial y} + \frac{1}{\rho}\frac{\partial}{\partial z}\left(A_z \frac{\partial V}{\partial z}\right) + \frac{1}{\rho}\left\{\frac{\partial}{\partial x}\left(A_x \frac{\partial V}{\partial x}\right) + \frac{\partial}{\partial y}\left(A_y \frac{\partial V}{\partial y}\right)\right\}. \quad (12.14)$$

Considering only steady state conditions ($\partial U/\partial t = \partial V/\partial t = 0$), and writing the stress terms such as $A_z\, \partial U/\partial z = \tau_{xz}$, etc.

$$-f\rho V = -\frac{\partial p}{\partial x} + \frac{\partial \tau_{xz}}{\partial z} + \frac{\partial \tau_{xy}}{\partial y} + \frac{\partial \tau_{xx}}{\partial x},$$

$$f\rho U = -\frac{\partial p}{\partial y} + \frac{\partial \tau_{yz}}{\partial z} + \frac{\partial \tau_{yx}}{\partial x} + \frac{\partial \tau_{yy}}{\partial y}. \quad (12.15)$$

In order, left to right, the terms represent the Coriolis effect, the ordinary pressure gradient, the vertical gradient of horizontal stress, the gradient of lateral stress and the lateral gradients of viscous pressure stresses.

If (12.15) is integrated vertically from $z = 0$ to $z = D$ where D is the depth of influence of wind stress (depth of the Ekman layer),

$$-fM_y = -\frac{\partial P}{\partial x} + (\tau_{xz})_0 + \frac{\partial \tau'_{xy}}{\partial y} + \frac{\partial \tau'_{xx}}{\partial x},$$

and

$$fM_x = -\frac{\partial P}{\partial y} + (\tau_{yz})_0 + \frac{\partial \tau'_{yx}}{\partial x} + \frac{\partial \tau'_{yy}}{\partial y}, \quad (12.16)$$

where, by definition,

$M_y \equiv \int_D^0 \rho V dz$, $M_x \equiv \int_D^0 \rho U dz$, are the components of mass transport,

$P \equiv \int_D^0 p dz$, is an integrated pressure term, and

$\tau' \equiv \int_D^0 \tau dz$, is an integrated stress terms.

The integration of the vertical stress term left only the surface stress because of the definition of D.

Differentiating the first equation (12.16) with respect to y, the second with respect to x and subtracting,

$$f\left(\frac{\partial M_x}{\partial x} + \frac{\partial M_y}{\partial y}\right) + M_y \frac{\partial f}{\partial y} = \left[\frac{\partial (\tau_{yz})_0}{\partial x} - \frac{\partial (\tau_{xz})_0}{\partial y}\right] + \left[\frac{\partial^2 \tau'_{yx}}{\partial x^2} - \frac{\partial^2 \tau'_{xy}}{\partial y^2}\right] + \left[\frac{\partial^2 \tau'_{yy}}{\partial x \partial y} - \frac{\partial^2 \tau'_{xx}}{\partial y \partial x}\right], \quad (12.17)$$

the integrated pressure gradient term being eliminated. This equation (12.17) is referred to as the vertically integrated vorticity equation. The first term, f times the horizontal divergence of mass transport, is zero in any model that does not allow for vertical flow into the layer, because of the continuity requirement. Moreover, with non-divergent mass transport, a stream function ψ for horizontal mass transport may be defined such that

$$M_x = -(\partial\psi/\partial y) \text{ and } M_y = (\partial\psi/\partial x).$$

The second term $M_y\,(\partial f/\partial y)$ is the "planetary vorticity tendency", it is a measure of the torque imposed upon the column as it moves to a region where the Coriolis parameter is altered. It is a consequence of the tendency to conserve angular momentum. The rate of change of f with latitude $\partial f/\partial y$ is often written β, and the planetary vorticity tendency becomes $M_y\beta$.

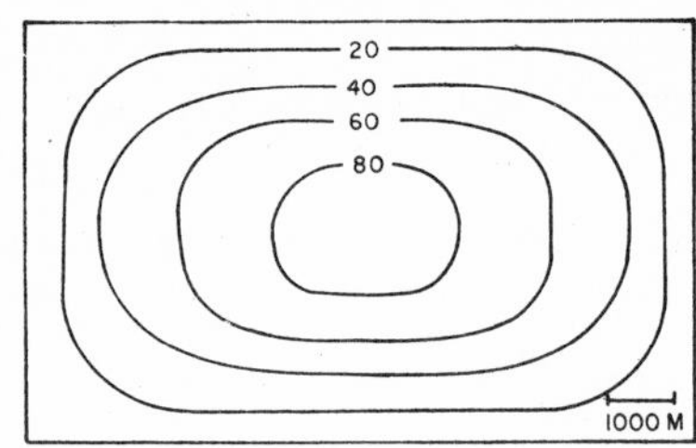

A. NON ROTATING OR UNIFORMLY ROTATING OCEAN (STOMMEL 1948 FIG. 2)

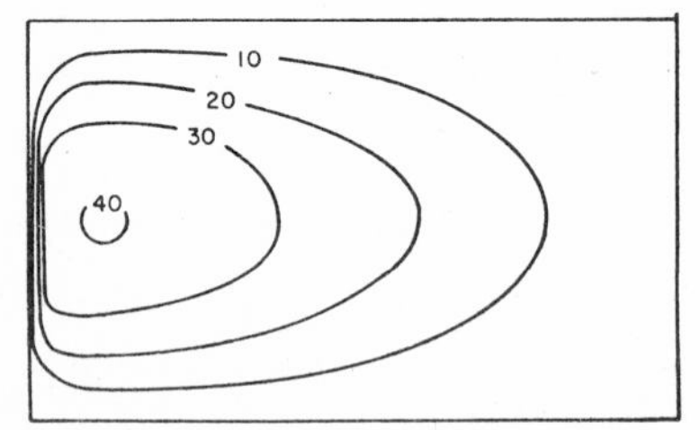

B. CORIOLIS PARAMETER A LINEAR FUNCTION OF LATITUDE (STOMMEL 1948 FIG. 5)

Fig. 12.3 Stream lines in a rectangular ocean of constant depth with wind stress a cosine function of latitude as given by Stommel (1948) for (A) non-rotating ocean or one with uniform rotation and (B) ocean where Coriolis parameter varies linearly with latitude.

The third term is, in vector notation, the vertical component of the curl of the wind stress, and is a measure of the torque about a vertical axis exerted on the column by the surface winds.

The last two terms are integrated torques exerted upon the column by virtue of the viscous stresses. The present state of knowledge does not permit of their evaluation in this form. Some simplifying assumption is usually introduced earlier in the development to permit the formulation of the viscous torque in a more tractable form.

Sverdrup (1947) and Reid (1948) neglected viscous stresses altogether and, by equating the planetary vorticity tendency to the surface wind torque (assuming a simplified mean wind field), produced reasonable representations in the east Central Pacific. Their solution was not applicable to the western side of the ocean where intense boundary currents obviously make internal viscous stresses more important.

Stommel (1948) introduced friction in a very simple form as being simply proportional to velocity, and showed that the balance of the three terms could produce the assymetrical circulation

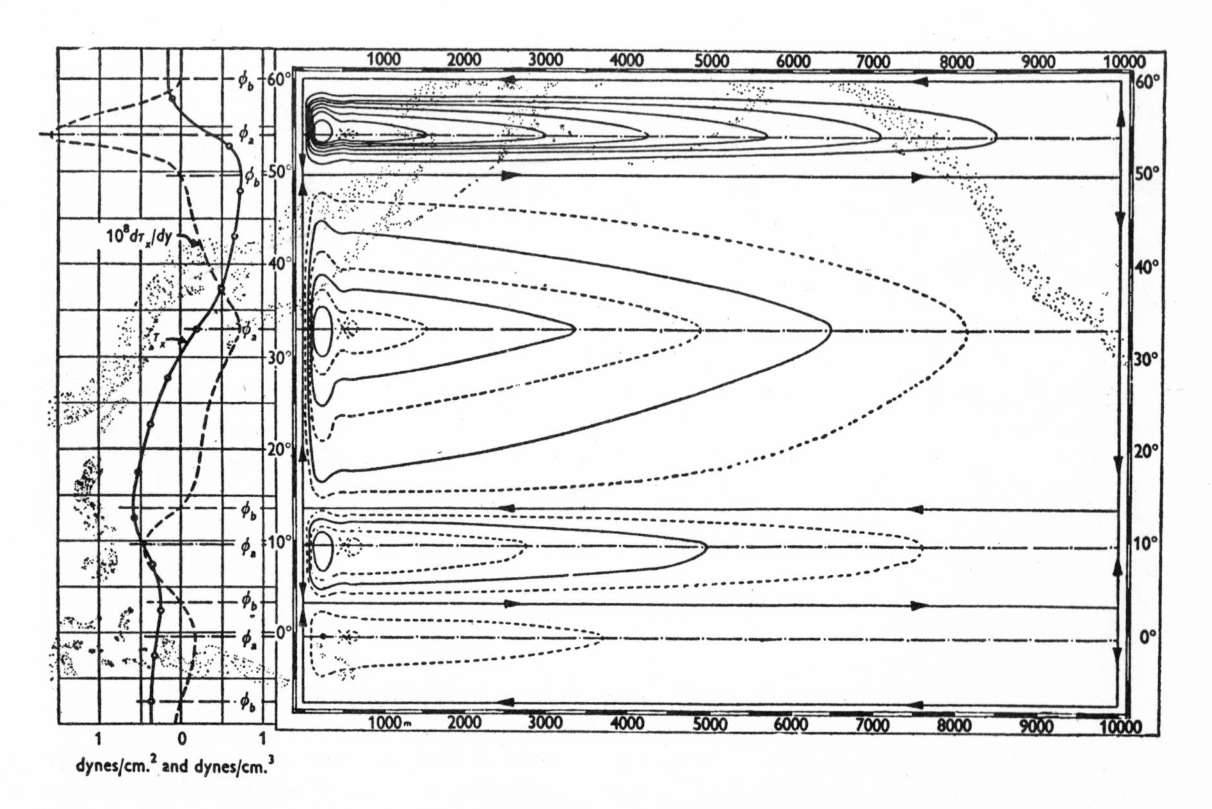

Fig. 12.4 Mass transport streamline in a rectangular ocean, as given by Munk for the Pacific. The mean annual zonal wind stress $\tau_x(y)$ over the Pacific and its curl $(d\tau_x/dy)$ are on the left (after Munk, 1950, Fig. 2).

observed in the oceans, with an intense western boundary current. Figure 12.3 shows mass transport streamlines in a rectangular ocean according to this theory with a constant Coriolis parameter (A) and with the Coriolis parameter a linear function of latitude (β constant) (B).

Munk (1950) assumed a single valued horizontal viscosity K_H so the right-hand terms of (12.14) became

$$K_H\,[(\partial^2/\partial x^2) + (\partial^2/\partial y^2)]\,U$$

and

$$K_H\,[(\partial^2/\partial x^2) + (\partial^2/\partial y^2)]\,V.$$

He further assumed that, in the vertical-integration of these shearing stresses, one could write

$$\int_D^0 K_H\left(\frac{\partial^2}{\partial x^2} + \frac{\partial^2}{\partial y^2}\right) U dz = A\left(\frac{\partial^2}{\partial x^2} + \frac{\partial^2}{\partial y^2}\right) M_x,$$

where $A \approx K_H$.

In this way, and by introducing the mass transport stream function ψ, he arrived at

$$\left[A\left(\frac{\partial^4}{\partial x^4} + \frac{2\partial^4}{\partial x^2\,\partial y^2} + \frac{\partial^4}{\partial y^4}\right) - \beta\frac{\partial}{\partial x}\right]\psi = \frac{\partial(\tau_{xz})_0}{\partial y} - \frac{\partial(\tau_{yz})_0}{\partial x}. \quad (12.18)$$

Introducing mean wind stresses and boundary conditions on ψ, Munk thus constructed the first really satisfactory analytical model of the circulation in a complete ocean. Figure 12.4 shows mass transport stream lines as computed by Munk for a rectangular Pacific in response to mean annual zonal wind stress. Note that the sub-tropical and boreal gyres both appear in the solution as well as the North Equatorial Current and North Equatorial Counter-Current.

References

EKMAN, V. W. (1902) Om jordrotationens inverkan på vindströmmar i hafvet. Nyt. Mag. F. Naturvid, 40. Kristiania.

EKMAN, V. W. (1905) On the influence of the earth's rotation on ocean currents. *Ark. f. Mat. Astr. och Fysik. K. Sv. Vet. Ak. Stockholm*, 1905–06 **2**, 11.

MUNK, W. H. (1950) On the wind driven ocean circulation. *J. Meteor.* **7**, 79–93.

REID, R. O. (1948) The equatorial currents of the eastern Pacific as maintained by the stress of the wind. *J. Mar. Res.* **7**(2), 74–99.

ROSSBY, C. G. (1932) A generalization of the theory of the mixing length with application to atmospheric and oceanic turbulence. *Papers in Phys. Oceanog. and Meteor.* **1**(4), 35 pp.

ROSSBY, C. G. and R. B. MONTGOMERY. (1935) The layer of frictional influence in wind and ocean currents. *Papers in Phys. Oceanog. and Meteor.* **3**(3), 101 pp.

STOMMEL, H. (1948) The westward intensification of wind driven ocean currents. *Trans. Am. Geophys. Union* **29**, 202–206.

SVERDRUP, H. U., M. W. JOHNSON and R. M. FLEMING. *The Oceans*. Prentice Hall, New York. 1942.

SVERDRUP, H. U. (1947) Wind driven currents in a baroclinic ocean; with application to the equatorial currents of the eastern Pacific. *Proc. Nat. Acad. Sci.* **33**, 318–326.

THORADE, H. (1914) Die Geschwindigkeit von Triftströmungen und die Ekmansche Theorie. *Ann. d. Hydrogr. u. Mar. Meteor.* **42**, 379–391.

VERONIS, G. and HENRY STOMMEL. (1956) The action of variable wind stresses on a stratified ocean. *J. Mar. Res.* **15**(1), 43–75.

Sources of Additional Information

The Gulf Stream. STOMMEL, H. University of California Press, Berkeley. 1958.

Dynamics of Ocean Currents. In *The Sea*, Vol. 1. FOFONOFF, N. P. Interscience, New York. 1962.

Some Studies on the Ocean Circulation. GARNER, D. M. Tech. Rept. (unpublished), New York Univ., College of Engineering. 1962.

CHAPTER 13

INERTIAL MOTION

WHILE the wind driven theories of ocean currents met with considerable success, there was a problem with the high value of lateral eddy viscosity that had to be invoked to give a reasonable representation of the western boundary currents. Also many observed features of the Gulf Stream were not explained. Recently, much of the theoretical work has concentrated upon the effect of inertial accelerations in ocean currents and it appears that lateral friction may be neglected throughout most of the models.

We will introduce the concepts of conservation of absolute vorticity and of potential vorticity, and the Bernoulli equation. The reader will, however, be left on his own to investigate the rapidly evolving literature on inertial currents.

13.1 MOTION IN THE CIRCLE OF INERTIA

Consider a fluid in horizontal motion along a curved path. Let the radius of curvature be R and the speed be C. Two accelerations act normal to the velocity; the centrifugal acceleration and the Coriolis acceleration. The centrifugal acceleration is directed outward from the center of curvature and is equal to $\omega^2 R$, where ω is the angular speed. This may also be written C^2/R. The Coriolis acceleration is $2\Omega \sin \psi\, C$ where ψ is the latitude (see Section 9.3), or simply fC, and is directed to the right of the motion in the northern hemisphere, to the left in the southern hemisphere.

If the motion is anticyclonic these accelerations are in opposition (Fig. 13.1) and, in the absence of other accelerations one can write the balance:

$$(C^2/R) = fC, \quad \text{or} \quad R = (C/f). \qquad (13.1)$$

If f can be considered constant the radius of curvature is proportional to the speed and the motion will be in closed circles.

The period for a complete rotation is given by

$$T = (2\pi R/C) = (2\pi/f). \qquad (13.2)$$

Since $f = 2\Omega \sin \psi$, where $\Omega = (2\pi/24 \text{ hr})$, (13.2) yields

$$T = (12 \text{ hr}/\sin \psi) \qquad (13.3)$$

That is, the period of rotation is one-half of a pendulum day, or one-half the time required for a complete turning of the plane in which a pendulum swings.

If the speed C is large, R also is large (13.1) and variation of f with latitude must be considered. The effect is that the radius of curvature is less for the poleward part of the rotation and greater through the equatorward part. The motion would then not complete a circle but would describe a spiral which migrates westward.

Motion in inertial circles has been observed in the ocean, for example, by Gustafson and Kullenberg (1936) as described by Sverdrup *et al.* (1942, p. 438). Inertial oscillations may be generated by impulsive disturbances such as the passage of a line squall.

Of interest is the fact that the period (13.3) of inertial rotation at 30°06′ latitude is identical to that of the principal diurnal (K_1) component of the tide (23.93 hr). Reid (1962) has observed pronounced rotary currents in the open Pacific at 30°N latitude and suggests that they were driven by the diurnal tide. A similar resonance effect might be expected at 75°04′ latitude where the inertial period (12.42 hr) coincides with that of the principal semi-diurnal (M_2) tidal component.

13.2 ROSSBY WAVES — ABSOLUTE VORTICITY

Consider non-divergent horizontal flow, with constant speed C towards the east, along a parallel of latitude ψ_0. If the flow is in geostrophic balance the cross stream pressure gradient acceleration will balance the Coriolis acceleration at this latitude.

If some perturbation should displace part of the stream poleward the fluid involved would experience a Coriolis acceleration greater than the pressure gradient acceleration and would be accelerated back towards the initial latitude. The curvature would be such that the centrifugal acceleration would balance the increase in Coriolis

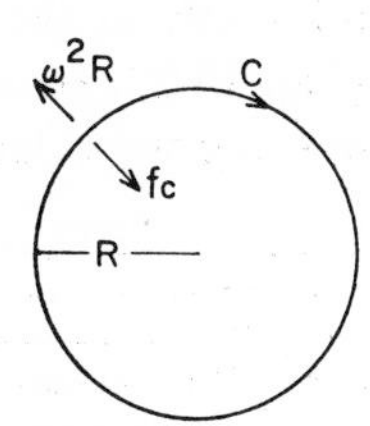

Fig. 13.1 Acceleration balance in inertial motion (Northern Hemisphere).

acceleration. The fluid would cross the initial latitude without curvature but with an equatorward velocity component that would carry it beyond, to where an opposite curvature in the flow would be required for balance. Thus, north–south oscillations in the flow will be repeated down stream.

Rossby (1939) investigated oscillations that might arise in this manner as applied to horizontal waves in the atmospheric westerlies. It is not known that waves of this type have any importance in oceanic circulation although Moore (1963) has shown that, under certain conditions, stationary Rossby waves with amplitude diminishing along the flow may be superimposed upon west to east flow. Rossby's techniques for dealing with inertial acceleration terms have, however, greatly influenced our modern theories of ocean currents.

The qualitative reasoning given above may provide insight into the physical phenomena but is not, of course, analytically satisfactory. We will rewrite the horizontal acceleration equations (12.14), omitting the frictional acceleration terms but adding the inertial terms.

$$\frac{\mathrm{d}u}{\mathrm{d}t} = fv - \frac{1}{\rho}\frac{\partial p}{\partial x}, \tag{13.4}$$

$$\frac{\mathrm{d}v}{\mathrm{d}t} = -fu - \frac{1}{\rho}\frac{\partial p}{\partial y}, \tag{13.5}$$

where $\mathrm{d}/\mathrm{d}t$ represents the time derivative following the motion. Thus

$$\frac{\mathrm{d}u}{\mathrm{d}t} = \frac{\partial u}{\partial t} + u\frac{\partial u}{\partial x} + v\frac{\partial u}{\partial y}, \tag{13.6}$$

where the last two terms are the so-called inertial acceleration terms, or field acceleration terms.

Expanding (13.4) and (13.5), cross differentiating, and subtracting yields

$$\frac{\mathrm{d}}{\mathrm{d}t}\left[\left(\frac{\partial v}{\partial x} - \frac{\partial u}{\partial y}\right) + f\right] = -\left(\frac{\partial u}{\partial x} + \frac{\partial v}{\partial y}\right)\left[\left(\frac{\partial v}{\partial x} - \frac{\partial u}{\partial y}\right) + f\right], \tag{13.7}$$

where terms involving the horizontal variation of density have been neglected. Since f is not a function of time or longitude $v\,\partial f/\partial y$ has been written $\mathrm{d}f/\mathrm{d}t$.

If it be required that there be no horizontal divergence,

$\partial u/\partial x + \partial v/\partial y = 0$, then (13.7) becomes

$$\frac{\mathrm{d}}{\mathrm{d}t}\left[\frac{\partial v}{\partial x} - \frac{\partial u}{\partial y} + f\right] = 0,$$

or

$$(\mathrm{d}/\mathrm{d}t)\,[\zeta + f] = 0. \tag{13.8}$$

Here $\zeta = (\partial v/\partial x) - (\partial u/\partial y)$ is the vertical component of vorticity relative to the chosen co-ordinate system. The horizontal Coriolis parameter f is the vertical component of vorticity at the location which arises from the earth's rotation. f has been called the "planetary vorticity".

Thus (13.8) states that, following the motion in horizontally non divergent flow, the absolute vorticity $(\zeta + f)$ is conserved.

Considering the conservation of absolute vorticity Rossby examined perturbations traveling along the stream without change in shape. He found that stationary waves could be present if the wavelength λ were

$$\lambda_s = 2\pi\,\sqrt{(C/\beta)}, \tag{13.9}$$

where C is the eastward flow velocity and $\beta = \partial f/\partial y$. For $C = 100$ cm/sec (approximately 2 knots) at 45° latitude $\lambda_s = 1540$ km.

Waves of greater length would travel westward and shorter waves would travel eastward along the stream.

13.3 Potential Vorticity

If the flow is simply required to be non-divergent, rather than horizontally non-divergent, this condition is written

$$\partial u/\partial x + \partial v/\partial y + \partial w/\partial z = 0,$$

and

$$\partial u/\partial x + \partial v/\partial y = -\,\partial w/\partial z. \tag{13.10}$$

Horizontal divergence can be replaced by vertical convergence $-\partial w/\partial z$. This in turn can be equated to the rate of stretching of a column of fluid of thickness D, divided by that thickness:

$$-\frac{\partial w}{\partial z} = -\frac{1}{D}\frac{\mathrm{d}D}{\mathrm{d}t}. \tag{13.11}$$

Thus, (13.7) can be written

$$\frac{\mathrm{d}}{\mathrm{d}t}(\zeta + f) = \frac{1}{D}\frac{\mathrm{d}D}{\mathrm{d}t}(\zeta + f),$$

or

$$\frac{\mathrm{d}}{\mathrm{d}t}\left[\frac{\zeta + f}{D}\right] = 0. \tag{13.12}$$

The quantity $(\zeta + f)/D$ is called the potential vorticity and (13.12) states that, for frictionless non-divergent flow, in which the thickness of the fluid layer (D) may vary, potential vorticity is conserved following a parcel of fluid along its trajectory. If the flow is stationary trajectories and streamlines coincide, and potential vorticity is conserved along streamlines.

Stommel (1955), in studying the Gulf Stream, found the potential vorticity to be uniform across the stream in at least one section.

If one considers only northward flow, assumes that potential vorticity is uniform across the flow, and that at some x, where the layer thickness is D_0, the velocity, velocity gradient, and relative vorticity are zero, the vorticity equation (13.12) may be written:

$$\frac{f + (\partial v/\partial x)}{D} = \frac{f}{D_0}. \tag{13.13}$$

Integrating

$$V = \int_{\infty}^{x} f\{(D/D_0) - 1\}\,\mathrm{d}x, \tag{13.14}$$

which describes the velocity variation across the stream.

Stommel showed that velocity computed this way for a Gulf Stream section compared extraordinarily well to velocity computed by means of the geostrophic equations. This is of interest, but no physical reasoning has been advanced to suggest that potential vorticity should be uniform throughout a current system. The conservation of potential vorticity along trajectories is, however, defensible and is part of many ocean current theories.

13.4 Flow Over a Ridge

One interesting consequence of the conservation of potential vorticity (13.12) can be seen in the flow of a uniform current over a ridge.

Consider west to east flow over a ridge that stretches north and south in the northern hemisphere. The flow (Fig. 13.2) extends to the bottom and, before encountering the ridge we will assume

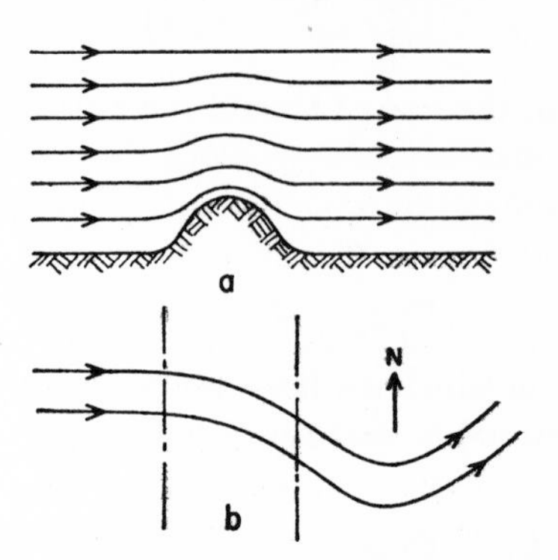

Fig. 13.2 Streamlines in vertical section (a) and plan (b) for eastward flow crossing a ridge in the Northern Hemisphere.

it to have zero relative vorticity ζ. We will consider that relative vorticity will take the form of flow curvature rather than shear.

As the flow is shallowed by the ridge (D decreases) anticyclonic curvature must develop, reaching maximum at the shallowest point. As the depth increases curvature should decrease so that the original value (zero) of relative vorticity might be attained at the foot of the ridge. However, the flow would be towards the southeast and towards decreasing values of f. Thus, some cyclonic curvature will be required. Once past the ridge, the latitude effect will be controlling and some oscillation about the original latitude might be expected as discussed in Section 13.2. Sverdrup *et al.* (1942, p. 466) have discussed this phenomenon in a stratified ocean and from a somewhat different point of view.

13.5 The Bernoulli Equation

An important element in inertial current theories is the Bernoulli equation. If one assumes a steady state $\partial u/\partial t = \partial v/\partial t = 0$, then, multiplying (13.4) by u, (13.5) by v and adding yields

$$u\left(u\frac{\partial u}{\partial x} + v\frac{\partial v}{\partial v} + \frac{1}{\rho}\frac{\partial p}{\partial x}\right)$$

$$+ v\left(u\frac{\partial u}{\partial y} + v\frac{\partial v}{\partial y} + \frac{1}{\rho}\frac{\partial p}{\partial y}\right) = 0.$$

Writing $p = \rho gz +$ constant (8.18) this becomes

$$u\frac{\partial}{\partial x}\left(\frac{u^2+v^2}{2}+gz\right) + v\frac{\partial}{\partial y}\left(\frac{u^2+v^2}{2}+gz\right) = 0 \qquad (13.15)$$

or, since we are considering a steady state

$$\frac{d}{dt}\left(\frac{u^2+v^2}{2}+gz\right) = 0. \qquad (13.16)$$

That is, the sum of kinetic and potential energy per unit mass is conserved along the trajectory.

If flow in one direction only is considered (13.16) reduces to

$$(V^2/2) + gz = \text{constant}, \qquad (13.17)$$

the form in which the Bernoulli equation is usually first presented to students of physics.

13.5 Inertial Current Theories

Consider a two-layer ocean where the top layer of density ρ_1 moves over a motionless bottom layer of density ρ_2. It has been shown (Section 10.2) that the geostrophic velocity may be evaluated from the slope of the interface. If Fig. 13.3 represents

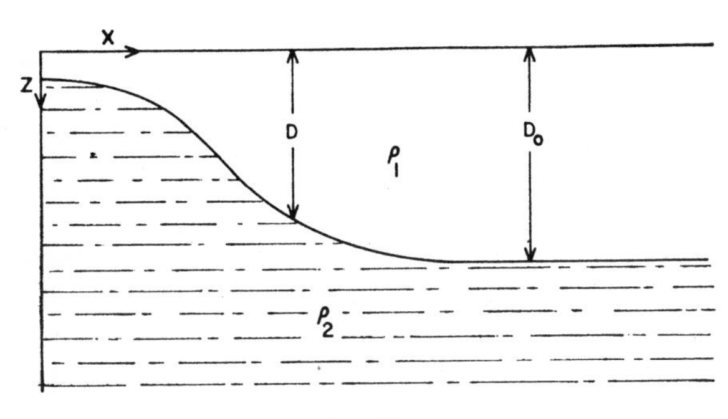

Fig. 13.3.

an east–west vertical section, we can write

$$v = \frac{g'}{f}\frac{\partial D}{\partial x}, \qquad (13.18)$$

where D is the thickness of the surface layer and $g' = g\,(\rho^2 - \rho_1)/\rho_1$.
Similarly

$$u = -\,(g'/f)\,(\partial D/\partial y). \qquad (13.19)$$

Using this type of simple geostrophic layered flow, the Bernoulli equation (13.16) and the conservation of potential vorticity (13.12), a number of theoretical models of ocean currents have been investigated. In particular, inertial theories have been successful in predicting observed characteristics of the Gulf Stream. This western boundary current in a wind driven system can be explained without invoking lateral friction as Munk (1950) did. A number of features that Munk's theory failed to display appear in the inertial models.

It is usual to apply these models mainly to the western boundary current where wind stress is of minor importance and to piece them together with the interior wind driven models of Sverdrup (1947) and Reid (1948) to give a complete solution. The reader is directed to papers by Fofonoff (1954), Charney (1955), Morgan (1956), etc.

References

Charney, J. G. (1955) The Gulf Stream as an inertial boundary current. *Proc. Nat. Acad. Sci.* **41** (10), 731–740.

Fofonoff, N. P. (1954) Steady flow in a frictionless homogeneous ocean. *J. Mar. Res.* **13**(3), 254–262.

Gustafson, T. and B. Kullenberg. (1936) Untersuchungen von Trägheitsströmungen in der Ostsee. *Sv. Hydr. Biol. Komm. Skr., Ny Ser. Hyder.* **13**, 28 pp.

Moore, D. W. (1963) Rossby waves in ocean circulation. *Deep Sea Res.* **10**(6), 735–747.

Morgan, G. W. (1956) On the wind driven ocean circulation. *Tellus* **8**, 301–320.

Munk, W. H. (1950) On the wind driven ocean circulation. *J. Meteor.* **7**, 79–93.

Reid, R. O. (1948) The equatorial currents of the eastern Pacific as maintained by the stress of the wind. *J. Mar. Res.* **7**(2), 74–99.

Reid, J. L. (1962) Observations of inertial rotation and internal waves. *Deep Sea Res.* **9**, 283–289.

Rossby, C. G. (1939) Relation between variations in the intensity of zonal circulation in the atmosphere and the displacement of the semi-permanent centers of action. *J. Mar. Res.* **2**(1), 38–55.

Stommel, H. (1955) In "Discussion on the relationship between meteorology and oceanography". *J. Mar. Res.* **14**(4), 504–510.

Sverdrup, H. U., M. W. Johnson and R. W. Fleming. *The Oceans.* Prentice Hall, New York. 1942.

Sverdrup, H. U. (1947) Wind driven currents in a baroclinic ocean; with application to the equatorial currents of the eastern Pacific. *Proc. Nat. Acad. Sci.* **33**, 318–326.

Sources of Additional Information

Dynamics of ocean currents. In *The Sea.* Vol. 1, pp. 323–394. Fofonoff, N. P. Interscience, New York. 1962.

The Gulf Stream. Stommel, H. University of California, Press, Berkeley. 1958.

CHAPTER 14

WAVES

ALTHOUGH elevations on our planet are almost universally referred to "sea level", the most striking characteristic of the air–sea boundary is its tendency to continuously change level.

At any location the surface is alternately raised above, and depressed below, its mean position. At any one time the surface presented shows alternate elevations and depressions in a horizontal direction. In order to describe the phenomena the following descriptive terms, illustrated for a very simple disturbance in Fig. 14.1, are introduced:

Elevation (η). The elevation is the instantaneous vertical distance of the surface at a point from a level representing the surface in the absence of wave disturbances.

Wave Height (H). The vertical distance between a "crest" (maximum elevation) and the adjacent "trough" (minimum elevation) is called the wave height.

Amplitude (a). The amplitude of a wave disturbance is one-half of the wave height.

Wavelength (L). The horizontal distance between neighboring crests (or troughs) in the direction of wave travel is called the wavelength. Related to this is the wave number (k).

$$k = 2\pi/L$$

Wave Period (T). The time interval between the occurrence of successive troughs (or crests) at a fixed position is called the period of the waves. The inverse $1/T$ is called the "frequency" and is a measure of the number of crests (or troughs) which occur at a fixed position in unit time. Related to this is the "angular frequency" (σ).

$$\sigma = 2\pi/T.$$

14.1 THE SPECTRUM OF SURFACE WAVES

On a world-wide, climatic basis the spectrum of energy density (Section 14.7) in waves of various periods may be represented by Fig. 14.2 (following Munk, 1950) where an arbitrary energy scale is employed. The usual designation for waves covering each portion of the spectrum is given, as is the generating mechanisms. Table 14.1 lists some of the characteristics.

Swell. In the absence of local winds the observed surface disturbances in deep water tend to be long, regular waves with periods in the range from 5 to 30 sec. The amplitude is small in comparison to the wavelength, and the surface configuration in the direction of wave travel approximates a sine function. The variation in time and space of the elevation (η) of the surface can be expressed by:

$$\eta = a \cos 2\pi \{(x/L) - (t/T)\} = a \cos (kx - \sigma t) \tag{14.1}$$

where t is time and x distance measured in the direction of progression of the waves.

In swell the crests and troughs form long, essentially straight, lines which stretch for at least 6 or 7 wavelengths perpendicular to the direction of progression. A single identifiable crest travels a distance L in a time T, and hence the "wave speed" or "celerity" is given by:

$$c = L/T = \sigma/k. \tag{14.2}$$

This is, strictly speaking, the "phase speed" of the disturbance. The energy associated with the disturbance is propagated at a speed which, for gravity waves in deep water, is less than c and is designated as the "group speed".

Swell represents wind waves which have traveled out of the area in which they were generated.

Wind Waves. The casual observer notes that the character of the sea surface varies with the local wind. The stronger the wind becomes the higher are the waves up to a point. Higher waves are associated with longer wavelengths and longer periods. When the local wind dies out the visible

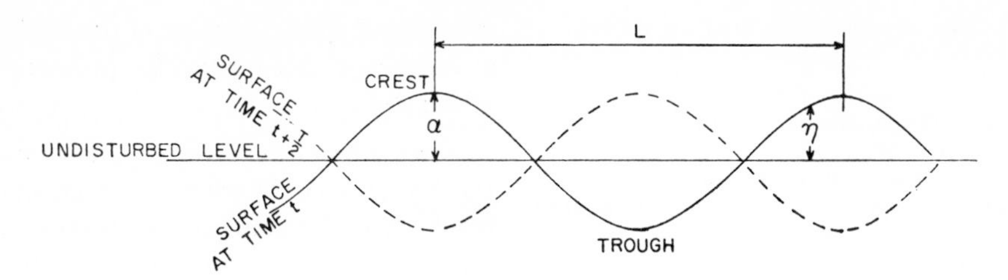

Fig. 14.1.

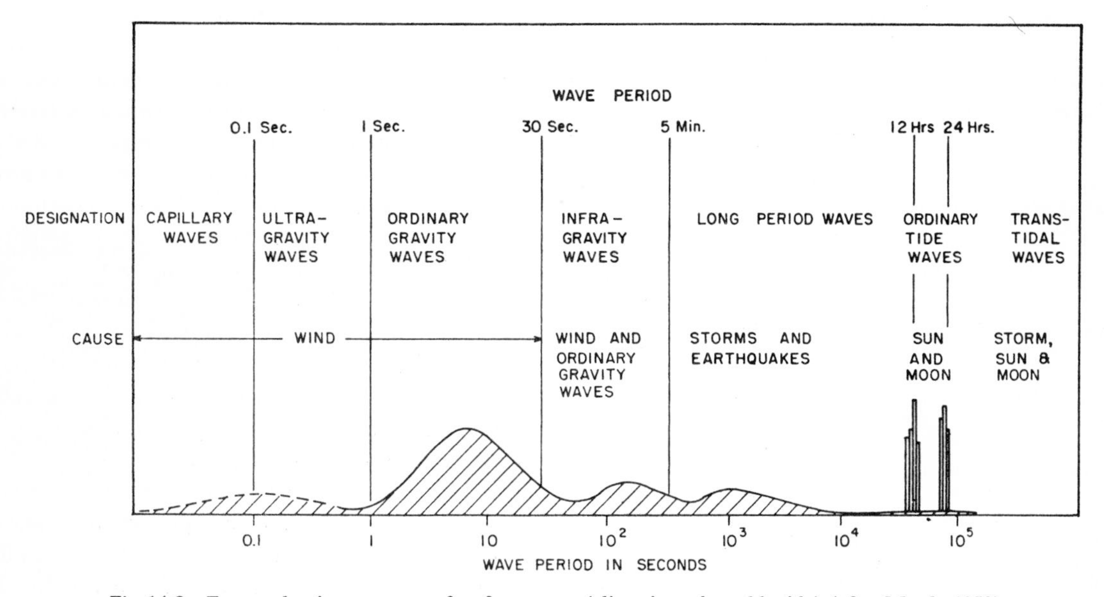

Fig. 14.2 Energy density spectrum of surface waves (climatic and world wide) (after Munk, 1950).

surface fluctuations soon take on the characteristics of swell.

The configuration of the sea surface in the presence of wind waves lacks the regular features of swell. The waves appear to be "short-crested". Waves of many different heights, lengths, and periods can be identified. The wave crests are noticeably more peaked than pure sine waves and they tend to be skewed in the direction of propagation. Although the general direction of progression coincides with that of present or recent wind direction, there appears to be considerable variation in the direction of individual waves. This results in the short-crestedness and is what is often termed a "confused sea". Similar irregularities are apparent in the time distribution of elevation at a fixed point.

Some of the peakedness of wind waves can be attributed to the interference of waves of different periods and speeds, but there are theoretical reasons why the individual components should not have pure sinusoidal form. This latter is true as well for swell.

The wide use of equations of the form (14.1) is due to the susceptibility of such functions to analytical treatment. Since a broad class of disturbance can be represented by the sum of sine and cosine terms the terminology which has been outlined above is retained.

In order to characterize the state of the sea it is necessary to report extremes or to perform some sort of averaging process. One might, for example, speak of a maximum wave height either as the variation between the maximum and minimum elevations observed at a point over a fixed time interval, or as the maximum difference in elevation between any trough and the subsequent crest.

The most generally accepted parameter for reporting is the "significant wave height" which is defined as the average height of the highest one-third of the waves observed over a fixed length of time. The "significant period" is the period associated with the waves of significant height. These parameters have proved useful in the statistical

TABLE 14.1. SPECTRUM OF OCEAN SURFACE WAVES

Type	Period Range	Forces Controlling Wave Characteristics	Generating Forces	Remarks
Capillary Waves	< 0.1 sec	Surface tension	Wind	
Ultra-Gravity Waves	0.1–1 sec	Surface tension and gravity	Wind	
Ordinary Gravity Waves	1–30 sec	Gravity	Wind	Wind waves and swell belong in this category
Infra-Gravity Waves	30 sec–5 min	Gravity, Coriolis acceleration	Wind and ord. grav. waves	Surf beat, seiches storm surges in this category
Long Period Waves	> 5 min	Gravity, Coriolis acceleration	Storms and earthquakes	Tsunamis, storm tides, etc.
Ordinary Tidal Waves	Fixed periods diurnal and semi-diurnal	Gravity Coriolis acceleration	Attraction of sun and moon	Astronomical tides predictable at coastal points
Trans Tidal Waves	> 24 hr	Gravity, Coriolis acceleration	Storms, sun and moon	Many long period components of the astronomical tides

study of waves and correspond well to the figures arrived at by visual estimation.

Wind waves are generated by the winds blowing over the ocean surface. The mechanism of coupling is not fully understood. Theories have been advanced which involve the "form drag" of the waves themselves and others involve impulsive generation by pressure fluctuations in the turbulent atmospheric boundary layer. It seems unlikely that these two mechanisms can be divorced, and, therefore, coupling through a combination of effects must be considered.

The horizontal extent of the water surface over which the wind blows prior to reaching the observation point is termed the "fetch". The time since the wind began blowing over the water is termed "duration". Waves build up gradually with time and distance to a maximum for the given wind speed. Minimum values of fetch and duration can be specified for a fully developed sea arising from a given wind speed. Because of the fetch requirement a windward shore provides protection regardless of duration.

Tides. Those who dwell on the sea coast note that there are slow oscillations in the general level of the sea surface. A maximum in elevation occurs twice during the day, or, in some locations, only once. The times of occurrence of low and high water can be predicted with accuracy. They occur approximately one hour later each day.

It has long been recognized that these disturbances result from the gravitational attraction of the sun and moon and the phenomena are referred to as "astronomical tides" or simply "tides". Through harmonic analysis of the records from any location the tides can be resolved into a combination of sinusoidal oscillations. Analysis usually recognizes four major components with periods close to 12 hr and three with periods close to 24 hr. In addition there are components with periods of a fortnight, about a month, half a year, and longer.

The tide producing potential can be uniquely formulated from astronomical information regarding the motions of the sun and moon relative to the earth. The water movements which result, however, behave as long waves and are greatly influenced by the configuration of the basins and by Coriolis acceleration. Just along the eastern coast of North America observed tides vary from the semi-diurnal tide of the Bay of Fundy, which has a range as great as 50 ft, to the diurnal tides in the Gulf of Mexico with a range of about 1 ft.

Storm Tides. Persistent winds blowing over the surface of the sea may pile up water against a coast, giving rise to abnormally high stands of sea level. Winds from other directions may result in abnormally low stands of sea level. These effects are often referred to as storm tides and may be treated as long period waves although the disturbances are, strictly speaking, not periodic. When the wind stress is relaxed periodic oscillations sometimes result which are characteristic of the local bottom topography.

Seiches. Any body of water will have natural frequencies at which it is particularly easy to set up oscillations. The result is complimentary variations in surface level at different locations. The phenomenon in a small scale is familiar to anyone who has attempted to carry a shallow container of fluid. In a natural body of water such oscillations are called "seiches". The frequencies of preferred oscillation are regulated by the depth, horizontal dimensions and configuration of the basin. Seiches may be impulsively generated by changes in meteorological conditions or by the tide producing forces when the preferred frequencies are close to the tidal frequencies or harmonics thereof.

Surf Beat. Anyone who has built sand castles is aware of a wave phenomenon called Surf Beat. Where waves are incident upon a sloping beach the periodic variations in sea level which result as the waves "run up" on the beach have superimposed upon them a longer period variation in average level with a period of several minutes. This represents a distinct mode of oscillation of the water which is excited by the action of the waves. The progression of surf beat is along the shore and it belongs to a class of phenomena called "edge waves".

Tsunami. Waves generated by impulsive disturbances in the sea bed occur at irregular intervals and may have spectacular results where they are incident upon the land. The Japanese name "tsunami" is indicative of their frequent occurrence in the Pacific. In the western world they are sometimes called tidal waves although they have no relation to the tides. At sea these short trains of long low waves pass unobserved although the energy transmitted is extremely great. At the shore they build up so that veritable walls of water tens of feet high may sweep inshore and cause great destruction. The periods involved are of the order of 10 to 30 min and the wavelengths in deep water are from several miles to hundreds of miles.

Capillary Waves. Close inspection of the surface of relatively quiet water will reveal very small wave disturbances which have a distinctly different appearance from small wind waves. Periods are characteristically of less than one-tenth of a second. The important restoring force in these oscillations is that resulting from surface tension while in wind waves it is that resulting from gravity. In capillary waves the group speed (speed at which energy is transmitted) is greater than the wave speed and this gives rise to their distinctive appearance.

14.2 Airy Theory of Gravity Waves

Equation (14.1) fully describes a plane wave of permanent form. By plane wave is meant one that is long crested. That is, the form of the disturbance is independent of the horizontal co-ordinate normal to the direction of propagation. By permanent form is meant that following the wave at the phase speed or celerity ($C = \sigma/k = L/T$), the fields of motion, pressure distribution, and surface elevation remain constant.

The surface disturbance is simple harmonic and of constant amplitude. Theoretically this type of wave train can exist only if the amplitude is very small relative to the depth of water and also relative to the wavelength. If these conditions are not satisfied then the surface configuration must approach a trochoidal form characterized by long flat troughs and narrow steep-sided crests. Particle motion in trochoidal waves is not purely oscillatory, some net translation of fluid occurs.

The classical or "Airy" wave theory deals with plane waves of permanent form. Since they are plane waves a two-dimensional solution will be complete.

Consider a co-ordinate system (Fig. 14.3) with its origin in the undisturbed surface. The x-dimension increases in the direction of wave propagation and z is measured vertically upward. u and w are the velocity components in the x- and z-directions respectively. The bottom is at $z = -h$ where h is the undisturbed depth.

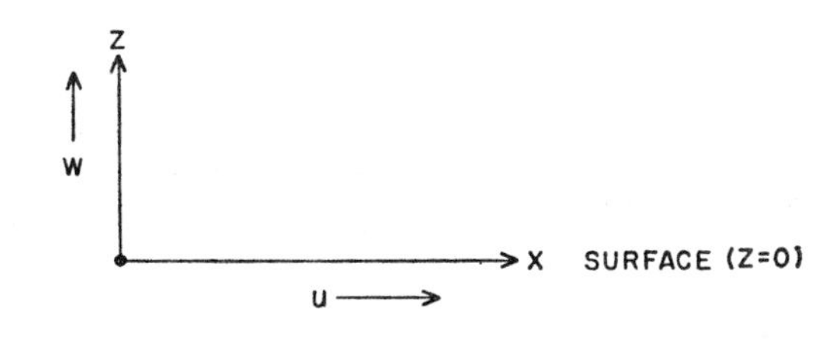

Fig. 14.3.

The following assumptions are made:

(1) The amplitude of the surface disturbance is very small compared to the wavelength and to the depth.
(2) The fluid is of uniform depth, h.
(3) The fluid is non-viscous and irrotational (without vorticity).
(4) The fluid is incompressible and homogeneous.
(5) Coriolis acceleration can be neglected.
(6) Surface tension can be neglected.
(7) The bottom is smooth and impermeable.
(8) The atmospheric pressure at sea level is uniform.

Assumption (5) excludes very long waves.
Assumption (6) excludes very short waves.
Assumption (4) excludes acoustic waves and internal waves.

The following differential equations must be satisfied for particle motion and pressure (p) in the system:

Irrotationality (Assumption 3)

$$\partial u/\partial z - \partial w/\partial x = 0;$$

Continuity (Assumption 4)

$$\partial u/\partial x + \partial w/\partial z = 0;$$

Acceleration in x-direction due to pressure gradient only

$$\partial u/\partial t = -(1/\rho)\,(\partial p/\partial x).$$

The following boundary conditions are to be applied:

$$\text{(a) } w = \partial \eta/\partial t \text{ at } z = 0,$$

an approximation valid only in the light of assumption (1),

$$\text{(b) } w = 0 \text{ at } z = -h,$$

required by assumption (7),

$$\text{(c) } p = p_a \text{ at } z = 0,$$

where p_a is atmospheric pressure. This too is an approximation based on assumption (1).

The free surface is defined by $z = \eta$, however, because of assumption (1) the boundary conditions (a and c) on p and w are applied at the mean water level $z = 0$.

These equations define a linear problem so a simple harmonic wave is a possible solution. Thus, if the surface is assumed to have the form

$$\eta = a \cos(kx - \sigma t), \tag{14.1}$$

then

$$u = a\sigma \frac{\cosh k(z+h)}{\sinh kh} \cos(kx - \sigma t), \tag{14.3}$$

$$w = a\sigma \frac{\sinh k(z+h)}{\sinh kh} \sin(kx - \sigma t), \tag{14.4}$$

and

$$p = p_a - \rho g z + \rho g a \frac{\cosh k(z+h)}{\cosh kh} \cos(ka - \sigma t). \tag{14.5}$$

satisfy (14.2) and boundary condition (b).

These relations will also satisfy boundary conditions (a) and (c), if

$$\sigma^2 = gk \tanh kh, \tag{14.6}$$

but, since the phase speed c is defined by $c = \sigma/k = L/T$, it follows that for waves of this type:

$$\begin{aligned} c^2 &= (g/k) \tanh kh, \\ &= (gL/2\pi) \tanh (2\pi h/L.) \end{aligned} \tag{14.7}$$

14.3 Airy Waves in Deep Water

Where the depth of water is greater than half a wavelength ($h/L > 1/2$, $kh > \pi$), $\tanh kh$ is not sensibly different from unity, and (14.7) can be written:

$$c^2 = (gL/2\pi), \tag{14.8}$$

or, since $T = (L/c)$

$$c = (gT/2\pi). \tag{14.9}$$

Thus,

$$L = (g/2\pi)\,T^2. \tag{14.10}$$

These are the conditions for what are called "deep water waves" or sometimes "short waves", the terms referring only to the relative values of depth and wavelength.

It is seen that the wave speed depends upon the wavelength or period and that these are uniquely related.

Taking L in feet and T in seconds one may write

$$L = 5.12\ T^2, \text{ and } c = 5.12\ T,$$

or for T in seconds, c in knots,

$$c = 3.03\ T.$$

TABLE 14.2. WAVELENGTH AND SPEED FOR RELATIVELY DEEP WATER WAVES OF VARIOUS PERIODS

T (sec)	1	2	4	6	8	10	15	20	1200 (20 min)
L (ft)	5.12	20.5	82	184	328	512	1150	2050	1500 miles
c (ft/sec)	5.12	10.2	20.5	30.8	41	51	77	102	Never a
c (m.p.h.)	3.5	6.9	14	21	28	35	52	70	Deep Water
c (knots)	3.0	6.0	12	18	24	30	46	61	Wave

Many observers use the approximation

$$L \text{ (ft)} = 5T^2,\ c \text{ (ft/sec)} = 5T \text{ or } c \text{ (knots)} = 3T.$$

Table 14.2 gives values for L and c for various wave periods using the deep water equations.

For deep water waves (14.3), (14.4), and (14.5) simplify to

$$u = a\sigma\, e^{kz} \cos (kx - \sigma t), \qquad (14.11)$$

$$w = a\sigma\, e^{kz} \sin (kx - \sigma t), \qquad (14.12)$$

and

$$\Delta p = \rho g a\, e^{kz} \cos (kx - \sigma t), \qquad (14.13)$$

where Δp is written for $p - p_a + \rho g z$ and represents the anomaly of pressure from the hydrostatic value.

Individual water particles move in closed circular orbits with radii ($a\, e^{kz}$) decreasing exponentially with distance below the surface. Fig. 14.4 depicts the orbits, instantaneous orbital velocities and stream lines (dashed lines) in a deep water wave. Just ahead of the crest there is an area of convergence and just behind the crest an area of divergence. Hence the surface rises ahead of the crest and falls behind it. This qualitatively describes the progression of the wave form.

The pressure anomaly is in phase with the surface elevation at all depths and the amplitude ($\rho g a\, e^{kz}$) of pressure fluctuations decreases exponentially with depth. Neither particle velocity nor pressure anomaly are dependent upon the depth (h) of water.

This is sometimes expressed by the statement that in depths greater than half a wavelength the waves do not "feel bottom".

14.4 CAPILLARY WAVES

The treatment given in the previous section is not strictly applicable to all waves in water deeper than a half wavelength. If the wavelength L is less than a few inches surface tension can no longer be neglected. Boundary condition c must be modified to include a term dependent upon the surface curvature. The resultant simple harmonic solution leads to a phase speed such that

$$c^2 = (gL/2\pi) + (2\pi S/\rho L) \qquad (14.14)$$

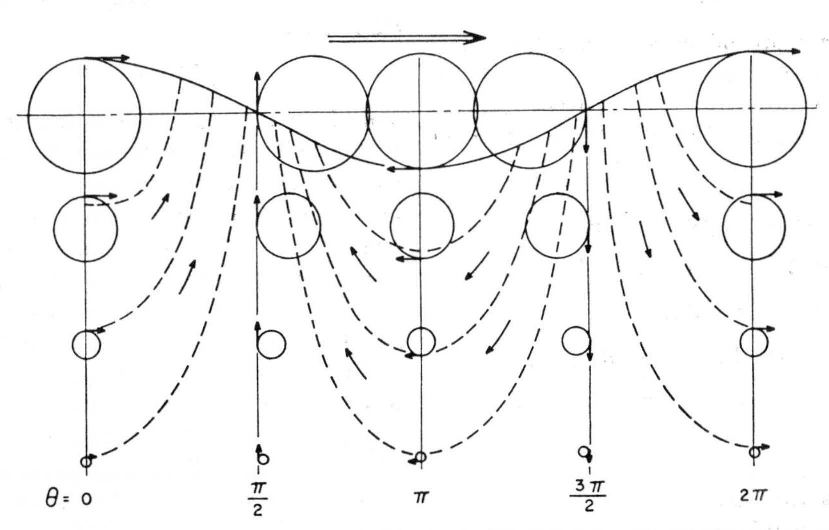

Fig. 14.4 Qualitative depiction of orbits, orbital velocities and stream lines in deep water waves.

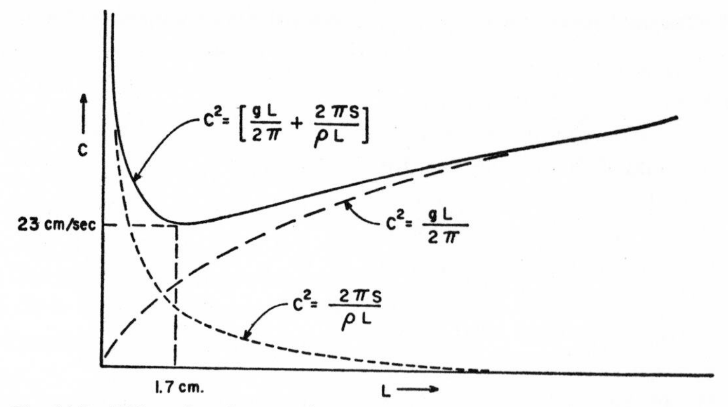

Fig. 14.5 Effect of surface tension on speed of water waves of short length.

where S is the surface tension (74 dynes/cm for an air–sea interface at 20°C).

The two parts of this expression and their sum are plotted against wavelength in Fig. 14.5. It can be seen that there is a minimum value for deep water wave speed corresponding to $L = 1.7$ cm (0.67 in.), $c = 23$ cm/sec (0.75 ft/sec), and a period $T = 0.07$ sec.

Waves of period or wavelength less than this belong in the category of "Capillary Waves". Those of longer period and wavelength, yet within the range where surface tension cannot be neglected, are classed as "Ultra-Gravity Waves".

14.5 Group Speed, Dispersion

Deep water is a dispersive medium for gravity waves. That is, the wave speed is a function of the wavelength or frequency. Specifically,

$$c = (gL/2\pi)^{1/2}. \qquad (14.8)$$

If two wave trains of the same amplitude but slightly different wavelengths and periods progress in the same direction the resultant surface disturbance can be represented as the sum of the individual disturbances.

$$\begin{aligned}\eta = \eta_1 + \eta_2 &= a \cos (kx - \sigma t) + \\ &a \cos [(k + \Delta k)\, x - (\sigma + \Delta\sigma)\, t] \\ &= 2a \cos 1/2\, [(2k + \Delta k)\, x - \\ &(2\sigma + \Delta\sigma)\, t] \cos 1/2\, (\Delta kx - \Delta\sigma t) \\ &\approx 2a \cos (kx - \sigma t) \cos 1/2\, (\Delta kx - \Delta\sigma t).\end{aligned} \qquad (14.15)$$

This disturbance appears as a series of successive groups of waves within which the amplitude varies from zero to $2a$ (Fig. 14.6), the modulation term in (14.15) being $\cos 1/2\,(\Delta kx - \Delta\sigma t)$.

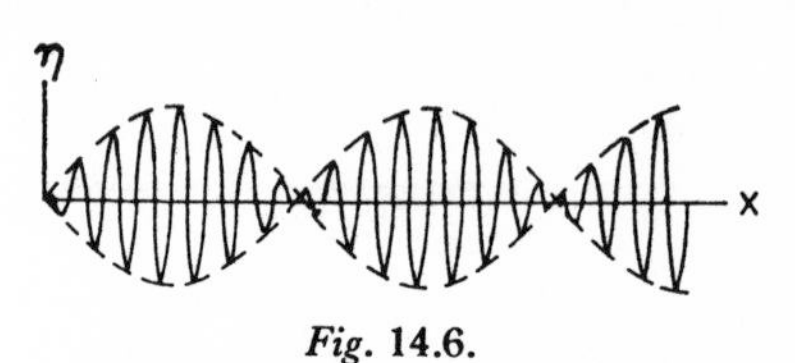

Fig. 14.6.

The distance between centers of successive groups is given by $2\pi/\Delta k$, and the time occupied by the system in shifting through this distance by $2\pi/\Delta\sigma$. The group speed C_g is thus given by

$$C_g = \Delta\sigma/\Delta k,$$

which, in the limit, becomes

$$C_g = \frac{d\sigma}{dk} = \frac{d(kc)}{dk} = c + k\frac{dc}{dk} = c - L\frac{dc}{dL}. \qquad (14.16)$$

For gravity waves in deep water, since $dc/dL = c/2L$, this becomes

$$C_g = (c/2) = (1/2)\,(gL/2\pi)^{1/2}. \qquad (14.17)$$

That is, the group travels at half the wave speed. It can be shown that the energy associated with a wave disturbance is propagated at the appropriate group speed. This has the effect that, where a wave train of a fixed period travels out from the generating area, the leading waves die out quickly and the front of the wave train progresses not at wave speed but at the appropriate group speed.

Another result of the dispersion of deep water waves is that, at a fixed distance from the generating area, waves of the longer periods (wavelength) arrive first. The effect this has on the spectra of wind generated waves will be discussed in Section 14.7.

14.6 Relation of Waves to Winds

Qualitatively it has long been recognized that high winds produce high waves, that high waves tend to be long waves, and that long wavelengths and long periods are associated. To obtain a more quantitative relationship a great amount of empirical data must be collected and correlated. Ships have historically kept logs containing observations of wind, sea, and swell. Standardized codes have been devised for reporting, yet there is so much latitude for subjective error in these observations that they are of little use for really quantitative analysis.

Perhaps the best collection of controlled visual observations is that of Cornish (1934) who spent a lifetime studying ocean waves and kindred phenomena. A resume of some of his findings is given in Table 14.3.

Table 14.3. Properties of Wind Waves at Sea (After Cornish, 1934)

Wind Speed U mph	Wave Speed c mph	Wave Period T sec	Wave Length L feet	Wave Height H feet	Wave Steepness H/L
31	25	7	250	22	0.088
35	28	8	330	24.5	0.074
42	33.5	9.5	470	29.5	0.063
50	40	11.5	670	35	0.052
59	47	13.5	930	41.5	0.045
68	54.5	15.5	1230	47.5	0.039
	$c = 0.8U$	$T = 2c/7$	$L = 41T^2/8$	$H = 0.7U$	

Cornish was, of course, attempting to measure "significant wave height" and the c, L, and T associated with the significant waves.

It is notable that these observations led him to the relationships $L = 5.01T^2$ and $c = 3.5T$ while the Airy theory for deep water yields $L = 5.12T^2$ and $c = 3.49T$.

Note that at higher wind speeds, while wave height increases, wave steepness decreases.

Some quite sophisticated methods have been developed for the prediction of wind wave conditions based on the variables Fetch, Duration, and Wind Speed. The system developed by Sverdrup and Munk (1947) is based on classical wave theory and uses a combination of theoretical and empirical relationships. The Pierson–Neumann–James (1955) system relies more heavily on theoretical consideration although empirical data on wave spectra are a basic input.

14.7 Spectra of Wind Generated Waves

Most of the recent work on ocean waves has concerned itself with the energy spectrum. Records of the surface elevation are taken continuously over a fixed length of time and the records are subjected mechanically to a Fourier analysis from which a spectrogram is constructed (Fig. 14.7).

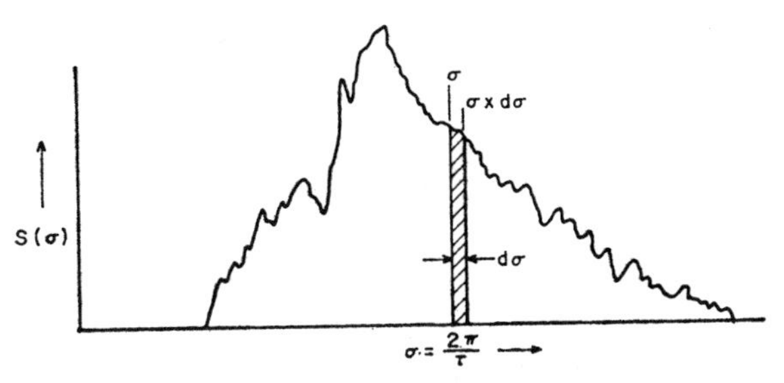

Fig. 14.7 A wave energy spectrum.

The spectral function $S(\sigma)$ is such that $S(\sigma)d\sigma$ is a measure of the contribution to the total energy which is associated with frequencies in the finite range from σ to $\sigma + d\sigma$. Analysis in this fashion does not assume anything concerning the shape of the individual wave components, nor does it imply that, because $S(\sigma)$ has a finite value associated with a certain value of σ, a wave component with that frequency is present.

The spectrum obtained will be influenced by the method of wave recording. Where the wave recorder is mounted on a fixed platform there is usually a real limit to the depth of water. The progress of waves into the relatively shallow water will have distorted the spectrum in a manner to be discussed in Section 14.8. To extrapolate to deep water conditions a filter function for the platform location must be generated and applied to the observed spectrum.

Sometimes the wave record is obtained from a bottom mounted pressure transducer and an additional filter function must be applied to correct for the attenuation of pressure anomaly with depth.

Some wave observations have been made by means of accelerometers mounted in ships or buoys. Here the observations may be made in deep water but compensation must be made for the non-linear response of the ship or buoy.

The present concept of the spectrum of a fully

developed sea (that is, a sea that is not limited by duration or fetch of the wind) is that the high frequency portion can be represented by a fixed curve that does not depend upon wind speed (Fig. 14.8). The functional form of this curve is close to

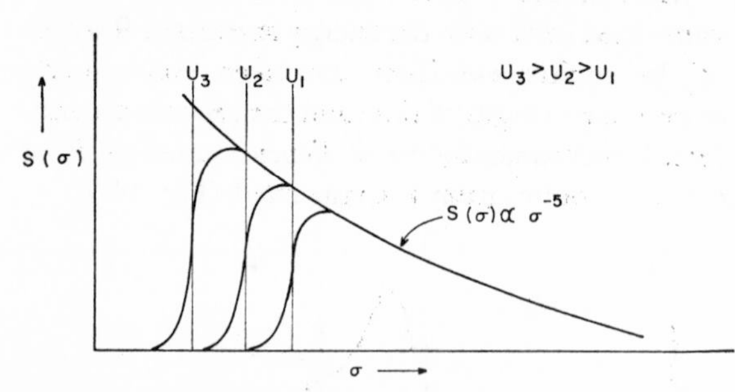

Fig. 14.8 Idealized spectra of fully developed wind waves for wind speeds U_1, U_2, and U_3.

$S(\sigma) \propto \sigma^{-5}$. The spectrum cuts off rather abruptly at the low frequency end at a value of σ which decreases with increasing wind speed.

Wave energy spectra can, of course, be constructed using period T as the variable rather than σ. The spectrum in a generating area might resemble that in Fig. 14.9(a). As the waves move

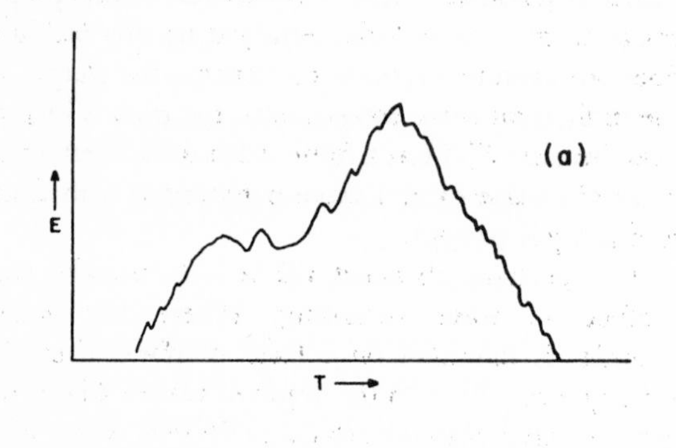

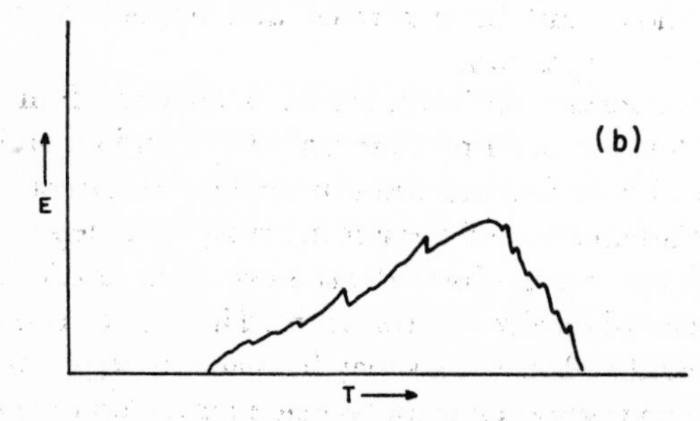

Fig. 14.9 Wave spectra as they might be observed in a generating area (a) and at some point remote from the generating area (b).

out from the area of generation the differential wave speed tends to alter the spectrum, long period energy reaching the observing location earlier. Also there is a tendency for the high frequency components (small T) to die out due to viscous damping. The spectrum at some location remote from the generating area might appear as in Fig. 14.9(b).

If spectral analyses are made regularly from observations on an exposed coast the following sequence sometimes occurs in the absence of local winds: After a period of quiet, wave energy suddenly appears with predominantly long periods. Subsequent spectra show an increase in total wave energy and a tendency toward peak distribution at shorter and shorter periods.

Figure 14.10 illustrates a hypothetical three day sequence. The period associated with maximum energy density for each spectrum may be picked, i.e. T_1, T_2, T_3, etc. Associated with these periods are the deeper water group speeds: $C_{g1} = (g/4\pi)\, T_1$, etc.

Since wave energy is propagated with group speed a line may be drawn on a distance–time (x–t) plot (Fig. 14.11) through $x = 0$ and $t =$ time of observation, with slope C_g. Such a line should pass through the distance–time location of the wave generation area. Experience has shown that these speed lines often intersect at points that check with known severe storms. This confirms that wave energy is propagated in the open ocean at essentially the group speed predicted by the Airy wave theory. Waves have been detected after traveling over 5000 miles.

Synchronized observations at two or more locations can provide a means of detecting severe meteorological disturbances that develop over unfrequented regions of the ocean (Munk, 1947).

14.8 Airy Waves in Shallow Water

Where the depth of water is less than 1/20 of a wavelength ($h/L < 1/20$, $kh < \pi/10$), tanh kh is not significantly different from kh, and the wave speed equation (14.7), reduces to

$$c^2 = gh. \qquad (14.18)$$

The medium is non-dispersive, that is, wave speed is independent of wavelength and period. It must, however, be remembered that the condition $h/L < 1/20$ is fulfilled at different values of h dependent upon L.

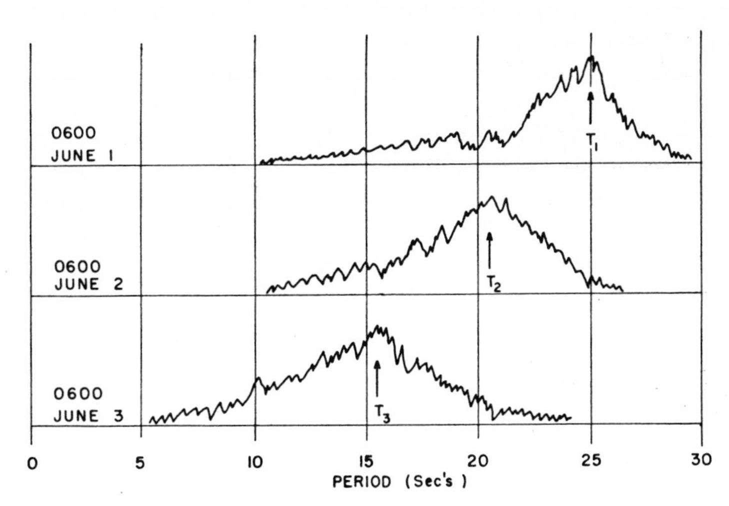

Fig. 14.10 Successive wave spectra at a coastal station.

The relationship between wavelength and period becomes

$$L = T\sqrt{(gh)}. \tag{14.19}$$

Since the number of waves passing a point in unit time must be invariant along the direction of progress, it follows that there must be a decrease in wavelength as the waves move into shallow water such that $L/L_0 = c/c_0$, where L_0 and c_0 refer to wavelength and speed in deep water. Hence,

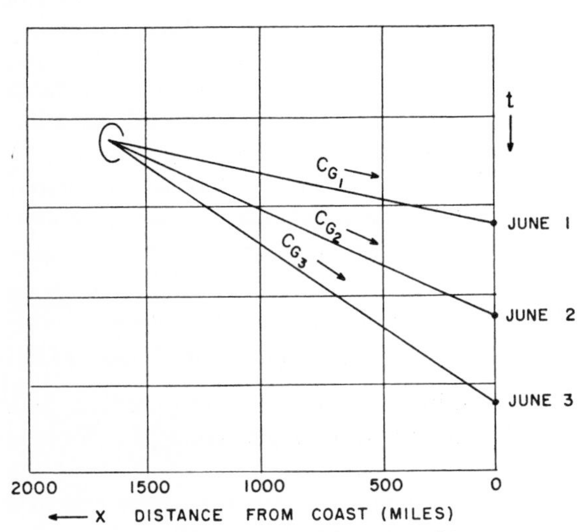

Fig. 14.11 *x–t* plot for location of generation area.

$$L_h = \sqrt{(2\pi h L_0)}, \tag{14.19}$$

where L_h is the wavelength observed in water of depth h. This provides a basis for assessing the bathymetry of an inshore area from aerial photographs in the presence of reasonably monochromatic swell.

For these arbitrarily defined shallow water conditions ($kh < \pi/10$), sinh kh and tanh kh can be replaced by kh, and cosh kh is essentially unity. Hence (14.3), (14.4), and (14.5) reduce to:

$$\begin{aligned} u &= (ac/h) \cos (kx - \sigma t) \\ &= a\sqrt{(g/h)} \cos (kx - \sigma t), \end{aligned} \tag{14.21}$$

$$\begin{aligned} w &= (ac/h)\, k(z + h) \sin (kx - \sigma t) \\ &= \sqrt{(g/h)}\, (2\pi/L)\, (z + h) \sin (kx - \sigma t), \end{aligned} \tag{14.22}$$

$$\Delta p = \rho g a \cos (kx - \sigma t). \tag{14.23}$$

While it might appear (14.21) and (14.23) that u and Δp are not dependent upon wavelength, it will be noted below that as L decreases (14.19) a must increase so that a dependence on L is retained. Horizontal velocity, it will be noted, is independent of z. The pressure anomaly (14.23) indicates a hydrostatic response to the total depth of water $h + \eta$.

The vertical particle velocity w retains a dependence upon L and decreases to zero at $z = -$ h. Even at the surface the maximum value of w is smaller than the maximum value of u by factor $2\pi h/L$.

In a shallow water wave, the particle trajectories are very flat ellipses (Fig. 14.12), the length of the horizontal axes being $aL/\pi h$, and of the vertical axes $2a(z + h)/h$.

The energy per unit surface area propagated with a water wave is proportional to the square

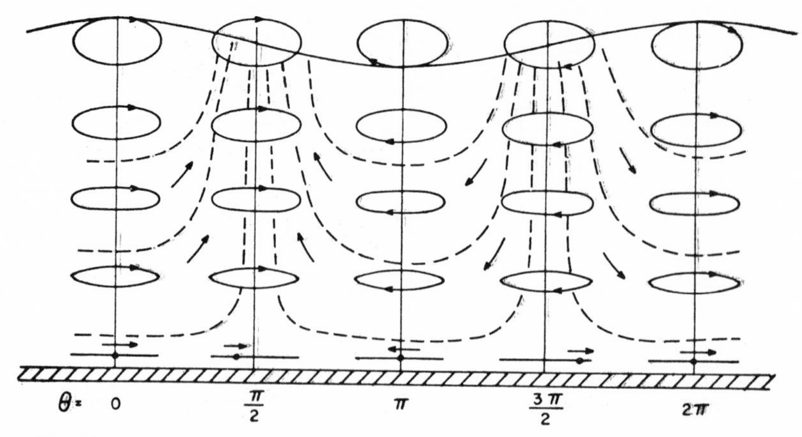

Fig. 14.12. Representation trajectories and stream lines for shallow water wave.

of the amplitude (see Section 14.12). In order to have continuity of energy flow, it can be seen qualitatively that, as the wavelength L decreases in shoaling water, the amplitude must increase. This explains the building up of swell as it approaches shore.

It should be noted that the predicted changes in wavelength and amplitude violate the initial conditions for waves of permanent form. Therefore (14.21), (14.22), and (14.23) cannot strictly be applied to swell moving into shallow water, but (14.18), $c = \sqrt{(gh)}$, turns out to be independent of wave form. All four equations should be applicable to tsunamis and tide waves in the open ocean with constant depth.

14.9 Wave Refraction

Since wave speed varies with depth ($c = \sqrt{(gh)}$), waves in shallow water are refracted towards regions of lesser water depth. Hence, on a long, straight beach with uniform slope all waves tend to approach normal to the shore line (Fig. 14.13).

Where a promontory juts out from a coast, waves tend to converge at the headland (Fig. 14.14a). This, of course, leads to a selective erosion of the headlands and hence a tendency toward straight coast lines.

Where a submarine valley cuts into a sloping beach there is divergence of the wave fronts (Fig. 14.14b). For this reason a favorable anchorage on an open coast can sometimes be found at the head of a submarine valley.

When a mixed wave train progresses into a region of diminishing water depth, the longer waves (T and L large) are the first to "feel bottom". Since wave energy is dissipated by bottom friction in the case of shallow water waves, it can be seen that there will be a selective attenuation of the energy associated with long periods. The wave spectrum as observed at an inshore location will be the deep water spectrum operated upon by a filter function which is characteristic of the location, and which discriminates against the lower frequencies.

14.10 Waves of Finite Amplitude

Two types of mathematical treatment of waves with finite amplitude will be mentioned here without going into the development.

The first type, known as "Gerstner–Rankine" waves, are described by the parametric equations:

$$x = X - a \sin (kX - \sigma t),$$

and

$$\eta' = a \cos (kX - \sigma t). \qquad (14.24)$$

These describe a trochoid, a curve traced out by a point, a distance a from the center of a circle of radius $1/k = (L/2\pi)$, which is rolled along the underside of a horizontal line at a distance $1/k$ above the reference surface $z = 0$.

The total wave height H is $2a$, as before, but mean water level is a distance $ka^2/2 = (\pi a^2/L)$ below the plane $z = 0$, so that the free surface, referred to mean water level is $\eta = (ka^2/2) + \eta'$.

Particle motion in these waves is in closed circular orbits and the wave speed is again given by $c = \sqrt{(gL/2\pi)}$. There is no net transport of water with the waves. The motion is, however, rotational, and the solution is sometimes objected to on these grounds.

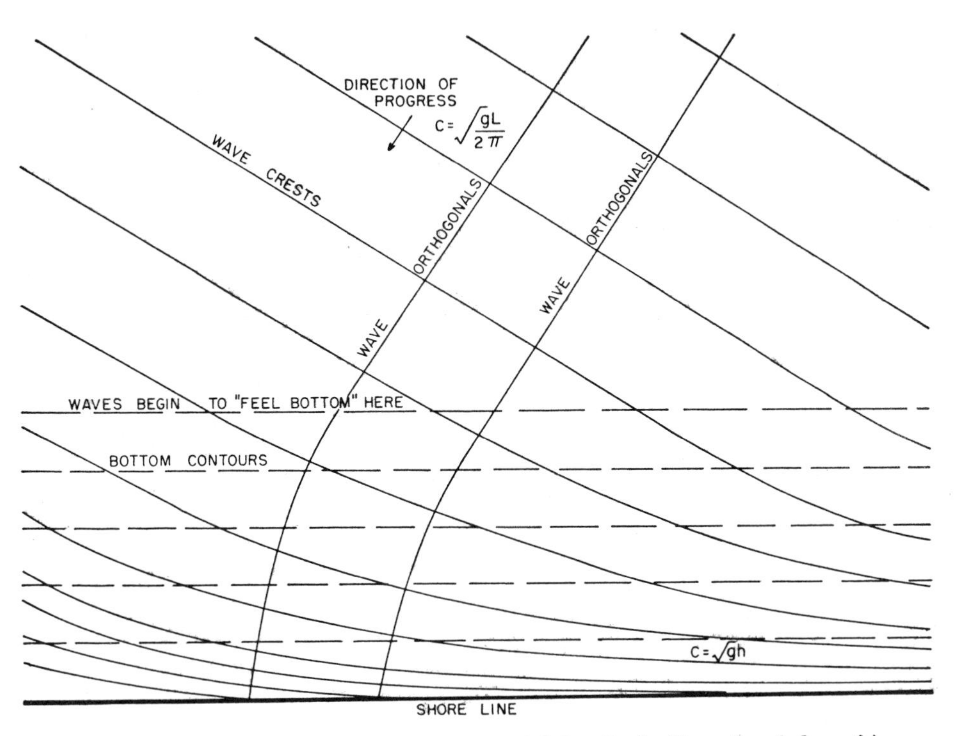

Fig. 14.13 Refraction of waves approaching a straight beach of uniform slope (schematic).

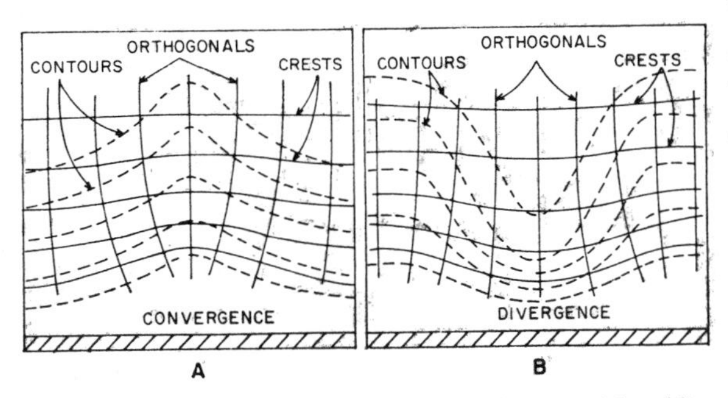

Fig. 14.14 Wave convergence inside a submarine ridge (A) and divergence inside a submarine valley (B).

Another solution for waves of finite amplitude was developed by Stokes (1847, 1880). The conditions for the Airy theory are retained except that finite amplitude is allowed and the boundary conditions are suitably modified. The Airy solution provides a first order approximate solution to the Stokes wave, but, for a better approximation, higher order terms must be used. The second order approximation is given by

$$\eta = a \cos (kx - \sigma t) + (1/2)\, ka^2 \cos 2\,(kx - \sigma t),$$

or $$(14.25)$$

$$\eta = a\,[\cos (kx - \sigma t) + (\pi H/2L) \cos 2\,(kx - \sigma t)]. \quad (14.26)$$

The second term in (14.26) is called the first order correction for wave steepness (H/L). (Remember that this quantity was considered to be zero in the Airy solution.)

The third order approximation yields

$$\eta = a\,[\cos (kx - \sigma t) + (\pi H/2L) \cos 2\,(kx - \sigma t) + (3\pi^2/8)\,(H/L)^2 \cos 3\,(kx - \sigma t)], \quad (14.27)$$

etc.

In Stokes waves the motion is irrotational. Particle trajectories are not closed figures and there is a net transport in the direction of wave travel. The phase speed for Stokes waves in relatively deep water is given by

$$c = \sqrt{[(g/k)\ \{1 + (ka)^2\}]}, \\ = \sqrt{[(gL/2\pi)\ \{1 + \pi^2\,\delta^2\}]}, \quad (14.28)$$

where the wave steepness H/L is written δ; in the case of relatively shallow water the celerity is

$$c = \sqrt{[gh\ \{1 + (a/kh^2)\}^2]}. \quad (14.29)$$

16.11 Breaking Waves — Surf

In waves of little steepness particle speeds are very small compared to wave speed. In the Stokes solution, as the waves become steeper the maximum particle speed at the crest approaches the wave speed. If the particle speed becomes greater than the wave speed the wave becomes unstable and will break.

If the shape of a wave at its crest is approximated by two straight lines meeting at an angle θ (Fig. 14.15) it can be shown that the minimum value of θ for stable waves is 120°. Observations at sea tend to confirm this.

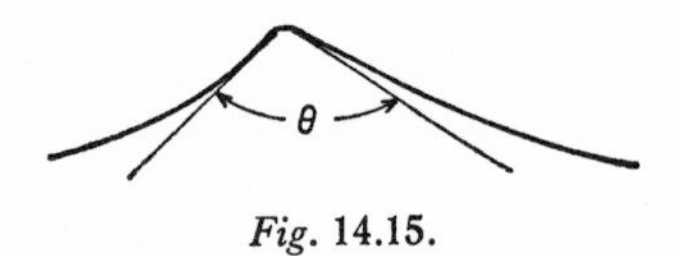

Fig. 14.15.

Another approach to the problem of breaking waves (Michell, 1893) assigns a maximum value to the steepness $\delta = H/L$ of 1/7. This criterion does not hold for breakers on a beach but seems to fit observations in relatively deep water reasonably well.

Neither the Airy theory nor the Stokes theory can adequately deal with the surf problem. For treatment of large waves in very shallow water, it is necessary to invoke the theory of solitary waves. This will not be presented here but the reader is directed to papers by Keller (1949), Munk (1949), and Daily and Stephan (1951).

The solitary wave theory takes account of the influence of the wave disturbance upon the effective depth of the water for wave propagation. Wave speed is given by

$$c = \sqrt{\{g(h + H)\}}, \qquad (14.30)$$

which it will be noted has the same form as (14.18). Horizontal particle velocity varies with depth (z) below the surface, unlike (14.21). Maximum horizontal particle velocity occurs under the crest and, at the water surface, is given by

$$u_M = Hc/h. \qquad (14.31)$$

This is similar in form to the Airy theory (14.21) but twice as great. At the bottom

$$u_M = Hc/2h, \qquad (14.32)$$

or just that predicted by (14.21). It can be seen from (14.31) that as the wave moves into shallow water a point will be reached where particle velocity at the crest exceeds the wave speed and the wave must break.

Solitary wave theory provides only for horizontal particle motion in the direction of wave travel and no return flow under the trough. Surf, therefore, involves shoreward transport of water. A necessary result is "longshore" currents which at discrete locations are unloaded by concentrated seaward flow in "rip currents" (Inman, 1963).

14.12 Wave Energy

Waves possess both potential and kinetic energy. In fact, it is the rythmic conversion of potential energy to kinetic and back again that maintains the oscillations.

If the undisturbed water depth is h, the local elevation η and the uniform density ρ, the potential energy of a vertical column with unit width along the wave front, and incremental width dx along the orthogonal, is given by

$$g[\rho(h + \eta)] \, \{ \frac{(h + \eta)}{2} \} \, dx = \rho g \, \{(h + \eta)^2/2\} dx.$$

For a complete wavelength L the potential energy per unit width is

$$\rho g \int_0^L (h + \eta)^2/2 \, dx.$$

With no wave disturbance the potential energy is

$$\rho g (h^2/2) \, L.$$

Subtracting leaves the potential energy due to the wave

$$1/2 \, \rho g \int_0^L \eta^2 \, dx + \rho g h \int_0^L \eta \, dx.$$

The last integral must be zero so we are left with the average potential energy per unit area due to the wave.

$$E_p = (1/2L) \rho g \int_0^L \eta^2 \, dx. \qquad (14.33)$$

For a sinusoidal wave, $\eta = a \cos kx$, this becomes

$$E_p = (1/4) \, \rho g a^2. \qquad (14.34)$$

The average over a wavelength of the kinetic energy per unit surface area can be written:

$$E_k = (\rho/2L) \int_0^L \int_{-h}^{\eta} (u^2 + w^2) \, dx \, dz. \quad (14.35)$$

For sinusoidal waves of small amplitude, making the approximation $\eta = 0$ as the upper limit in the integral with respect to z, and substituting (14.3) and (14.4) for u and w, one obtains

$$E_k = \frac{1}{4} \rho \frac{(a\sigma)^2}{k} \coth kh,$$

which, in view of (14.6), becomes

$$E_k = (1/4) \, \rho g a^2. \qquad (14.36)$$

The total energy per unit surface area is

$$E = E_p + E_k = (1/2) \, \rho g a^2.$$

or, as more often written

$$E = (1/8)\ \rho\, gH^2. \qquad (14.37)$$

The wave energy per unit area is equal to that necessary to raise a layer of water of thickness equal to wave height H a distance $H/8$. If 1 m is taken as a conservative estimate of the average wave height over the oceans the total wave energy is 4.5×10^{24} ergs.

Wave energy progresses at the group speed c_g (Section 14.5) so that the wave power per unit width of wave front is given by

$$P = E\, c_g,$$

$$= 1/8\ \rho\, gH^2\, c_g. \qquad (14.38)$$

For Airy waves in deep water, referring to (14.17) and (14.9),

$$P = (1/32\pi)\ \rho\, g^2\ T\, H^2. \qquad (14.39)$$

Consider, for example, waves of 1 m height and period 10 sec progressing in a front 1 km long. The power involved would be 10^{14} ergs/sec or 10^4 kW.

In shallow water, phase speed and group speed are identical ($\sqrt{(gh)}$) and

$$P = (1/8)\ \rho\, gH^2 \sqrt{(gh)}. \qquad (14.40)$$

For continuity of energy transmission wave height must increase as water depth decreases so that the product $H^2\sqrt{h}$ remains constant.

14.13 Standing Waves — Seiche

If one surface wave train as defined by (14.1), $\eta_1 = a \cos (kx - \sigma t)$, is added to another with identical a, k, σ but progressing in the opposite direction, i.e. $\eta_2 = a \cos (kx + \sigma t)$, the resulting surface elevation can be written

$$\eta = \eta_1 + \eta_2 = 2a \cos kx \cos \sigma t. \qquad (14.41)$$

This is called a "standing wave". The surface elevation varies with a frequency σ (period $T = 2\pi/\sigma$), but the amplitude of the variation varies horizontally from zero at $kx = \pi/2, 3\pi/2, \ldots$ to a maximum of $2a$ at $kx = 0, \pi, 2\pi. \ldots$ Locations where the variations in elevation are zero or a minimum are called "nodes"; locations where the variations are maximum are referred to as "antinodes".

Particle motion is such that at the antinodes it is entirely a vertical oscillation and at the nodes entirely a horizontal, back and forth, motion. This is illustrated for the case of shallow water in Fig. 14.16.

Where progressive waves are incident upon a vertical fixed boundary some of the wave energy is reflected from the boundary. With a perfectly reflecting boundary normal to the direction of wave travel the interference between the incident and reflected wave trains would set up a standing wave system with an antinode at the boundary. For a less than perfect reflection the resultant can be considered as a standing wave with a progressive wave superimposed.

In an enclosed body of water, where the speed o long waves is a unique function of location, there exists, for any direction across the basin, a discrete set of frequencies for which standing waves can be set up. Antinodes must occur at the boundaries. The simplest mode is that wherein a single node occurs somewhere between the boundaries. Any number of nodes would, however, be permissible.

In the simplest case, where depth is constant across the basin, the wave speed is single valued and all permissible modes are harmonics of the fundamental. In real basins, with complex geometry, there may be a complex set of frequencies depending upon the direction considered. These

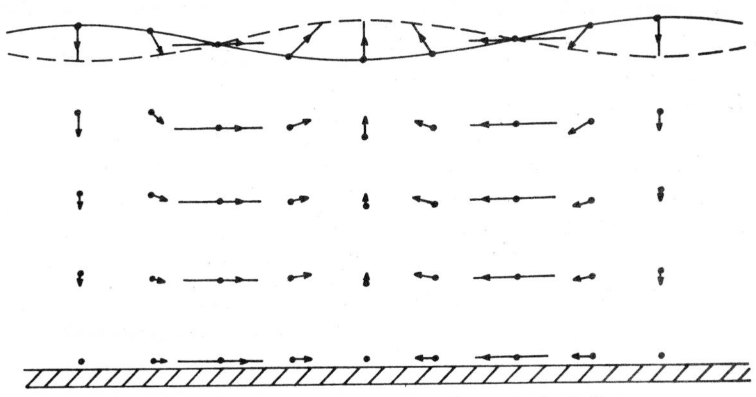

Fig. 14.16 Particle trajectories for a standing wave in shallow water.

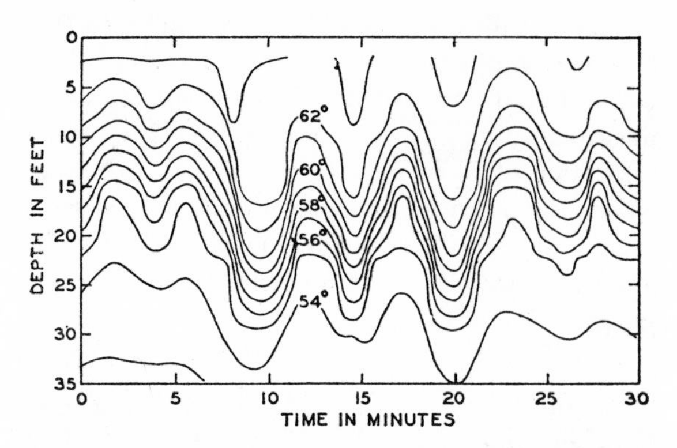

Fig. 14.17 Example of a series of internal waves which were observed in 60 ft of water off the coast at San Diego, California. Isotherms are shown in 1°F intervals (after Lee, 1961).

natural periods of oscillation are the "seiche periods" for the basin. The standing wave motion is called a "seiche". Seiche motion may be set up by an impulsive disturbance, or driven by periodic disturbances which have approximately the same period as one of the seiche modes. Standing waves often play an important role in determining the nature of the astronomical tides at a given location.

14.13 Internal Waves

The waves discussed so far are those that manifest themselves in an oscillation of the air–sea interface. Surface waves are the only permissible gravity waves in a homogeneous, incompressible, fluid. In developing the theoretical models the density of the atmosphere is assumed to be negligible.

It can be shown that similar oscillations are possible at the boundary between any two fluids of different densities. The energy involved in the oscillations depends upon the ratio of density difference to density (virtually unity for surface waves). Where the density difference is a small fraction of the density, waves of large amplitude can be propagated with very little energy. The theory of waves on a surface of discontinuity has been treated by Lamb (1932, p. 370) in some detail.

The two-layer case has, of course, little application to the real ocean where continuous density stratification is encountered. Fjeldstad (1933) has treated the general case in some detail. The reader is also directed to an exposition by Defant (1961, Chapter XVI).

Experience has shown that, almost every time a time series of observations at a fixed location has been made, fluctuations in the observed variables occur which may be attributed to "internal waves". Figure 14.17 shows an example given by Lee (1961); the observed variable is temperature, and the waves appear as oscillations in the depth of the various isotherms.

References

Cornish, V. *Ocean Waves and Kindred Phenomena.* Cambridge. 1934.

Daily, J. W. and S. C. Stephan. (1951) Characteristics of the solitary wave. *Proc. Am. Soc. Civ. Eng.* **77**(107), 13 pp.

Defant, A. *Physical Oceanography,* Vol. II. Pergamon Press, New York. 1961.

Fjeldstad, J. E. (1933) Internes. Wellen. *Geofysiske Publikasjoner* **10**(6), 53 pp. Oslo.

Inman, D. L. Ocean waves and associated currents. In *Submarine Geology by Francis P. Shepard anp others* Harper & Row, New York, 1963.

Keller, J. B. (1949) The solitary wave and periodic waves in shallow water. *Ann. N. Y. Acad. Sci.* **51,** 345–350.

Lamb, H. *Hydrodynamics* (sixth edition). Cambridge Univ. Press, Reprinted 1945 by Dover, New York. 1932.

Lee, O. S. (1961). Effect of an internal wave on sound in the ocean. *J. Acoust. Soc. Am.* **33**(5), 677–681.

Michell, J. H. (1893) On the highest waves in water. *Phil. Mag.* **36**, 430–435.

Munk, W. H. (1947) Tracking storms by forerunners of swell. *J. Meteor.* **4** (2), 45–57.

Munk, W. H. (1949) The solitary wave theory and its application to surf problems. *Ann. N. Y. Acad. Sci.* **51,** 376–424.

Munk, W. H. (1950) *Origin and generation of waves,* Proc. 1st. Conf. Coastal Eng., 1–4, Council on Wave Research, Berkeley.

Pierson, W. J., G. Neumann and R. W. James. (1955) *Practical methods for observing and forecasting ocean waves by means of wave spectra and statistics.* U.S. Navy Hydrog. Office, H.O. Pub. No. 603, Washington.

Stokes, G. G. (1847) On the theory of oscillatory waves. *Trans. Camb. Phil. Soc.* **8**, 441.

Stokes, G. G. (1880) Supplement to a paper on the theory of oscillatory waves, *Math. and Phys. Papers,* Cambridge, 314–326.

Sverdrup, H. U. and W. H. Munk. (1947) *Wind, sea, and swell: theory of relations for forecasting.* U.S. Navy Hydrog. Office, H. O. Pub. No. 610. Washington.

Sources of Additional Information

Hydrodynamics. Lamb. H., Dover, New York. 1945.

Wind waves at sea, breakers and surf. Bigelow, H. B., and W. T. Edmondson, U.S. Hydrographic Office (H.O. Pub. 602), Washington, 177 pp. 1944.

Observing and Forecasting Ocean Waves. Pierson, W. J., G. Neumann and R. W. James. U.S. Hydrographic Office (H. O. Pub. 603) Washington. 1955.

Physical Oceanography, Vol. 2. Defant, A. Pergamon Press, New York, pp. 1–244. 1961.

Proceedings—Conference on Ocean Wave Spectra. Easton, Maryland, May 1961, Prentice Hall. 1962.

CHAPTER 15

TIDES

THE longest ocean waves are those associated with the astronomical tides. Wavelengths are everywhere much greater than water depth so that wave progression is governed by the shallow water wave speed. This may be about 400 knots for a depth of 4000 m or 60 knots for a depth around 100 m. The principal semi-diurnal tide with period 12.42 hr would have wavelength 5000 nautical miles or 750 nautical miles under these conditions. Simple two-dimensional wave theories cannot be applied since Coriolis acceleration and other inertial accelerations cannot be neglected. Moreover, because of the limited size of the ocean basins, wave trains of several wavelengths do not occur.

These waves are driven by external forces with discrete periodicities. Theoretical treatment must consider the response of the fluid in basins of complex geometry to these forcing functions.

We shall limit ourselves to a descriptive treatment aimed at an understanding of the complex variations in sea level that are observed at any location around the margin of an ocean basin.

15.1 Description of the Tides

At the edge of the ocean the water surface does not remain at a fixed level but alternately rises and falls. It will slowly rise to a maximum elevation which we call "High Water" then fall to a minimum ("Low Water") from which it begins to rise again. The difference in elevation between High Water and Low Water is called the "Range of the Tide". This fluctuation usually takes place twice in a day so that there are two High Waters and two Low Waters. Where there is a long bay or river mouth on the coast the rising of water level is accompanied by an inward flow known as the "Flood" and the falling by an outward flow or "Ebb". The vertical oscillations are referred to as the "Tide" and the back and forward movement the "Tidal Stream". As the direction of the tidal stream changes, there is a period of no horizontal movement due to tidal forces. This is called "Slack Water". The occurrence closest in time to High Water is called "High Water Slack" and that closest to Low Water, "Low Water Slack".

In the open ocean, away from coasts, variations in elevation are difficult to detect and the accompanying horizontal movement usually must be represented by a rotating vector rather than a simple back and forth movement. These horizontal movements are the "Tidal Currents".

A closer examination of the phenomena reveals that:

(1) The range of the tide is not the same at every location but varies from virtually zero to over 50 ft.

(2) At a given place High Water occurs approximately an hour later each day, getting back to approximately the same time in 14 or 15 days. The "mean tidal interval", or average time from one High Water to the next, is 12 hr, 25 min, 14 sec or precisely one-half "Lunar Day".

(3) The range of tide at any location is not constant but varies periodically from maximum to minimum values. There are usually two complete cycles in a month, though at some locations only one. Periods when the range is a maximum are known as "Springs" and the tides occurring at the time are "Spring Tides". Periods when the range is a minimum are known as "Neaps" and the tides as "Neap Tides".

Spring Tides generally occur when the moon is full or new while Neap Tides occur with the moon in its quarters.

(4) At many locations, the two tides of the day may have unequal ranges. At such locations, the nature of the "Diurnal Inequality" varies throughout the month, usually with a recurrence of type in approximately a

month. The shape of the tide curve may vary greatly, but usually a maximum elevation ("Higher High Water") is followed by a suppressed minimum ("Higher Low Water") after which there is a suppressed maximum ("Lower High Water") and a minimum elevation ("Lower Low Water"). In the extreme "Higher Low Water" and "Lower High Water" may be equal and a long "Stand" of the tide is observed.

There may also be recurring inequalities in "tidal interval" or time between successive high waters. In the extreme, one interval in the day might be as much as 14 hr and the succeeding one only 11 hr.

15.2 Tidal Stations—Tide Tables—Low Water Datum

In the harbors and along the coasts of the world, stations have been established for the recording of tides. From the records accumulated over long periods of time it is possible to predict into the future the nature of the astronomical tides. At "Principal Tidal Stations" recordings are continuous and the "Tide Tables" computed for them predict the times of occurrence of high and low water, the elevations to be expected at these times, and, in some cases, the times of slack water in near-by navigation channels. At other locations, tidal observations are made for a sufficient period to permit correlation to a Principal Tidal Station.

The predicted elevations in the Tide Tables are referred to a fixed level called the "Low Water Datum" and inshore navigation charts show depths of water below this Datum. It is important for the navigator to know what datum is used, since depths less than chart depth may sometimes be encountered. The datum used varies from place to place. Some of the reference levels in common use are:

Mean Sea Level. This is the average value of the water level taken over a long period. This datum is almost never used in tide tables or as a chart datum but is an important reference in terrestrial surveying. For this latter purpose precise leveling is used to carry the datum inland from principal tidal stations.

Mean Low Water. This is an average value of the elevations observed at all low waters over a suitably long period. This datum is commonly used in surveys along the Atlantic Coast of the United States.

Mean Lower Low Water. This is an average value of the elevations observed at "Lower Low Water" over a suitably long period. This is a better datum in areas with pronounced diurnal inequalities and is generally used along the Pacific Coast of the United States.

Mean Low Water Springs. This is an average value of the elevations observed at low water during spring tides. This datum is widely used as a reference in foreign countries but, by the U.S. Survey, only on the Pacific Coast of the Panama Canal Zone.

Lowest Low Water Springs. This is a computed level representing the lowest stand of sea level at spring tides that can be expected due to astronomical tides. This datum is used by Brazil and Portugal.

Low Water Datum. In some charts and Tide Tables the datum is given simply as Low Water Datum with an indication that datum is taken at a fixed distance below mean low water springs. The datum, thus arbitrarily selected, is such that levels lower than datum can be expected to occur very rarely.

15.3 Equilibrium Theory of the Tides

The earliest theory which attempted to explain the tides was the equilibrium theory. While it fails to give an adequate picture of what actually happens, it does provide some insight into the nature of the tide generating forces. Since observations make it obvious that the tides are primarily caused by the moon, one examines the forces that the moon exerts on the fluid envelope of the earth.

The force of gravitational attraction coupling the earth and moon (Fig. 15.1) is $\gamma ME/R^2$, where $\gamma =$ the gravitational constant, $M =$ mass of the moon, $E =$ mass of the earth, and R is the distance between centers.

The acceleration experienced by the earth is then equal to $\gamma M/R^2$ directed towards the moon.

A particle at P experiences an acceleration in the same direction equal to $\gamma M/(R - r)^2$, while at Q acceleration is $\gamma M/(R + r)^2$, where r is the radius of the earth. At O the acceleration $\gamma M/(R')^2$ is directed at a slight angle to the others.

Subtracting the acceleration of the earth as a whole from that at Q gives the relative acceleration at Q equal to

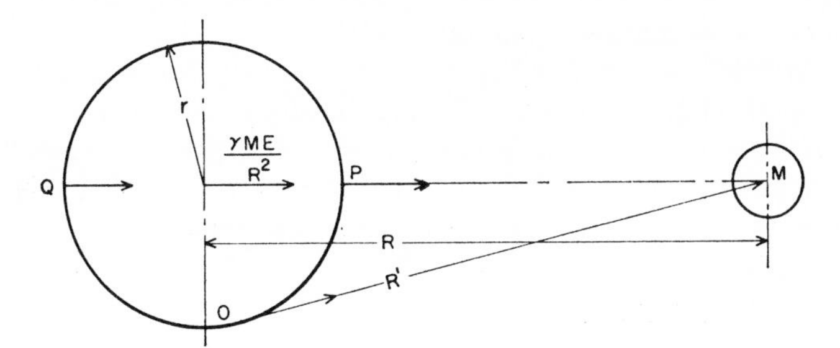

Fig. 15.1.

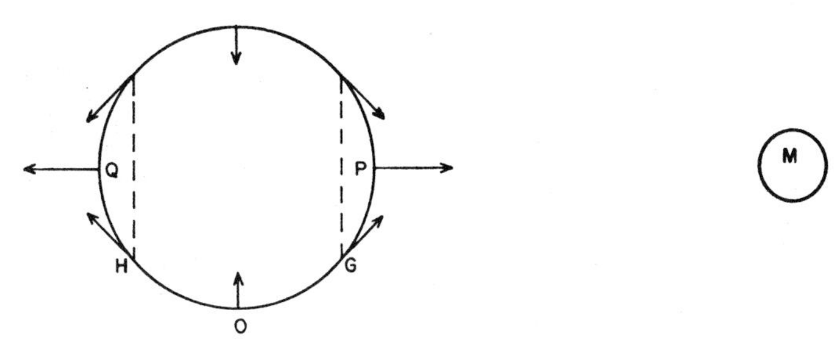

Fig. 15.2.

$$\gamma M/(R+r)^2 - \gamma M/R^2,$$

which can be written

$$-\frac{\gamma M}{R^2}\left[1-\frac{1}{(1+r/R)^2}\right]$$
$$=-\frac{\gamma M}{R^2}\left[\frac{2r/R+(r/R)^2}{(1+r/R)^2}\right].$$

Since r/R is approximately 1/60 for the earth–moon system, we can make the following approximations: $(r/R)^2 = 0$, $(1 + r/R) = 1$, leaving relative acceleration at $Q = -2\gamma Mr/R^3$. That is, the relative acceleration is directed away from the moon and is inversely proportional to the cube of the moon's distance R.

Similarly for P the relative acceleration is $+ 2\gamma Mr/R^3$. The resultant at O can be shown to be directed towards the center of the earth and equal to $\gamma Mr/R^3$.

The relative acceleration experienced at the earth's surface is shown qualitatively in Fig. 15.2. At P and Q the acceleration is normal to the surface and directed outward. At O it is normal inward. At other locations there are both normal and tangential components except for two rings (G and H) where the acceleration is entirely tangential.

If now we assume an earth covered with an ocean of uniform depth, an equilibrium can be visualized where the vertical component of this acceleration anomaly is balanced by a displacement of the free surface in the geopotential field. The surface configuration would be distorted relative to a geopotential surface as indicated in Fig. 15.3.

This figure is drawn as if we were looking down on the earth at the North Pole. The equilibrium surface (with moon) shows two elevated areas on each side of the planet and two depressed areas in the other quadrants. As the earth rotates it can be seen that an observer on the small island would see two high waters and two low waters per day.

For an equilibrium tide due to the moon, the displacement from the no moon equilibrium would be 35.4 cm at the maxima and − 17.7 cm at the minima.

One might construct a similar component for equilibrium tides due to the sun. While the mass of the sun is very much larger, its great distance from the earth results in a tide generating potential that is about 46 per cent of that due to the moon. Theoretical elevation anomalies being 16.2 cm and − 8.2 cm.

When the sun and the moon are in line with respect to the earth (Full and New moon) the effects are additive, hence "Spring Tides". When the sun and moon are in quadrature the effects tend to cancel one another—hence "Neap Tides". When the tide generating body is displaced from the equatorial plane of the earth (declination)

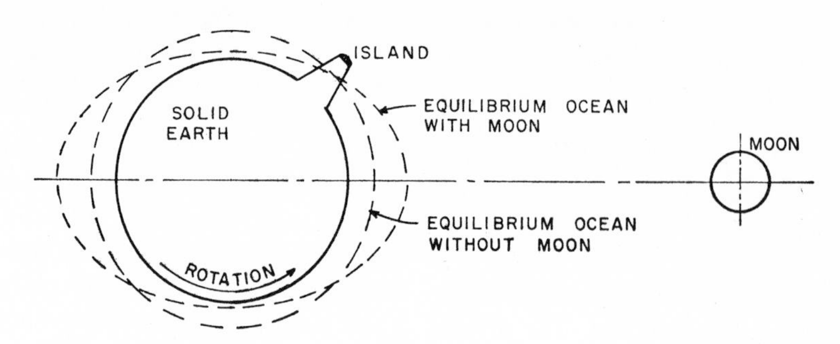

Fig. 15.3.

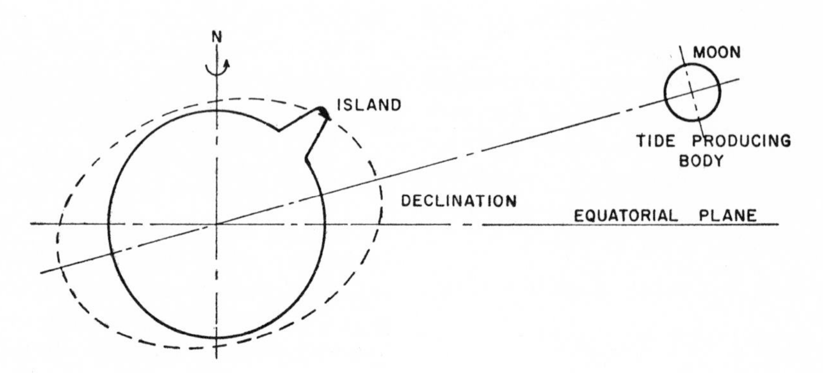

Fig. 15.4.

the equilibrium configuration viewed in a meridional plane would be as shown in Fig. 15.4. It can be seen that at the hypothetical island there would be a marked inequality in the two tides observed during the day.

While the equilibrium theory of the tides provides an insight into the generating forces and a qualitative explanation of many features of the tide, it fails to explain the actual amplitudes observed or the phase of the tides, which may be vastly different from the phase of the generating forces.

The failure can be attributed to the following causes:

(1) The oceans have real meridional boundaries.
(2) Tidal oscillations constitute wave motion for which the speed of progression is limited by the characteristic shallow water equation $C = \sqrt{(gh)}$.
(3) For motion of this type the rotation of the earth (Coriolis acceleration) is important.
(4) The various basins which enclose the oceans possess natural modes of oscillation "seiche periods" which influence their response to the tide generating forces.

15.4 Dynamical Theory of the Tides

The dynamical theory of the tides deals with the hydrodynamic response of the real oceans to the tide generating forces. While this approach makes notable contribution to an understanding of the tidal motions in the open ocean, the complexity introduced by the boundary configurations makes it useless for detailed prediction of tides in harbors, estuaries or exposed coastal locations. Theoretical models must be verified on the basis of observations at tidal stations where the tide wave has been distorted through passage over a continental shelf of complex topography.

15.5 Harmonic Analysis

The practical study of tides, aimed at predicting surface elevations and times, involves the empirical treatment of observations made at the desired location over an extended period of time. The motion of the heavenly bodies relative to the earth is known with great precision so that the tide generating potential at any place and time can be computed. Mathematically the potential can be resolved into a finite number of strictly periodic components which, upon addition, produce the total potential. Doodson (1922), lists some 390 components of the tide generating potential, of which about 100 are of long period, 160 diurnal, 115 semi-diurnal and 14 one-third diurnal. To each can be assigned an exact period and an amplitude. The amplitude is usually stated as a relative coefficient which relates it to the amplitude of the principal lunar semi-diurnal component M_2.

Many of the components are of insignificant amplitude for practical consideration. The principal components are listed in Table 15.1. In practice only seven components are widely used: 4 semi-diurnal components M_2, S_2, N_2, K_2, and 3 diurnal components K_1, O_1, P_1.

The records for a station are analyzed for components of the chosen frequencies. For each component an amplitude and a phase angle are determined. Then the elevation (η) of the sea surface at any time (t) can be computed from an equation of the form

$$\eta = D + a_1 \cos(\sigma_1 t + \delta_1) + a_2 \cos(\sigma_2 t + \delta_2) + a_3 \cos(\sigma_3 t + \delta_3) + \ldots.$$

D is the vertical distance from mean sea level to the desired low water datum, a_1 and δ_1 are the amplitude and phase angle, respectively, as determined for the component with angular frequency σ_1, and so on.

Offices charged with the preparation of the tide tables now use machines into which the a's and δ's can be inserted with the result that the machine will construct the tide curve for the station and the operator can read off the time and elevation for each predicted high or low water. Tide predicting machines have been built which take account of as many as 63 components or "partial tides".

15.6 Movements of the Sun and Moon

Every movement of the sun and moon relative to the earth has its influence upon the tide. To develop an understanding of the reasons for the complexity of the tide, we will consider some of the major features of the motion of sun and moon from a geocentric point of view.

Table 15.1. Principal Tidal Harmonic Components

Name of Partial Tides	Symbol	Speed (degrees per mean solar hr)	Period in solar hr	Coefficient ratio $M_2 = 100$
Semi-diurnal components				
Principal lunar	M_2	28.98410°	12.42	100.0
Principal solar	S_2	30.00000	12.00	46.6
Larger lunar elliptic	N_2	28.43973	12.66	19.2
Luni-solar semi-diurnal	K_2	30.08214	11.97	12.7
Larger solar elliptic	T_2	29.95893	12.01	2.7
Smaller lunar elliptic	L_2	29.52848	12.19	2.8
Lunar elliptic second order	$2N_2$	27.89535	12.91	2.5
Larger lunar evectional	ν_2	28.51258	12.63	3.6
Smaller lunar evectional	λ_2	29.45563	12.22	0.7
Variational	μ_2	27.96821	12.87	3.1
Diurnal components				
Luni-solar diurnal	K_1	15.04107°	23.93	58.4
Principal lunar diurnal	O_1	13.94304	25.82	41.5
Principal solar diurnal	P_1	14.95893	24.07	19.4
Larger lunar elliptic	Q_1	13.39866	26.87	7.9
Smaller lunar elliptic	M_1	14.49205	24.84	3.3
Small lunar elliptic	J_1	15.58544	23.10	3.3
Long-period components				
Lunar fortnightly	M_f	1.09803°	327.86	17.2
Lunar monthly	M_m	0.54437	661.30	9.1
Solar semi-annual	S_{sa}	0.08214	2191.43	8.0

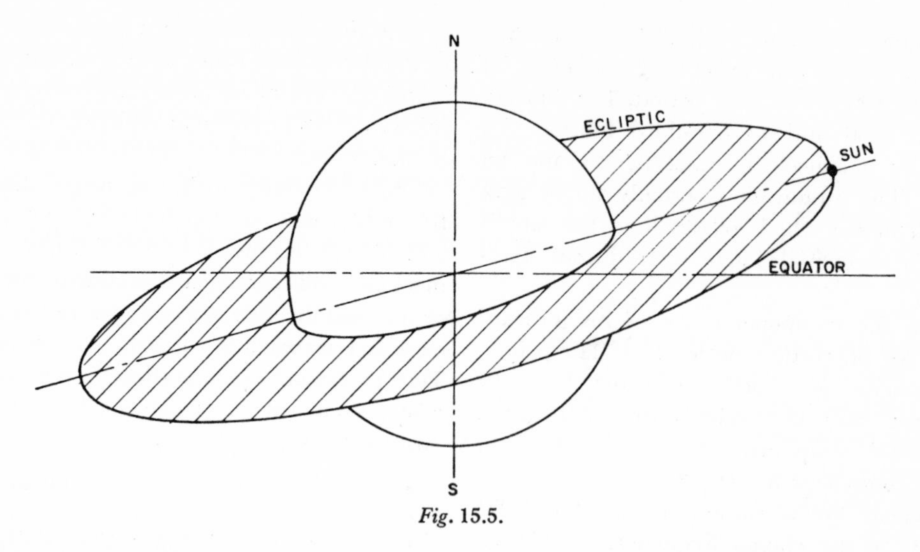

Fig. 15.5.

Declination

The path of the sun on the face of the heavens Fig. 15.5 is a line, called the ecliptic, which lies in a plane that is inclined to the equatorial plane. The angle which a line from the earth's center to the center of the sun makes with the equatorial plane is called the declination of the sun. The sun, as it travels along the ecliptic during the course of the year, crosses the equator (zero declination) about 21 March, and goes gradually further north until it reaches 23–1/2° north declination about 21 June then goes south crossing the equator in September and, on reaching 23–1/2° south declination in December, turns northward again. The points at which it crosses the equator are the "Equinoxes" and the turning points where it reaches maximum declination north and south are termed the "Summer and Winter solstici" respectively.

The moon moves in a similar way with a period of 27 days, 7 hr 43.2 min (27.3217 days) or one "sidereal month". The maximum declination, or the angle between the plane of the moon's orbit and the equatorial plane, varies from 18–1/2° to 28–1/2° with a complete cycle of variation in 18.6 years.

Distance

The earth's orbit around the sun is an ellipse with the sun at one of the foci (Fig. 15.6). Thus, there is a variation in the solar distance as the earth moves from one extension of the major axis to the other.

When the sun is at its maximum distance, it is said to be in "Aphelion", and when it is at the minimum distance, it is said to be in "Perihelion". While the variation in distance is a small fraction of the mean distance, the tide generating forces vary inversely as the third power of the distance and so an appreciable variation in the tides can be expected. At the present perihelion occurs a few days after the winter solstice but there is a secular variation with recurrence in some 25,800 years.

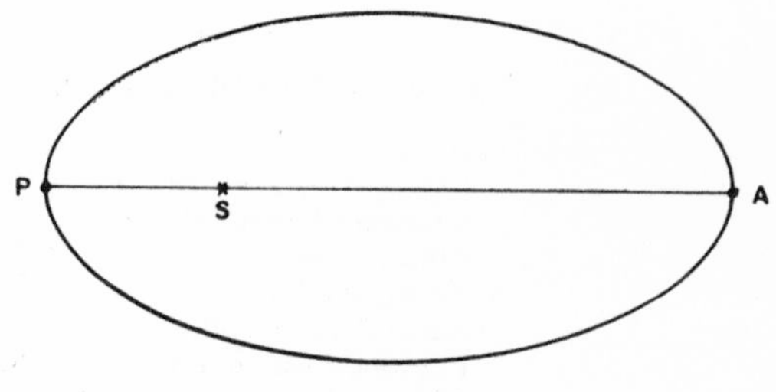

Fig. 15.6.

Similarly, the moon's orbit is an ellipse with the earth at one focus. The moon at its extremes of distance is said to be in "Apogee" or "Perigee". Its tide generating force is 18 per cent greater at Perigee and 15 per cent less at Apogee than it is at mean distance. The variation from perigee to perigee or apogee to apogee takes place in an "Anomalistic month" of 27 days, 13 hr, 12.6 min (27.5546 days).

Relative Position — Moon's Phases

The "Phase" of the moon is described as the relative amount of its surface that appears to an observer on earth to be illuminated by the sun.

When the sun, earth, and moon are in line, with the moon on the same side of the earth as the sun, the moon presents a completely darkened face and is said to be "New". When they are in line, with the moon opposite the sun, it presents a completely illuminated face and is said to be "Full". The tide generating potentials of sun and moon are in phase at Full and New moon and in quadrature at the quarters.

The period from new moon to new moon is called the "Synodic Month". It is longer than the moon's orbital period (Sidereal Month) because, in the course of the month, the earth has moved almost 1/12 of its distance around the sun. The Synodic Month is 29 days, 12 hr, 44 min (29.5306 days).

Inequalities in the Half Synodic Month

As the moon moves in its orbit from Apogee (*A*) to Perigee (*P*), it will pass point *B* (Fig. 15.7) one quarter of an Anomalistic Month after *A*. Similarly, from Perigee (*P*) to Apogee (*A*), it will pass point *C* one quarter of an Anomalistic Month after *P*.

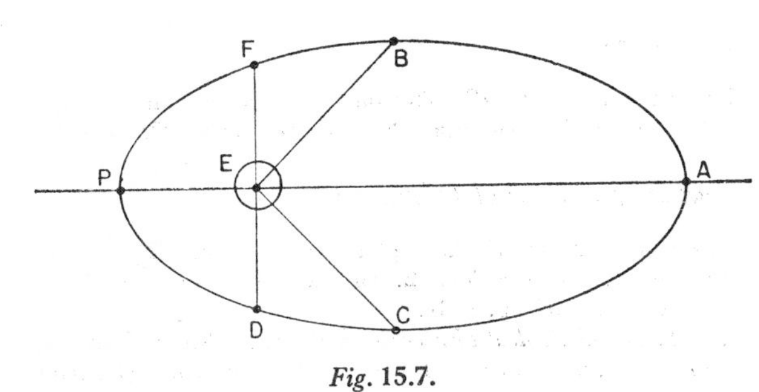

Fig. 15.7.

If the sun lies along the extension of *P.E.A.* the moon will be Full at Perigee and New when it is approximately in Apogee. The time from New to Full moon will be approximately the same as the time from Full to New Moon, each period being close to one-half synodic month (14 days, 18 hr, 22 min).

With the sun along the extension of *F.E.D.* the moon will be Full at *F* and New at *D* and the period from Full to New will be much less than the period from New to Full. In the extreme, the two "halves" of the synodic month may be 13 days, 22 hr, 32 min and 15 days, 14 hr, 12 min.

Revolution of the Axis of the Moon's Orbit

The anomalistic month, or time from Perigee to Perigee (27.5546 days) is slightly longer than the sidereal month, or time for a full revolution of the moon around the earth relative to a fixed star (27.3217 days), because the axis of the moon's orbit rotates around the earth, making a complete cycle in 8.85 years.

Oscillation of the Plane of the Lunar Orbit (Nutation)

As mentioned above, the inclination of the plane of the moon's orbit to the equatorial plane varies from a minimum of 18–1/2° to a maximum of 28–1/2° with a period of about 18.6 years.

Tide Generating Potential

The preceeding description of some of the major modes of motion of the tide producing bodies relative to the earth should give some appreciation of the reasons for the complexity of the tides. One can see qualitatively how the tide generating potential of sun and moon add to give a great variation in their resultant. The maximum value of this potential at a point on the earth's surface will occur when the declination of sun and moon are equal to each other and equal to the latitude of the point, when the sun is in Perihelion, the moon is Perigee and the moon is Full or New. Such an unusual conjuction is extremely rare.

Since the dynamics of tidal motion are greatly influenced by the configuration of the basins, it is not sufficient to formulate the total tide producing potential at the location under study. The response of the local tide to each of the partial tides must be determined and the summation of these responses computed.

15.7 Types of Tides

The tides at a given locality are sometimes classified on the basis of the mode of lunar motion which most influences the range.

The Synodic Type

These are tides in which the major variation in range occurs with the change in phase of the moon. Spring tides occur with Full or New moon. Neap tides occur with the moon in its quarters. Because the two "halves" of the Synodic Month may be quite unequal, the same is true for the periods from spring tide to spring tide.

For tides of this type, a figure known as the "Establishment" (sometimes "Local Establishment" or "Vulgar Establishment") gives a great deal of information concerning the local tide. The "Establishment" is the time interval between the meridional passage of a full or new moon and the occurrence of the following High Water. The "Luni-Tidal Interval" or time interval between the moon's meridional passage and the following High Water varies through the synodic month. The establishment is a particular value of the Luni-Tidal Interval.

The Anomalistic Type

The leading variation in range in this type occurs with variations in the moon's distance.

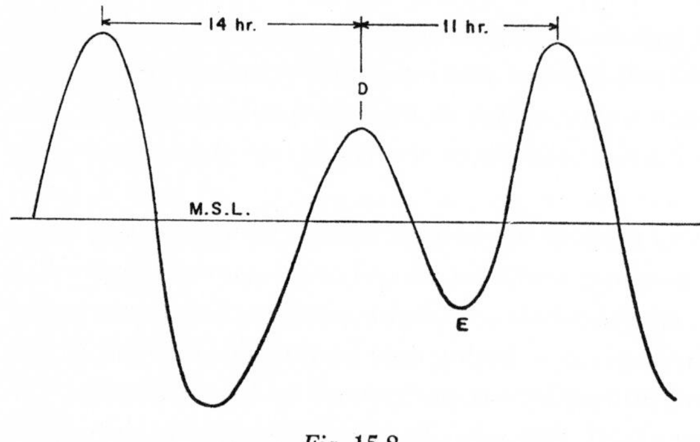

Fig. 15.8.

The greatest range occurs at Perigee and the least at Apogee. The cycle recurs in an Anomalistic Month or 53–1/4 tidal intervals.

The Declinational Type

In this type, the variations due to the moon's declination predominate over other modes of lunar motion. With the moon on the equator, the two tides of the day are equal in range and interval. These are called "Equatorial Tides". With the moon in maximum declination, the two tides of the day show a maximum in "Diurnal Inequality" where a "Large Tide" and a "Half Tide" alternate. These are called "Tropical Tides". The time interval between successive high waters may also become quite unequal (Fig. 15.8).

At some localities the inequality becomes so great that there is no fall from *D* to *E* and this part of the cycle represents a long "Stand" of the tide. At some localities, the diurnal inequality may influence only the high waters and the elevations at low waters remain essentially equal.

In regions where tides are of the Declinational type, the declination of the sun also has a marked influence. The solar inequality is similar to the lunar inequality, being zero at the equinoxes and maximum at the solstices.

Mixed Types

At most locations it is not possible to characterize the tide as being purely Synodic, Anomalistic, or Declinational, but some combination of these influences must be considered. These are called "Mixed Tides" or "Combined Tides".

References

Doodson, A. T. (1922) The harmonic development of the tide-generating potential. *Proc. Roy. Soc.* **A100**, 305–000.

Sources of Additional Information

The Tide. Marmer, H. A. Appleton, New York, 282 pp. 1926.
Physical Oceanography, Vol. 2. Defant, A. Pergamon Press New York, 598 pp. 1961.
The Tides and Kindred Phenomena in the Solar System. Darwin, G. H., San Francisco, Freeman, 378 pp. 1962 (Reprint of 1898 book).
The Tides and Tidal Streams. Bell Dawson, W. Ottawa, Dept. of Naval Services, 43 pp. 1920.
Tide, In *Encyclopedia of Science and Technology,* pp. 632–640, Groves, G. W. McGraw-Hill, New York. 1960.

PART III

SELECTED TOPICS

THERE is a broad range of topics that might reasonably be considered under the heading of physical oceanography. In the first two parts of this book we have covered material that is necessary background for almost any specialized study in the field. We now choose to present an introduction to five topics which, it is felt, are of rather wide interest to oceanographers.

Sound propagation is important because of the increasing use of acoustic methods in studying the bottom structure, currents, and distribution of marine life. There are challenging opportunities in the application of under water sound to military problems, but it will be clear that the treatment given here barely introduces the reader to the complexities of the applied problem.

Light in the sea is of importance in the study of marine life and, at several laboratories, advances are being made in the use of optical measurements for identifying water masses and studies of sedimentation processes. The consideration of light penetration leads naturally to the heat budget of the ocean which plays a major role in establishing the climate of our planet. The interaction of sea and atmosphere is understood only in a gross general way, and it seems certain that a major effort will soon be directed towards the interface problem.

The thermohaline circulation might well have been included in Part II since it is an important mode of oceanic movement. It is a mode, however, for which both reliable field data and satisfactory analytical treatments are lacking.

Estuaries provide fertile ground for both field and theoretical study, and even the oceanographer who specializes in the deep ocean will encounter these features as he sets out and returns from his investigations.

PART III

SELECTED TOPICS

[illegible]

[illegible]

[illegible]

[illegible]

[illegible]

CHAPTER 16

SOUND PROPAGATION

THE only efficient method currently available for the transmission of intelligence through bodies of water of oceanic dimensions involves the propagation of compressional waves in the medium. Although the frequencies in use vary from below to far above the audible range (subsonic to supersonic), and sophisticated instrumentation may obviate any aural presentation, the terms "sonic" or "acoustic" are generally applied to the techniques and devices used.

Uses include submarine signalling, depth measurements, echo ranging and detection, location and tracking of instrument packages, and telemetering of information from free floating or bottom mounted transducers.

16.1 PROPAGATION SPEED FOR ACOUSTIC WAVES

Compressional waves are propagated in a fluid with a speed or celerity (C) which is given by

$$C = \sqrt{(\text{elasticity}/\text{density})}. \qquad (16.1)$$

By elasticity, we mean the adiabatic bulk modulus

$$E = -\,\alpha(\partial p/\partial \alpha)_s,$$

α being the specific volume, p the pressure, and the subscript s indicating the value of the thermodynamic partial derivative under adiabatic conditions.

The celerity may be written:

$$C = \sqrt{(1/K_s \rho)},$$

with K_s representing the adiabatic compressibility $-(1/\alpha)\,(\partial \alpha/\partial p)_s$. The isothermal compressibility K is more often known. $K = (1/\alpha)\,(\partial \alpha/\partial p)_T$, and $K = \gamma K_s$ where γ is the ratio of specific heats at constant pressure and constant volume ($\gamma = c_p/c_v$). We may thus write

$$C = \sqrt{(\gamma/K\rho)}. \qquad (16.2)$$

On the basis of laboratory measurements, equations for computing the speed of sound for the range of temperature, pressure, and salinity in the ocean have been produced by Matthews (1927, 1939), Kuwahara (1939), Del Grosso (1952), and Wilson (1960).

Wilson's results are generally considered the most accurate at this time. For sea water of 35‰ salinity at 30°C and atmospheric pressure, he gives a sound speed of 1546.16 m/sec, or 5072.6 ft/sec.

As typical sound speeds for the ocean, one frequently quotes 1500 m/sec or 5000 ft/sec, bearing in mind that the actual value is a function of temperature, salinity and depth (pressure).

Wilson's empirically derived equation, valid for salinities in the range from 33‰ to 37‰ is

$$C = 1449.2 + C_t + C_p + C_S + C_{S,t,p}, \qquad (16.3)$$

where

$$C_t = 4.6233T - 5.4585 \times 10^{-2}T^2 + 2.822 \times 10^{-4}T^3 - 5.07 \times 10^{-7}T^4,$$

$$C_p = 1.60518 \times 10^{-1}p + 1.0279 \times 10^{-5}p^2 + 3.451 \times 10^{-9}p^3 - 3.503 \times 10^{-12}p^4,$$

$$C_S = 1.391\,(S - 35) - 7.8 \times 10^{-2}(S - 35)^2,$$

and

$$C_{S,t,p} = (S - 35)\,(-1.197 \times 10^{-2}T + 2.61 \times 10^{-4}p - 1.96 \times 10^{-7}p^2 - 2.09 \times 10^{-6}pT) + p(-2.796 \times 10^{-4}T + 1.3302 \times 10^{-5}T^2 - 6.644 \times 10^{-8}T^3) + p^2\,(-2.391 \times 10^{-7}T + 9.286 \times 10^{-10}T^2) - 1.745 \times 10^{-10}p^3T.$$

C is in m/sec, T in °C, S in ‰, and p in kg/cm^2.

Physically, and with reference to (16.2), an increase in temperature results in a decrease in density with a resultant increase in C. The increase is approximately 3 m/sec/°C (5.5 ft/sec/°F) in average surface layer conditions.

Although an increase in salinity increases the density, the decrease in compressibility produces a

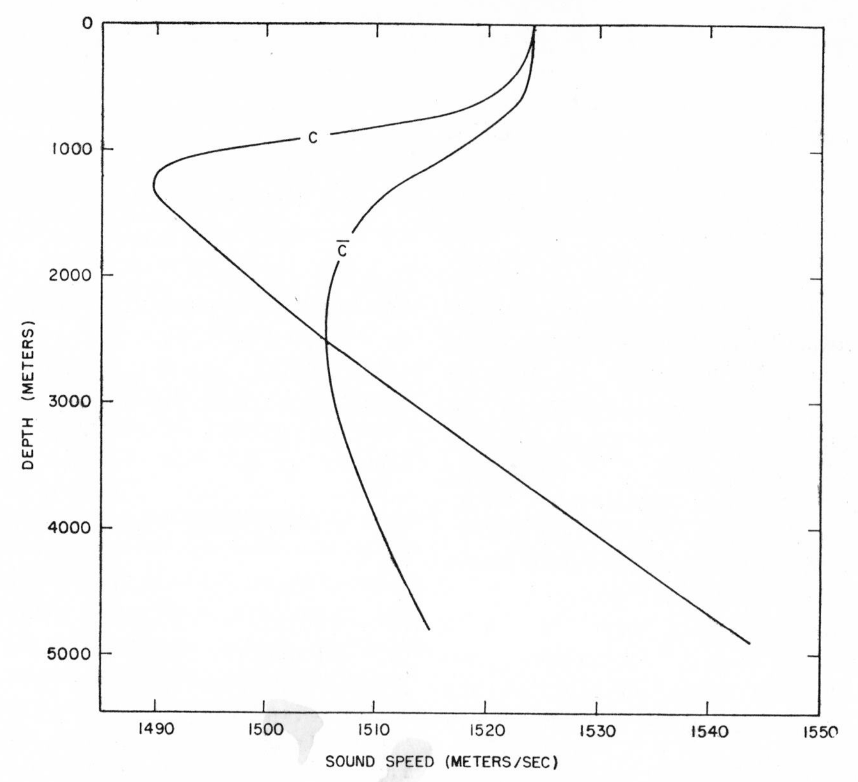

Fig. 16.1 Typical depth variation of sound speed (C) and mean sounding speed $\bar{C}$ in the North Atlantic.

greater effect so that C increases. This increase is approximately 1.3 m/sec/‰ (4.3 ft/sec/‰).

Similarly, with an increase in depth (pressure), the increase in density is less important than the decrease in compressibility and C increases. In the surface layers the increase is approximately 1.8 m/sec per 100 m (1.8 ft/sec/100 ft).

At a typical location in the open ocean, the dominant influence on sound speed in the upper layers is the decrease in temperature with depth. Sound speed decreases to a depth of some 700 to 1500 m. Below this the influence of increasing pressure dominates so that sound speed increases with depth. Figure 16.1 shows schematically the sort of vertical variation with depth that is typical of most regions. The layer of minimum speed is an almost world-wide feature important in long range signalling (to be discussed in Section 16.7). Also shown in Fig. 16.1 is the sort of variation to be expected in the mean speed from surface down to a given depth. This is the important parameter in echo sounding (Section 16.3).

16.2 Attenuation of Sound

There are a number of ways in which the energy level in a sound field may be expressed.

First there is the "sound pressure" or the anomaly in pressure introduced into the medium due to the existence of the sound field. Since the pressure fluctuations will be time variable and of alternating sign, it is most meaningful to consider the "root mean square sound pressure" (p) where it is understood that the averaging process is extended over an appropriate period of time for the frequencies involved.

The "energy density" (W) at a point is the energy in a unit volume of the medium centered on the point, that is associated with the sound field. This is given by

$$W = \frac{p^2}{\rho C^2},$$

where p is the r.m.s. sound pressure, ρ the undisturbed density and C the speed of sound in the medium. With p in dynes/cm^2, ρ in g/cm^3, and C in cm/sec, W will be in ergs/cm^3.

Another parameter in common use is "energy flux" (F) which, at a point, has the value of the energy passing in unit time through a unit area containing the point and normal to the direction of propagation. In the case of the simplest unidirectional sound field, $F = CW = p^2/\rho C$ ergs/sec/cm^2.

Perhaps the most often used parameter is the "intensity" (I) defined by

$$I = p^2 \text{ dynes}^2/\text{cm}^4.$$

Along the path of progression of a sound disturbance energy is absorbed by the medium through viscous effects, and converted from orderly progression to omni-directional disturbances through scattering by suspended matter within the medium.

With viscous absorption the rate of decrease in sound (or intensity) along the direction (x) of propagation of a plane wave is proportional to the sound pressure (or intensity).

$$dp/dx = -\nu p.$$

The sound pressure p_x at a distance x from where the value was p_0 is given by

$$p_x = p_0 e^{-\nu x}.$$

Similarly, for intensity,

$$I_x = I_0 e^{-2\nu x}. \quad (16.4)$$

Here ν is the absorption coefficient which can be expressed (Raleigh, 1945 Pt. II, p. 316) as

$$\nu = \frac{8}{3}\frac{\pi^2\mu}{\lambda^2\rho C} = \frac{8}{3}\frac{\pi^2\mu f^2}{\rho C^3}, \quad (16.5)$$

μ being the coefficient of viscosity, λ the wavelength and f the frequency ($C = f\lambda$).

The fact that absorption is proportional to the frequency squared becomes important in the choice of operating frequencies for underwater sound applications.

The characteristic absorption distance, x_e, over which the intensity falls to $1/e$ of its value is a convenient parameter for quantitatively describing the rate of attenuation or absorption.

$$x_e = \frac{3\rho C^3}{16\,\pi^2\mu f^2}. \quad (16.6)$$

Taking $\mu = 15 \times 10^{-3}$ c.g.s. units, $\rho = 1.025$ g/cm^3 and $C = 1.5 \times 10^5$ cm/sec, Table 16.1 evaluates this parameter for various frequencies. The wavelength, λ, is also tabulated for the assumed sound speed.

Actually for frequencies in the kilocycle range, the measured attenuation coefficient for sound in sea water turns out to be some 100 times as great as the simple theory would predict from viscous absorption. For some time this discrepancy was attributed to an ill defined phenomena referred to as "anomalous dispersion". Suspected causes included scattering by bubbles, although this has subsequently proved to be theoretically impossible. Lieberman (1948) showed that the effect was not observable in pure water and that the coefficients for sea water and pure water become identical at frequencies somewhat higher than a megacycle. He postulated that the excess energy absorption was due to some physical–chemical reaction being driven by the pressure fluctuations. The relaxation time for the reaction in question was calculated to be about 1.1×10^{-6} sec. Liebermann (1949) reported experiments by R. W. Leonard which indicate clearly that it is the magnesium sulfate in sea water which gives rise to this effect.

TABLE 16.1

f (sec^{-1})	λ	x_e(km)
50 cycles	30 m	1.75×10^7
500 cycles	3 m	1.75×10^5
5 kc	30 cm	1750
10 kc	15 cm	437
15 kc	10 cm	194
25 kc	6 cm	70
50 kc	3 cm	17.5

Theoretical wavelength (λ), and characteristic absorption distance (x_e) for various frequencies of sound in sea water assuming $C = 1.5 \times 10^5$ cm/sec, $\rho = 1.025$ g/cm^3, $\mu = 15 \times 10^{-3}$ c.g.s. units.

To the attenuation arising from viscous and chemical effects must be added the geometrical effects upon the sound beam projected from the device in use. For a transducer that may be approximated as a point source, radiating into a finite solid angle, the geometric drop off in intensity or spreading loss will be proportionate to the square of the distance.

Energy may also be lost from a sound beam through reflection from suspended particles. This is referred to as scattering. Losses due to scattering by suspended materials are extremely variable both spatially and temporally and introduce uncertainties into the performance of sonic devices.

16.3 ECHO-SOUNDING

In echo-sounding an acoustic transducer is located near the surface of the water, frequently mounted in the hull of the ship. This transducer is caused to emit a short burst of sound or a "ping" which is directed in a cone with a vertical axis.

Some of the sound is reflected from the bottom of the ocean and the return echo is received, usually by the same transducer, at the ship. The time interval from the initiation of the ping to the reception of the echo is a measure of the distance (depth) that the signal has traveled to and from the bottom.

The precision of the measurement is dependent only upon the precision of the time measuring device used, which is usually integral with a strip chart recorder. It is essential to remember that it is time that is measured, and the accuracy of the depth termination is dependent upon multiplication by the proper value of the mean sounding speed (Fig. 16.1), that is, the average speed for the whole vertical column.

It is usual for the recording device to produce a record graduated in units of length and this requires the adoption of some standard sounding speed. In virtually all U.S. made equipment the assumed speed is 4800 ft/sec, or 400 fathoms/sec both ways. It is important to know whether soundings presented on charts, or in reports, have been corrected for actual sounding speed. One can appreciate that, with a uniform assumed speed, uncorrected sounding depth may be the most readily usable parameter.

16.4 Sub-bottom Recordings

Given sufficient power in the outgoing signal and adequate sensitivity in the receiver, echo returns may often be received from below the physical bottom of the ocean area. Wherever a marked increase in propagation speed takes place in a vertical distance of the order of one quarter wavelength or less, a fraction of the acoustic energy is reflected. Thus, it is possible to examine the configuration of structures below the surface sediments of the ocean floor. The propagation speed within the various layers of sediments is seldom known precisely and so it is the custom to speak of distances to sub-surface features in terms of equivalent water depths. Figure 16.2 shows a record with sub-bottom horizons. The efficiency of an echo-sounding system for recording a sub-bottom topography is dependent upon the frequency employed as discussed in the following section.

16.5 The Choice of Frequencies

In the design of acoustic signalling devices one is usually faced with the necessity for a compromise in the choice of operating frequency. Table 16.1 would indicate that, purely on the basis of efficiency of transmission, the lower the frequency the better. However, it is often desirable to concentrate the acoustic energy transmitted within a narrow beam and to have comparable directivity in the receiving transducer. This is accomplished by having the transducer large with respect to a wavelength so that the various parts act as individual sources and there is constructive interference in the desired direction. The beam width turns out to be proportional to the ratio λ/d, where λ is the wavelength and d the characteristic dimension of the transducer. See, for example, Horton (1957, Chapter 4). Since there must be a realistic limitation on the permissible size of the transducer, the directivity criterion favors the higher frequencies. Shallow water echo sounders are usually designed to operate at frequencies above 20 kc/s, thus providing high resolution with relatively small transducers. Units which sound to maximum ocean depths are, because of energy considerations, usually designed to operate in the 10 to 15 kc/s range.

In sub-bottom devices optimum resolution of the small scale features which are of interest in coastal waters is achieved at some 8 to 10 kc/s. Deep penetration requires frequencies of 1 kc/s or below, with a sacrifice of definition because of the longer wavelength. Some of the more sophisticated systems utilize high energy, nondirectional, multi-frequency sound sources, such as explosives or spark discharge. Wide band receivers and equipment capable of displaying reflected energy in a number of frequency bands are used.

16.6 Refraction

If a wave front progresses from a medium where the propagation speed is C_1 to one where the speed is C_2, and the initial direction of progress makes an angle θ_1 (not 90°) with the interface, the direction of travel is altered towards the region of lower propagation speed. This refraction can quantitatively be expressed by Snell's law

$$\frac{C_1}{\cos\,\theta_1} = \frac{C_2}{\cos\,\theta_2} = \frac{C_3}{\cos\,\theta_3}, \text{ etc.}$$

This is illustrated in Fig. 16.3 for single rays where C is a step function in depth.

Stratification is almost universal in the upper layers of the ocean with the result that refraction

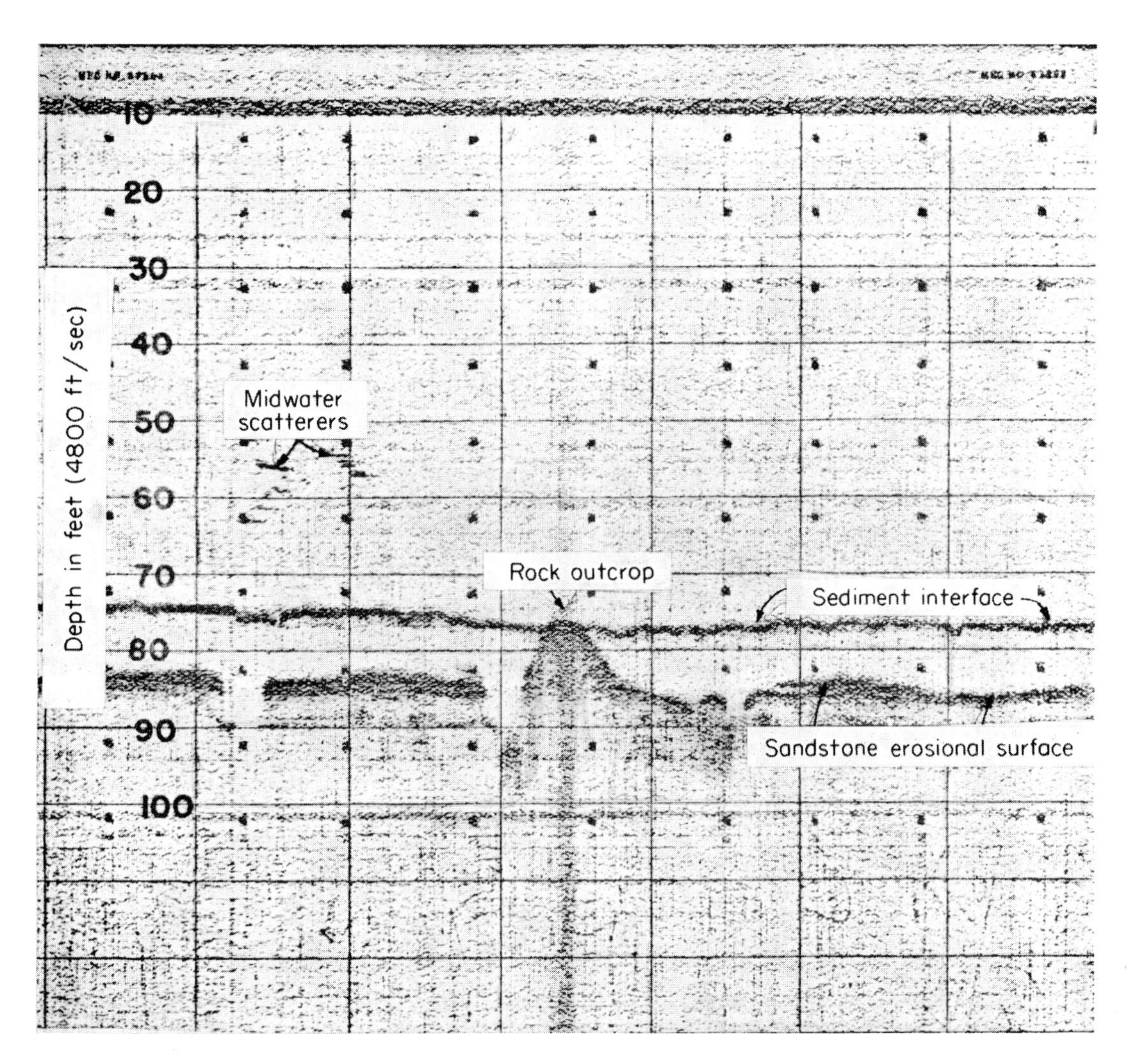

Fig. 16.2 Section of marine sonoprobe record from the Arabian Gulf (courtesy of Rayflex Corporation).

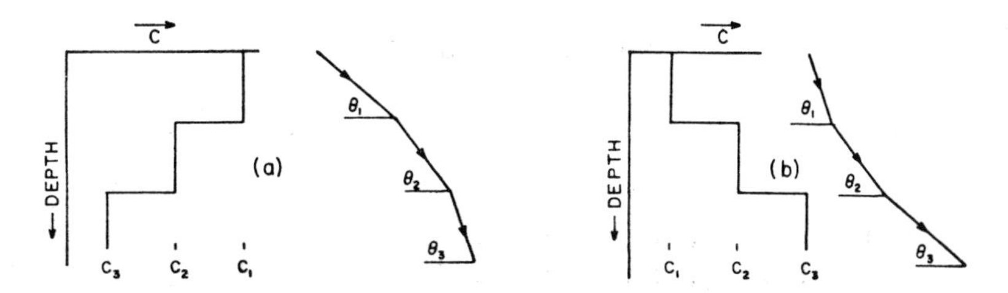

Fig. 16.3 Refraction of ray travelling into regions of progressively lower (a) and higher (b) propagation speed.

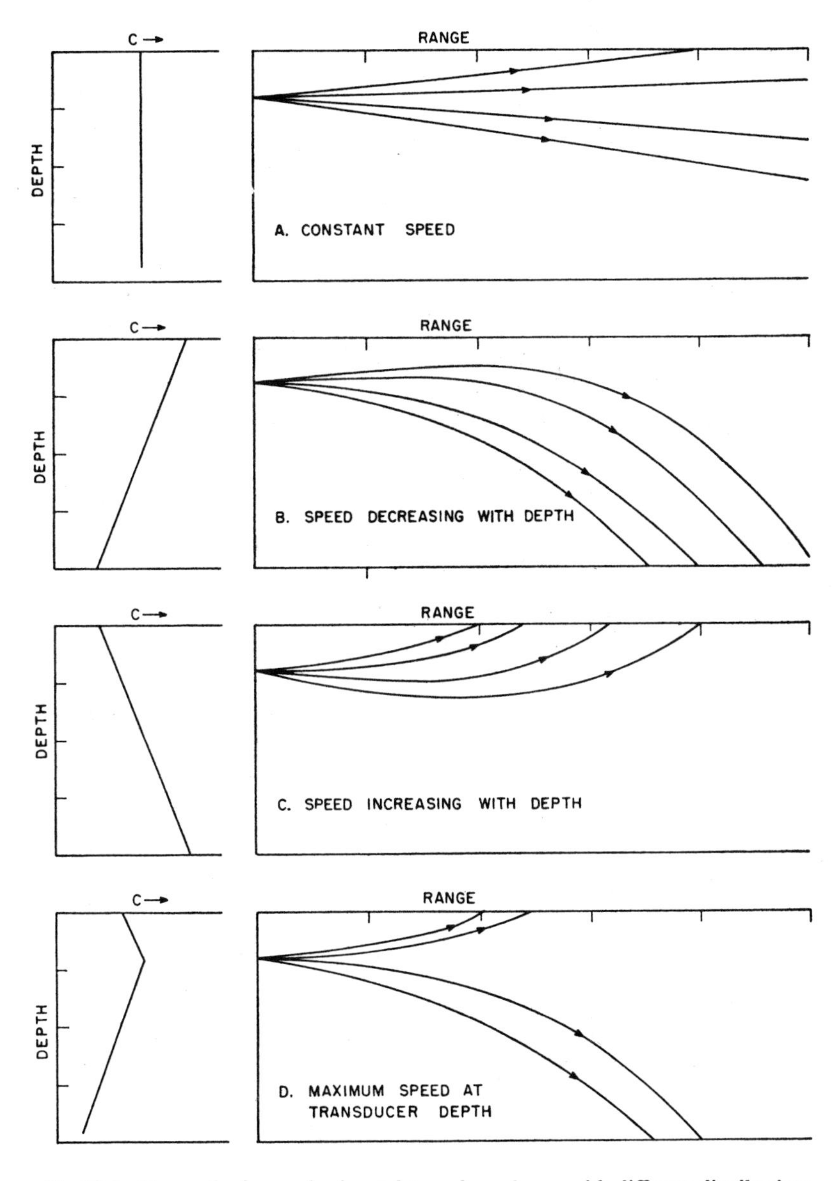

Fig. 16.4 Ray paths from a horizontal transducer beam with different distributions of sound speed.

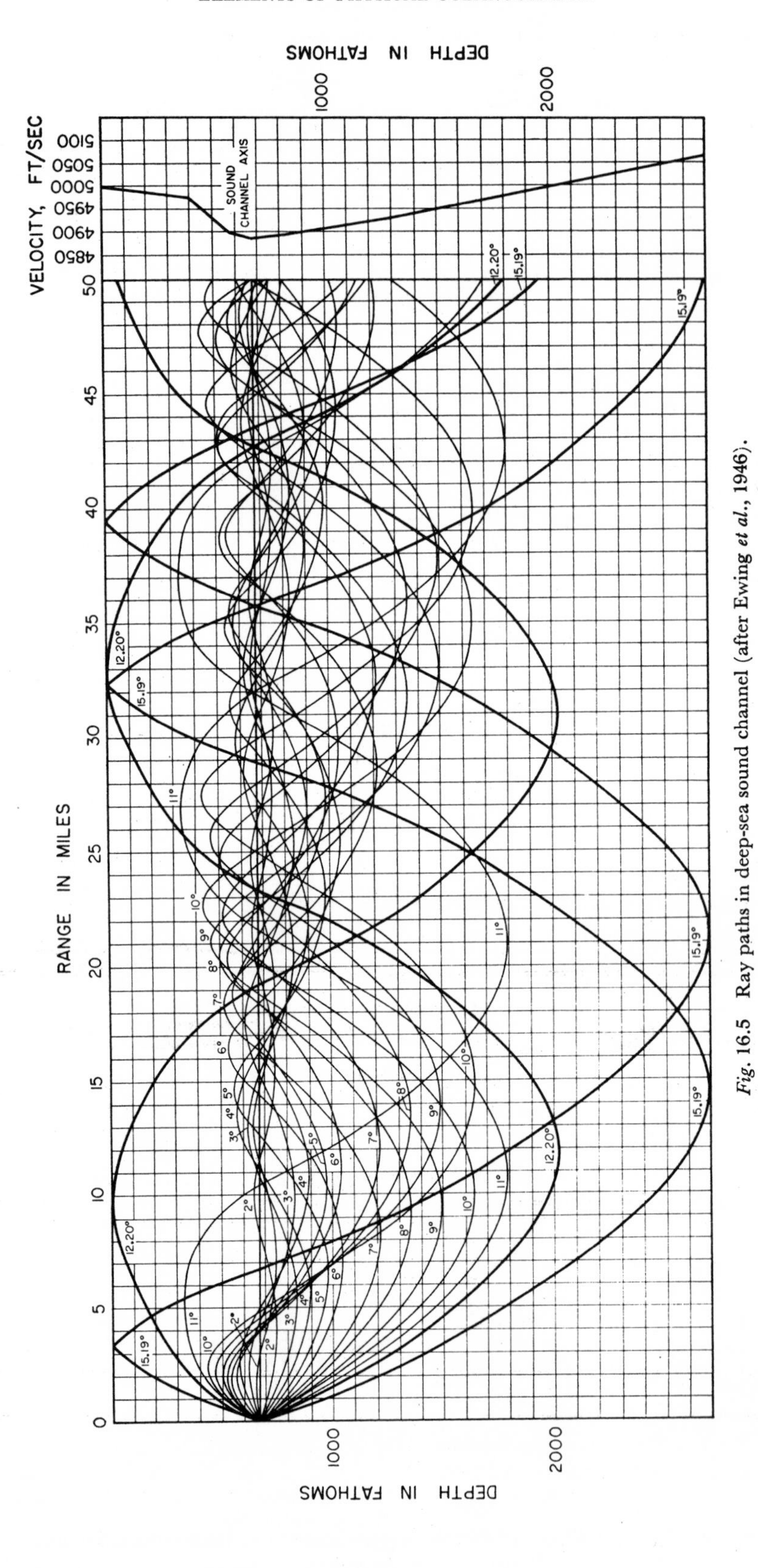

Fig. 16.5 Ray paths in deep-sea sound channel (after Ewing *et al.*, 1946).

becomes extremely important in such applications as horizontal acoustic ranging (sonar). In sonar devices a transducer located at some shallow depth projects a narrow beam of sound in a horizontal, or nearly horizontal, direction. Ideally this insonifies an area as shown in Fig. 16.4(a), where the paths of individual rays under conditions of constant C are drawn. Should C decrease uniformly with depth, the beam will be refracted downwards as in Fig. 16.4(b). If the speed increases with depth the beam is refracted upward (Fig. 16.4(c)) or, with a composite gradient it may be split as in Figure 16.4(d). The variants in the real ocean are unlimited and it becomes necessary to know the sound speed structure in the water in order to assess the limitations of the equipment. Frequently improved performances may be obtained by tilting the beam or by altering the depth of the transducer. Consequently much of the military effort in oceanography has been directed towards predicting conditions in the surface layer so that the tactical limitations of sonic devices may be predicted.

16.7 Sofar

The existence of a minimum sound speed at depth in most ocean areas (Fig. 16.1) provides opportunity for particularly efficient acoustic signalling at this depth. The energy from a sound source at these depths tends to be refracted towards the layer of minimum speed. Energy propagated within a large solid angle undergoes total refraction and is trapped within this "permanent sound channel". The spreading loss for energy within this two-dimensional channel is proportionate to the distance traveled rather than the square of the distance as in propagation in three dimensions, hence much greater signalling distances are practical. Signals from relatively small explosive sources have been detected up to several thousands of miles from the source (Ewing *et al.*, 1946). Furthermore the ray geometry is such that a well defined "last arrival time" can be measured, and, with the minimum sound speed known quite precisely, triangulation on sources within this "sofar" channel is practical. Ewing *et al.* (1959) have suggested that the precision available is suitable for establishing bench marks in ocean areas to extend the geodetic network heretofore confined to the land areas. Figure 16.5 shows an example of sound ray paths in the sofar channel, after Ewing *et al.* (1946).

16.8 Biological Effects

The animal populations of the ocean create problems in the use of acoustic devices by introducing noise into the environment and by presenting false targets for echo ranging devices.

A very large number of aquatic organisms have been found to produce noises which can be detected by passive listening devices. In some cases seasonal maxima in the noise production of certain species may raise the noise level to the point that acoustic ranging systems become inoperative. At the same time, the opportunity is presented to study the distribution and behavior of the organisms by acoustic means.

Whales and large shoals of fish present well defined targets to acoustic equipments. More mysterious are the so called "scattering layers" that have been detected over many parts of the ocean. These show up on the records of sensitive echo sounders as echoes weaker and less well defined than bottom echoes. Most of these can be observed to make dramatic vertical migrations towards the surface at sundown and downward again at sunrise. Since this is precisely the behavior of many forms of zooplankton, the scattering layers are clearly associated with plankton. Observations have confirmed this relationship. The echoes result from the backward scattering of a fraction of the energy in the outgoing pulse. Disturbingly, it can be shown on theoretical grounds that the plankton organisms themselves cannot account for the back scattering observed. It has been postulated that concentrations of larger animals feeding on the plankton must give rise to the observed echoes. Although much work has been concentrated on this problem, there has been no clear identification of the responsible organisms to date.

References

Del Grosso, V. A. (1952) *The velocity of sound in sea water at zero depth.* Rept. 4002, Naval Research Laboratory, Washington, D.C.

Ewing, M., G. P. Woollard, A. C. Vine and J. L. Worzel. (1946) Recent results in submarine geophysics. *Bull. Geol. Soc. Am.* **57**, 909–934.

Ewing, M., J. L. Worzel and M. Talwani. (1959) Some aspects of physical geodesy. Am. Geophys. Union Monograph 4 *Contemporary Geodesy*, pp. 7–21.

Horton, J. W. *Fundamentals of Sonar*. United States Naval Institute, Annapolis, Md. (1957).

Kuwahara, Susumu. (1939) Velocity of sound in sea water and calculation of the velocity for use in sonic sounding. *Hydrogr. Rev.* **16** (2), 123–40. Monaco.

Liebermann, L. N. (1948) The origin of sound absorption in water and in sea water. *J. Acoust. Soc. Am.* **20**, 838–873.

LIEBERMANN, L. N. (1949) Sound propagation in chemically active media. *Phys. Rev.* **76**, 1520–1524.

MATTHEWS, D. J. (1927) *Tables of the velocity of sound in pure water and sea water for use in echo-sounding and sound-ranging.* 29 pp. British Admiralty, Hydrogr. Dept., H. D. No. 282, 1927 and 1939.

RAYLEIGH, LORD. *The Theory of Sound.* Dover, New York. 1945. Reprinted from earlier editions 1877, 1894, etc.

WILSON, W. D. (1960) Speed of sound in sea water as a function of temperature, pressure and salinity. *J. Acoust. Soc. Am.* **32**, 641.

Sources of Additional Information

Fundamentals of Sonar. HORTON, J. W. U.S. Naval Institute. Annapolis, Md. 1957.

Principles and Applications of Underwater Sound. U.S. Dept. of Com. Office of Tech. Services, P.B. 161682. 1946.

Introduction to the theory of sound transmission with application to the ocean. OFFICER, C. B., McGraw-Hill. New York.

EWING, MAURICE and J. L. WORZEL. (1948) Long range sound transmission, propagation of sound in the ocean. *Geol. Soc. Am. Mem.* **27**, 1–35.

Underwater Sound Transmission. MARSH, H. W. and M. SCHULKIN. Con. Avco Corp., New London. 1962.

The Sea, Vol. 1. HILL, M. N. (editor). Interscience, New York. 1962.

Chapter 12, Sound in the Sea. VIGOREAUX, P. and J. B. HERSEY.

Chapter 13, Sound scattering by marine organisms. HERSEY, J. B. and R. H. BACKUS.

Chapter 14, Sound production by marine animals SCHEVILL, W. E., R. H. BACKUS and J. B. HERSEY.

CHAPTER 17

LIGHT IN THE SEA

THE penetration of sunlight to moderate depths in the ocean makes possible the plant growth that is the basis for an enormously rich and diverse biological population. The plant pigments responsible for photosynthesis are adapted to absorb most efficiently light energy in those wavelengths which are most efficiently transmitted through the water. Many marine organisms have evolved light producing organs of high efficiency whose output is mainly in the band of most favored frequencies.

The absorption of solar energy through the surface layers of the ocean provides storage for vast quantities of heat. In a variety of forms this heat is subsequently released to the atmosphere.

Light is attenuated much more rapidly than sound in the ocean so that acoustic devices have been used in applications where it is desired to "see" through the water. With the development of laser techniques it is probable that optical scanning devices will be reconsidered. The high energy output and comparative ease of focusing a beam may offset the high attenuation. A laser operating in the frequency band of minimum absorption has not been reported to date but this surely is only a matter of time.

17.1 ATTENUATION

The flux of radiant energy per unit time through a unit area normal to the direction of propagation in a light beam is referred to as the "intensity". The units might be ergs/cm²/sec, cal/cm²/sec, watts/cm², etc. The energy flux is associated with some finite range of wavelengths or frequencies. Energy flux is distributed through the range of wavelengths in a spectrum.

We write I_λ as the spectral density of energy flux, per unit increment in wavelength, centered at wavelength λ. The beam intensity in a band of wavelengths from λ_1 to λ_2 is written

$$I_{(\lambda_1-\lambda_2)} = \int_{\lambda_1}^{\lambda_2} I_\lambda \, d\lambda. \qquad (17.1)$$

Similarly the total intensity is

$$I = \int_0^\infty I_\lambda \, d\lambda. \qquad (17.2)$$

Parallel light will suffer a decrease in intensity on passing through sea water because of:

(a) Absorption of energy by the sea water.
(b) Absorption of energy by suspended material including organisms in the water.
(c) Scattering by the sea water.
(d) Scattering by suspended particles.

The magnitude of each effect will be a function o the wavelength. The general law governing the decrease in intensity due either to absorption or to scattering by uniformly distributed particles is

$$dI_\lambda = - k_\lambda I_\lambda \, dz, \qquad (17.3)$$

where z is distance measured in the direction of propagation and k_λ is the "extinction coefficient" appropriate to the wavelength λ.

It is a consequence of (17.3) that, if k_λ is not a function of z,

$$I_{\lambda_z} = I_{\lambda_0} \, e^{-k_\lambda z}, \qquad (17.4)$$

where I_{λ_z} is the spectral density a distance z along the propagation path from where the value is I_{λ_0}. $k_\lambda z$ must be non-dimensional, i.e. k_λ has dimensions such as m⁻¹, cm⁻¹, etc.

The value of I_λ decreases by $1/e$ in traveling a distance z_e equal to $1/k_\lambda$. Thus z_e is sometimes called the characteristic "extinction distance".

To examine the consequences of scattering we may write

$$k_\lambda \equiv k_\lambda' + k_\lambda''$$

where k_λ' represents the effect of absorption and is appropriately called the absorption coefficient, and k_λ'' represents the effect due to scattering.

Provided that the scattering particles have dimensions small compared to the wavelength the scattering will be of the Rayleigh type where

$$k_\lambda'' \propto c/\lambda^4,$$

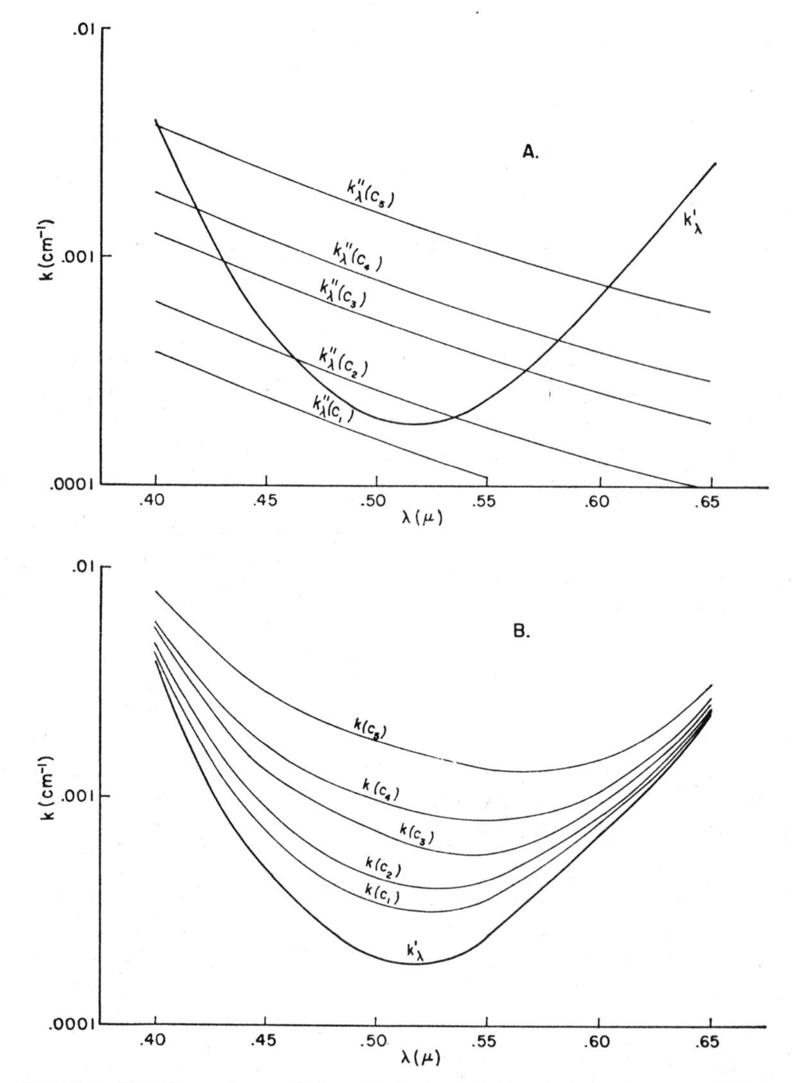

Fig. 17.1 (A) Absorption coefficient k_λ' for hypothetical substance and coefficients of scattering attenuation k_λ'' for various concentrations (c_1–c_5) of scatters. (B) Attenuation coefficients ($k_\lambda' + k_\lambda''$) for various concentrations (c_1–c_5) of scatters.

c being the volume concentration of the scattering particles.

Figure 17.1(a) shows k_λ' vs. λ for an hypothetical pure substance exhibiting a minimum k_λ' at a wavelength about 0.52 microns (μ). Also shown are curves of k_λ'' for various concentrations (c_1, c_2, etc.) of scatterers where $c_{i+1} > c_i$. The resulting extinction coefficients k_λ are shown in Fig. 17.1(b). It can be seen that the attenuation at all wavelengths increases with increasing concentration of scatterers and, at the same time, the wavelength of minimum attenuation is shifted towards longer wavelengths.

In Fig. 17.2 is shown the variation of extinction coefficient and extinction distance with wavelength

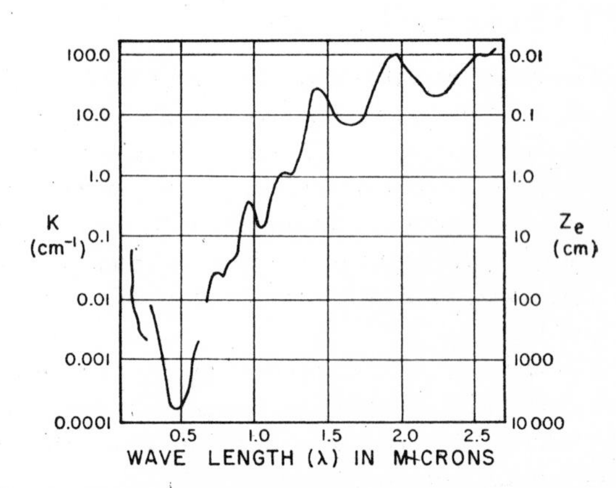

Fig. 17.2 Extinction coefficient for pure water (from various sources, after Defant, 1961).

in pure water. The minimum value of k_λ is observed for wavelengths 0.46 to 0.48 microns, in the middle of the visible range. Attenuation increases rapidly towards short wavelengths (ultraviolet) and towards longer (red and infrared) wavelengths. At $\lambda = 0.46\ \mu$, $k_\lambda = 0.00015\ \text{cm}^{-1}$, and the characteristic extinction distance (z_e) is 67 m. At $\lambda = 1.5\ \mu$ $k_\lambda = 19.4\ \text{cm}^{-1}$, and the characteristic extinction distance is 0.5 mm.

Although the attenuation coefficient, or the attenuation distance, are the generally preferred parameters for expressing the effects of absorption and scattering some writers use a "transmission coefficient per unit distance" (T) defined such that

$$T = I_{\lambda_{z+1}}/I_{\lambda_z},$$

where z is the distance in the specified units. Also used is "per cent transmission per unit distance" (T per cent) where

$$T\% \equiv 100\ T.$$

17.2 The Quality of Light in the Sea

The radiation reaching the surface of a natural body of water from the sun and sky contains energy distributed over a wide range of wavelengths. Ninety-nine per cent of the energy is in the range of wavelengths from 0.15 μ to 4.0 μ and over 50 per cent in the visible range, with peak spectral density at 0.47 μ.

By selective absorption the spectrum is altered as the radiation penetrates deeper into the water, eventually leaving significant amounts of energy only in the wavelengths near the middle of the visible range, i.e. in the blue–green region of the spectrum. This is shown schematically for pure water in Fig. 17.3. In the ocean a wide range is

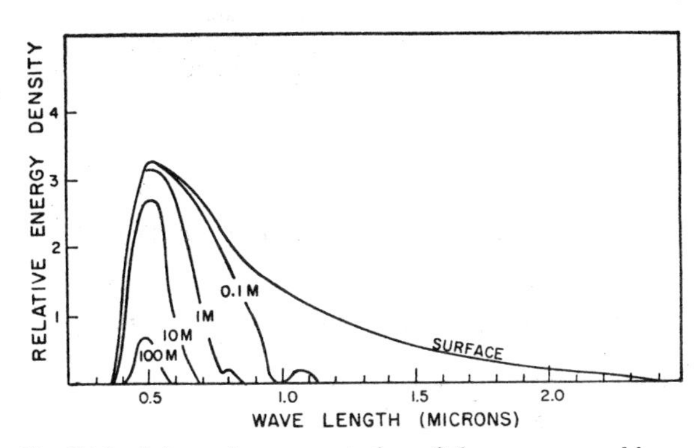

Fig. 17.3 Schematic representation of the energy reaching the surface and various depths in pure water (after Sverdrup *et al.*, 1942).

found in the additional factors that contribute to the attenuation of the radiation, and, while it is difficult to specify the conditions expected at any location, some generalization is possible. Transmission is generally quite efficient in the open ocean, especially in regions of low organic productivity. Coastal waters, on the other hand, are generally more opaque, an effect attributed to higher organic content and the presence of suspended material which gives rise to scattering. In Fig. 17.4 is shown the type of variation in the

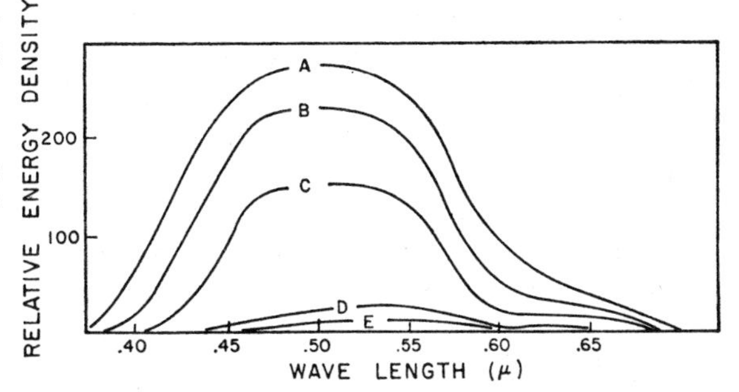

Fig. 17.4 Schematic energy spectra at a depth of 10 m in: (A) Pure Water, (B) Clear Oceanic Water, (C) Average Oceanic Water, (D) Average Coastal Water, and (E) Turbid Coastal Water (after Sverdrup *et al.*, 1942).

spectrum after traversing 10 m of water in various categories. In the regions of lower transmission, the spectral peak tends to be shifted from the blue–green to the yellow–green part of the spectrum. This is shown in more dramatic form in Fig. 17.5.

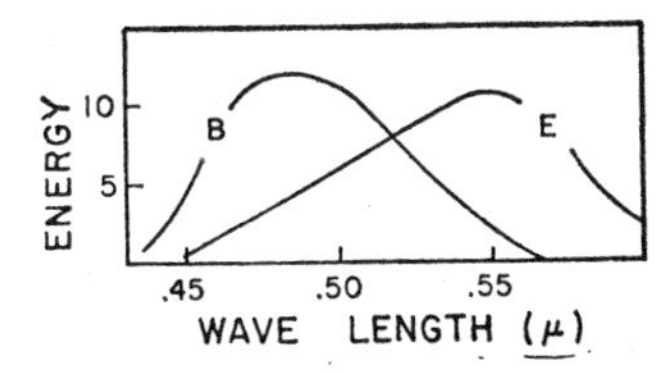

Fig. 17.5 Energy spectra at 100 m in Clear Oceanic Water (B) and at 10 m in Turbid Coastal Water (E) (after Sverdrup *et al.*, 1942).

It may be noted (17.2) that the areas under the individual curves for energy spectra (Figs. 17.3, 17.4 and 17.5) show, on insertion of the vertical scale factors, the energy flux through the stated surface (cal/cm²/min e.g.), which is the total intensity of radiation.

Yentsch (1960) gives the following representative values for the wavelength of maximum transmission and the per cent transmission per meter at that wavelength.

Type of Ocean Water	Wavelength of Maximum Transmission	% Transmission per meter
Clearest Oceans	0.470	98.1
Average Oceans	0.475	89.0
Clearest Coastal	0.500	88.6
Average Coastal	0.550	72.4
Average Inshore	0.600	60.8

The shift in wavelength of maximum transmission has generally been attributed to the combined effect of selective scattering by suspended material and absorption by an undefined dissolved yellow substance ("gelbstoff") in the water (Kalle, 1938, 1939). Some investigators have suggested that the "gelbstoff" might indeed be organic compounds such as humic acid.

Yentsch (1960) has investigated the absorption spectra of living phytoplankton and shown a general distribution in optical density as illustrated by Fig. 17.6. The maximum absorption by algal pigments occurs at the wavelengths of maximum transmission by pure water, with a second peak, attributed to the red chlorophylls, around 0.67 μ in the region of high absorption by water. He has shown that addition of varying concentrations of phytoplankton could cause the sort of shift in spectral composition that is observed in natural waters.

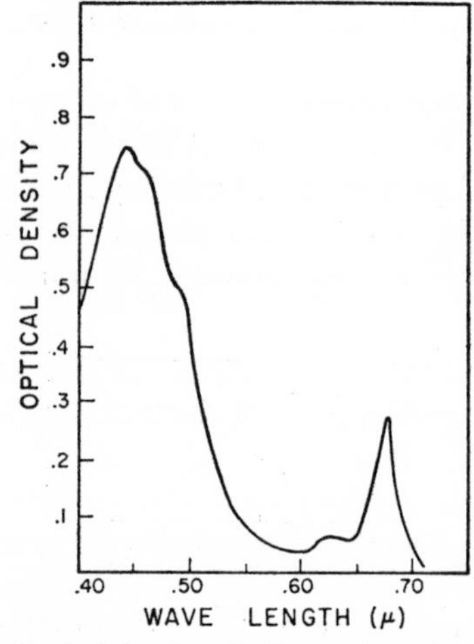

Fig. 17.6 Optical density of a living phytoplankton population as a function of wavelength (after Yentsch, 1960).

Thus, we see that the observed variations in intensity and spectral composition in sea water may be explained on the basis of scattering by suspended fine particles, absorption by dissolved organic material or absorption by phytoplankton pigment. It is likely that all three processes are active to a varying degree in any given situation.

Wide variations in the optical properties of the sea water can be expected to occur in the vertical, accompanying variations in the amount of suspended particulate matter. Recent investigations by Jerlov (1951) and co-workers have added significantly to our knowledge in this field. Levels of increased stability, for example, may serve to concentrate materials that contribute to light attenuation (Jerlov, 1959).

Clarke and Wertheim (1956), using a sensitive bathyphotometer, have found that an important contribution to the illumination at depth may come from the organisms found there. Many organisms produce light in short but intense flashes. At night it was found at some stations that the background light at depths greater than 300 m remained virtually constant. On one occasion illumination at 600 m on a night station was found to be as high as at the same depth during daylight hours.

17.3 Reflection and Refraction

When radiation of intensity I is incident upon the surface of fluid at an angle i from the vertical, part is reflected at an equal angle, with intensity R, and part is transmitted with an intensity T, being refracted so as to enter at an angle r to the vertical (Fig. 17.7).

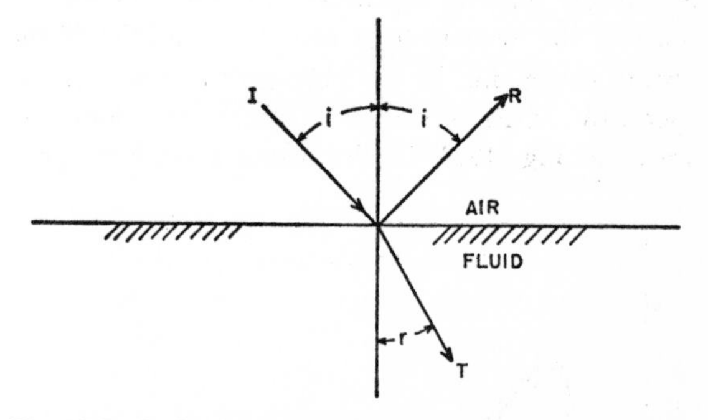

Fig. 17.7 Reflection and refraction of radiation incident upon an air–fluid interface.

The angles i and r are related by Snell's law:

$$\frac{\sin i}{\sin r} = \frac{\text{speed of light in air}}{\text{speed of light in fluid}}$$

$$= \frac{\text{index of refraction of fluid}}{\text{index of refraction of air}}$$

Taking the index of refraction of air as unity

$$\sin i/\sin r = \eta,$$

where η is the index of refraction of the fluid. For pure water at 20°C, $\eta = 1.333$, and r has a maximum value, when $\sin i = 1$, given by $\sin r = 1/\eta$. This is the critical angle r_c, which for pure water at 20°C is 48°35′. Light from within the fluid, incident upon the interface at angles greater than the critical angle will be totally refracted and not transmitted into the air.

The ratio of the intensity (I) of incident to that (R) of the reflected radiation is given by Fresnel's law:

$$\frac{R}{I} = \frac{1}{2}\left[\frac{\sin^2 (i - r)}{\sin^2 (i + r)} + \frac{\tan^2 (i - r)}{\tan^2 (i + r)}\right].$$

The intensity (T) of transmitted radiation is given by $T = I - R$.

For $I = 100$, $\eta = 1.333$ the following table gives values for r, R and T corresponding to various values of i.

i	0°	10°	20°	30°	40°	50°	60°	70°	80°	90°
r	0	7°29′	14°52′	22°02′	28°50′	35°05′	40°31′	44°40′	47°38′	48°35′
R	2.0	2.1	2.1	2.1	2.5	3.4	6.0	13.4	34.8	100
T	98.0	97.9	97.9	97.9	97.5	96.6	94.0	86.6	65.2	0.0

The reflection for normal incidence is only 2 per cent. This increases slowly with angle up to 60°, beyond which reflection increases rapidly. Under these conditions diffuse radiation (coming equally from all angles) is reflected 6.6 per cent. Powell and Clarke (1936) observed the reflection from the sea surface during overcast days, when all radiation was diffuse, to be 8 per cent.

The high reflection associated with large values of i explains the very bright image of the sun reflected from water surfaces at low angles. The variation with angle gives rise to the dancing highlights reflected from the sea surface when it is disturbed by wind. The occurrence of waves, by presenting surface facets at varying angles to the incoming radiation, alters the reflection and transmission of solar energy. Cox and Munk (1954) have used the glitter patterns produced by the sun's reflection from the sea surface in a study of the statistical distribution of surface slopes under various conditions.

Although the value $\eta = 1.333$ has been quoted for pure water at 20°C it should be noted that the index of refraction varies with wavelength being 1.331 for $\lambda = 0.6563\ \mu$ and 1.342 for $\lambda = 0.4102\ \mu$. Characteristic values decrease with increasing temperature. In sea water the index of refraction increases with chlorinity as well.

Since the refractive index varies with wavelength, a standard for experimental work must be chosen. This has usually been the Sodium D line (0.5893 μ). Utterback, Thompson, and Thomas (1934), Bein, Hirsehorn, and Moller (1935), and Miyake (1939) have all published results of careful measurements. The refractive index at temperature t may be expressed as

$$\eta_t = \eta_{0,t} + k_t \text{ Cl}. \tag{17.6}$$

Here $\eta_{0,t}$ represents the index for pure water at the same temperature, Cl is the chlorinity and k_t is a constant appropriate for that temperature.

For the sodium D line at 25°C, Utterback *et al.* obtained

$$\eta_{25} = 1.33250 + 0.000328 \text{ Cl}$$

and Miyake obtained

$$\eta_{25} = 1.332497 + 0.000334 \text{ Cl}.$$

A plot of the values for various temperatures and chlorinities as obtained by Utterback *et al.* is shown in Fig. 17.8.

All of the ions in solution contribute to the establishment of the refractive index but the effect of chloride, bromide and iodide ions is comparatively

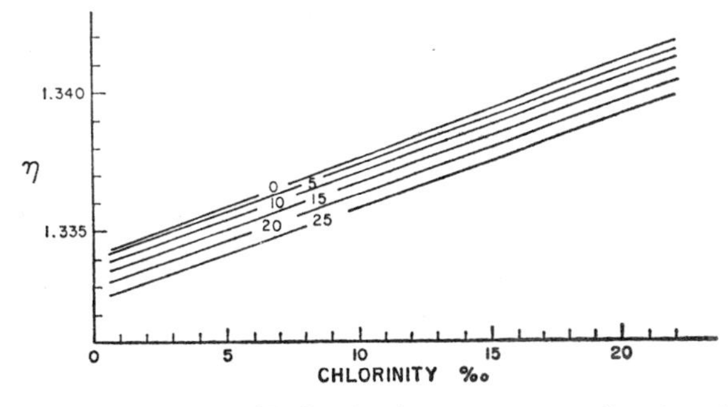

Fig. 17.8 Index of Refraction for sea water as a function of chlorinity at temperatures 0, 5, 10, 15, 20, 25°C (after Utterback *et al.*, 1934).

great. For this reason chlorinity, as determined by measurement of refractive index, might be expected to check more closely with titration chlorinity in inshore waters than would chlorinity determined by conductivity measurements. The use of present-day differential refractometers, capable of high precision, makes this method attractive for certain routine measurements. As with conductive salinometers, calibration with samples carefully diluted from a chosen standard permits greater precision than is justified by our knowledge of the functional relationship between refractive index and chlorinity.

References

BEIN, W., H-G. HIRSEHORN and L. MOLLER. *Knostantenbestimmungen des Meerwassers und Ergebnisse uber Wasserkorper*. Berlin, Universitat. Institut F. Meereskunde Veroff., N. F., A. Geogr.-naturwiss. Reihe, Heft 28, pp. 240. 1935.

CLARKE, G. L. and G. K. WERTHEIM. (1956) Measurements of illumination at great depths and at night in the Atlantic ocean by means of new bathyphotometer. *Deep Sea Res.* **3** (3), 189–205.

COX, C. and W. MUNK. (1954) Statistics of the sea surface derived from sun glitter. *J. Mar. Res.* **13** (2), 198–227.

DEFANT, A. *Physical Oceanography*. Pergamon Press, New York. 1961.

JERLOV, N. G. (1951) Optical studies of ocean waters. *Repts. Swedish Deep-Sea Exped., Phys. Chem.* **3** (1), 1–59.

JERLOV, N. G. (1959) Maxima in the vertical distribution o particles in the sea. *Deep Sea Res.* **5** (3), 173–184.

KALLE, K. (1938) Zum Problem der Meereswasserfarbe. *Ann. d. Hydrogr. u. Mar. Meteor.* **66** (5), 1–13.

KALLE, K. (1939) Die Farbe des Meeres. *Rapp Cons. Explor. Mer.* **109**, 98, Copenhagen.

MIYAKE, Y. (1939) Chemical studies of the western Pacific Ocean IV. The refractive index of sea water. *Chem. Soc. Japan.* **14** (6), 239–42.

POWELL, W. M. and G. L. CLARKE. (1936) The reflection and absorption of daylight at the surface of the ocean. *J. Optical Soc. Amer.* **26**, 111–120.

SVERDRUP, H. U., M. W. JOHNSON and R. H. FLEMING. *The Oceans*. Prentice Hall, New York. 1942.

UTTERBACK, C. L., T. G. THOMPSON and B. D. THOMAS. (1934) Refractivity–chlorinity–temperature relationships of ocean waters. Conseil Perm. Intern. p. l'Explor. de la Mer. *J. du Conseil*, **9**, 35–38.

YENTSCH, C. S. (1960) The influence of phytoplankton on the color of sea water. *Deep Sea Res.* **7**(1), 1–9.

Sources of Additional Information

The Sea, Vol. 1. HILL, M. N. (editor). Interscience, New York. 1963.

Chapter 8, Light. TYLER, J. E. and R. W. PRIESENDORFER, pp. 397–451.

Chapter 9, Underwater visibility. DUNTLEY, S. Q., pp. 452–455.

Chapter 10, Light and animal life. CLARKE, G. L. and E. J. DENTON, pp. 456–468.

STRICKLAND, J. D. H. (1958) Solar Radiation Penetrating the Ocean. *J. Fish. Res. Bd. Can.* **15** (3), 453–493.

CHAPTER 18

THE HEAT BUDGET OF THE OCEAN

OUR planet receives energy from the sun in the form of electromagnetic radiation, mostly at wavelengths shorter than 4 microns. Somewhat less than 20 per cent is absorbed by the atmosphere and its clouds, and the remainder is stored temporarily in the solid earth and in the oceans. The release of this temporarily stored energy powers the circulations of the atmosphere and ocean which redistribute the energy and maintain the climatic conditions which we observe. The capacity of the oceans to store heat make them particularly important in the global energy system.

Unfortunately the pertinent exchange processes between sea and atmosphere are neither well understood nor particularly easy to study, and our knowledge, though progressing, remains rudimentary. A particularly good review of the current status has been given by Malkus (1962).

18.1 RADIATION FROM THE SUN AND SKY

The intensity of radiation in all wavelengths coming from the sun and incident upon the outer boundary of the earth's atmosphere (measured in a plane normal to the sun's direction) is called the "solar constant" (S). The currently accepted value corrected to mean solar distance is

$$S = 2.00 \text{ cal/cm}^2\text{/min or}$$

$$S = 2.00 \text{ langleys/min.}$$

The radiation is partially absorbed and scattered by the atmospheric gases and contaminants, so that the intensity is significantly decreased before reaching the surface of the earth.

The differential equation expressing the attenuation may be written

$$\mathrm{d}I = kI\mathrm{d}Z,$$

where I is the intensity, Z is the path distance and k is the all wavelength attenuation constant.

If one considers a standard pressure, dry clear atmosphere when the sun is in the zenith position (Fig. 18.1), and measures distance z from the outer boundary of the atmosphere to the earth's surface ($z = l$), integration yields for the intensity at the earth's surface.

$$I = S \exp - \int_0^l k\mathrm{d}z.$$

k will, of course, be a function of z. It is convenient to write

$$\int_0^l k\mathrm{d}z = a_m,$$

where a_m is called the "standard zenith optical path length". a_m is non-dimensional and has a value of 0.128.

If ϕ is the sun's angle measured from zenith and one assumes a flat outer boundary to the atmosphere parallel to the tangent plane at the earth's surface, one can write

$$I = S\, \mathrm{e}^{-a_m \sec \phi}$$

for the intensity of radiation reaching the earth's surface (measured normal to the direction of the sun) through a standard, clear, dry atmosphere. The assumption of a flat outer boundary is shown to be a good approximation where ϕ is less than 70°, but in some treatments an empirical correction

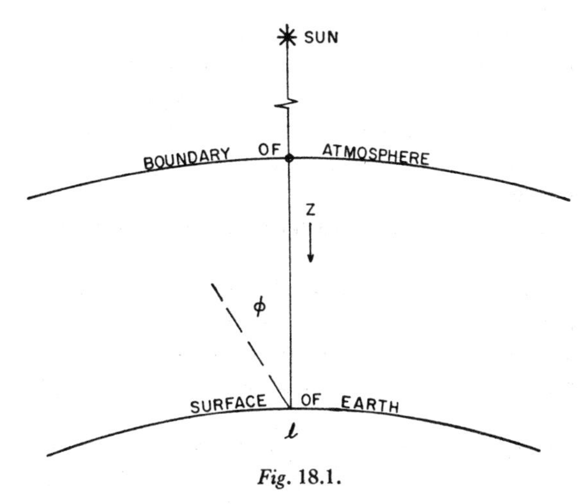

Fig. 18.1.

is applied by writing

$$a_m = 0.128 - 0.054 \log \sec \phi.$$

To take care of temporal and spatial variations in atmospheric attenuation a parameter T the "turbidity" is introduced. Turbidity can be defined as the number of clear, dry dust-free standard atmospheres that would be required to give the observed amount of attenuation. Then

$$I = S\, e^{-T a_m \sec \phi}. \qquad (18.1)$$

The flux of solar radiation unto a level surface on the earth is given by

$$Q_s' = S\, e^{-T a_m \sec \phi} \cos \phi. \qquad (18.2)$$

A portion of the incident radiation is reflected from the sea surface (Section 17.3) depending upon the sun's angle, the state of the sea, etc., so that the energy penetrating the surface is given by

$$Q_s = Q_s' (1 - a), \qquad (18.3)$$

where a is termed the albedo and is generally less than 0.1 except for very low angles.

With a cloudy sky, radiation from the sun and sky reaches even those portions of the sea surface from which the sun is obscured. In fact, since some radiation may be reflected downward from clouds, portions of the surface from which the sun is not obscured may receive even more radiation than they would have without clouds. On the average, however, there is a net decrease and Mosby (1936) found the following empirical relationship applicable to long term mean values:

$$Q_{sc} = Q_s (1 - 0.071\, C), \qquad (18.4)$$

where Q_{sc} is the incoming radiation under cloudy conditions and C is the fractional cloud cover in tenths.

In using this relationship (18.4) it should be recognized that no account is taken of the thickness of the cloud cover. Also, visual estimates of the fractional cloud cover from a point can be strongly influenced by the height and thickness of the cloud elements.

To obtain a climatological value for radiation received in an area over, say, a month (18.2), could be integrated over the range of sun angles appropriate to the latitude and time of year, (18.3) applied using some average value for the albedo, and the correction for climatological mean cloudiness made according to (18.4). Sverdrup *et al.* (1942) presented the data in Table 18.1 as calculated from the work of Kimball (1928). Programs of radiation measurements from research vessels have not yet provided the basis for generalization.

The radiation from the sun and sky which penetrates the sea surface is absorbed by, and temporarily stored in, the upper few hundred meters of water as discussed in Chapter 17.

18.2 Back Radiation

The sea surface, by virtue of its temperature, emits long wave radiation to the atmosphere. The emissivity* is very close to unity, so that the rate of back radiation Q_b approximates that from a black body as given by the Stephan–Boltzmann law,

$$Q_b = \sigma T^4, \qquad (18.5)$$

where T is the temperature in degrees Kelvin and σ, the Stephan–Boltzmann constant, has a value 5.735×10^{-5} ergs/sec cm^2 degree^4. The radiated energy is distributed over a wide band of wavelengths with the wavelength of maximum emission (λ_m) given by Wien's displacement law,

$$\lambda_m = K/T.$$

K has the value 2880μ degrees. Thus, for a surface at 20°C (293°K),

$$\lambda_m = 2880/293 = 9.85\mu.$$

Over most of its spectrum this radiation is absorbed efficiently by carbon dioxide and water vapor in the atmosphere. Since the air, with its water vapor, itself radiates by virtue of its temperature, the loss of heat by back radiation is reduced by the humidity of the atmosphere over the sea surface. Sverdrup *et al.* (1942) have presented (Fig. 18.2) a graphical relationship of effective back radiation to a clear sky as related to sea surface temperature and relative humidity measured a few meters above the sea surface. This shows that, for a constant relative humidity, effective back radiation decreases with increasing temperature. This relationship may at first appear strange but it should be noted that, for constant relative humidity, the concentration of water vapor in the atmosphere is greater at the higher temperatures. Also the radiation efficiency of the air itself increases with temperature.

* A "black body" is defined as one that completely absorbs all incident radiation. Such a body is also the most efficient radiator. Radiation from a body with emissivity ϵ is given by $Q_b = \epsilon \sigma T^4$, where ϵ has a maximum value of unity for a black body.

TABLE 18.1. AVERAGE AMOUNTS OF RADIATION FROM SUN AND SKY, EXPRESSED IN g cal per sq cm per min, WHICH EVERY MONTH REACHES THE SEA SURFACE IN THE STATED LOCALITIES (AFTER KIMBALL)

Locality													
Latitude	Longitude	Jan.	Feb.	Mar.	Apr.	May	June	July	Aug.	Sept.	Oct.	Nov.	Dec.
60°N	7°E – 56°W	0.002	0.053	0.125	0.207	0.272	0.292	0.267	0.212	0.147	0.074	0.006	0.0
60 N	135 –170 W	0.005	0.078	0.155	0.208	0.269	0.260	0.242	0.185	0.127	0.077	0.015	0.0
52 N	10 W	0.048	0.089	0.148	0.219	0.258	0.267	0.251	0.211	0.160	0.104	0.062	0.041
52 N	129 W	0.053	0.091	0.135	0.185	0.246	0.250	0.230	0.214	0.158	0.097	0.058	0.039
42 N	66 – 70 W	0.094	0.138	0.212	0.272	0.306	0.329	0.302	0.267	0.230	0.174	0.115	0.086
42 N	124 W	0.100	0.151	0.210	0.286	0.331	0.360	0.320	0.274	0.231	0.174	0.113	0.092
30 N	65 – 77 W	0.146	0.165	0.238	0.285	0.317	0.310	0.301	0.282	0.239	0.188	0.169	0.142
30 N	128 –130 E	0.141	0.153	0.199	0.241	0.258	0.238	0.256	0.260	0.219	0.178	0.153	0.135
10 N	61 – 69 W	0.254	0.276	0.299	0.305	0.272	0.276	0.285	0.292	0.287	0.269	0.248	0.239
10 N	116 – 80 W	0.226	0.257	0.292	0.278	0.255	0.239	0.240	0.242	0.247	0.237	0.224	0.219
0	7 – 12 E	0.239	0.248	0.244	0.230	0.210	0.196	0.188	0.194	0.220	0.240	0.239	0.235
0	48 W&170 E	0.261	0.265	0.282	0.297	0.309	0.300	0.300	0.340	0.386	0.362	0.339	0.278
10 S	14 E – 36 W	0.329	0.328	0.301	0.254	0.219	0.206	0.232	0.278	0.312	0.324	0.317	0.320
10 S	72 –171 E	0.290	0.308	0.315	0.289	0.266	0.253	0.269	0.306	0.332	0.313	0.301	0.303
30 S	17 &116 E	0.452	0.406	0.340	0.254	0.186	0.148	0.166	0.214	0.274	0.362	0.401	0.430
30 S	110 W	0.380	0.330	0.260	0.209	0.162	0.130	0.145	0.176	0.237	0.321	0.340	0.390
42 S	73 W; 147 E	0.343	0.297	0.223	0.154	0.104	0.085	0.092	0.135	0.187	0.264	0.310	0.348
52 S	58 W	0.289	0.237	0.167	0.112	0.062	0.039	0.049	0.097	0.150	0.222	0.273	0.302
60 S	45 W	0.213	0.171	0.105	0.056	0.011	0.0	0.003	0.054	0.111	0.156	0.204	0.221

Air and water vapor are almost transparent to radiation in a band of wavelengths from about 8 μ to 14 μ which embraces the wavelength of maximum emission from the sea surface. This band of high transparency is sometimes known as "Simpson's window". The long wavelength cut-off in this window is accomplished by a strong absorption band due to CO_2. Water vapor gives almost complete absorption at the still longer wavelengths.

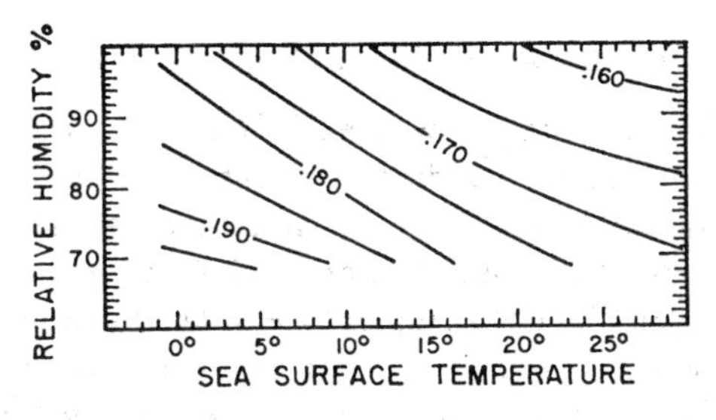

Fig. 18.2 Effective back radiation in gcal/cm²/min from the sea surface to a clear sky represented as a function of sea-surface temperature and relative humidity of the air at a height of a few meters.

The earth is heated by short wave solar radiation which passes efficiently through the atmosphere and, because of atmospheric absorption of the longer wavelengths, the surface temperature rises to where the wavelengths of maximum emission falls within the window. At these surface temperatures a balance of incoming and outgoing radiant energy can be effected, and the skin temperature of the earth is stabilized in this range. Because of the similarity to the effect created by horticulturists with glass roofed enclosures this is called the "greenhouse effect".

Liquid water in clouds is opaque to terrestrial radiation including that in the 8 μ to 14 μ range of wavelengths, and, since the cloud bases radiate back to the sea, their presence further decreases the effective back radiation. A gross empirical relationship given by Asklöff (1920) may be used to express this effect:

$$Q_{bc} = Q_{bo}\,(1 - 0.083\,C), \qquad (18.6)$$

where Q_{bc} is the effective back radiation to a cloudy sky, Q_{bo} the same for a clear sky, and C the cloud cover in tenths. It should be recognized that (18.6) takes no cognizance of the nature of the particular clouds. If a more refined treatment were practical, one would expect the cloud effect to be highly dependent upon the temperature at cloud base.

The intensity of long wave radiation from the

sea surface provides a method of measuring the "skin temperature" with infrared radiometers. Such measurements have shown that, because of heat loss by evaporation and radiation, the "skin" is cooler than the water just below the surface except under quite special circumstances (Ball, 1954; Ewing and McAlister, 1960). The discrepancy between skin temperature and surface temperature as measured by dipping a bucket of water from the surface can be of the order of 0.5°C.

18.3 Radiation Surplus

The difference between the incoming radiation from sun and sky Q_s and the effective back radiation Q_b is known as the radiation surplus, Q_r, i.e.

$$Q_r = Q_s - Q_b.$$

The relative stability of temperature on a global basis leads us to believe that for the earth as a whole $Q_r = 0$. Back radiation takes place continuously from the whole surface of the earth ($4\pi a^2$), where a is the mean radius. Incoming radiation is, however, intercepted by the projected area (πa^2), or is only incident upon a point during daylight hours.

The radiation surplus is positive in the tropics where the sun angle is high and the daylight hours uniformly long. Higher surface temperatures would tend to make back radiation more efficient, but increased evaporation from the sea surface in these latitudes results in high humidity and widespread cloudiness, both of which cut down the radiative loss.

Toward the poles the sun angle is generally low, so that Q_s is decreased by the longer optical path and by the obliquity of incidence to the earth's surface. Back radiation is slightly lower in polar regions, due to low surface temperatures, but the radiation surplus is negative. At about 38° latitude the radiation surplus is zero on an annual basis. The variation of radiation surplus with latitude for the earth and atmosphere as a whole is shown in Fig. 18.3 as given by Budyko (1956).

As a result of this unequal heating of polar and tropical regions, a transport of heat poleward by the oceans and atmosphere is required. Jung (1956) has discussed the question of relative importance of transport in the two regimes. Perhaps 10 per cent of the transport is accomplished by major ocean circulation. The majority of the heat exchange is accomplished by the atmosphere, not in steady organized flow, but mainly in violent random disruptions of the mean flow configuration. The most spectacular of these outbreaks are, of course, the tropical cyclones (hurricanes or typhoons).

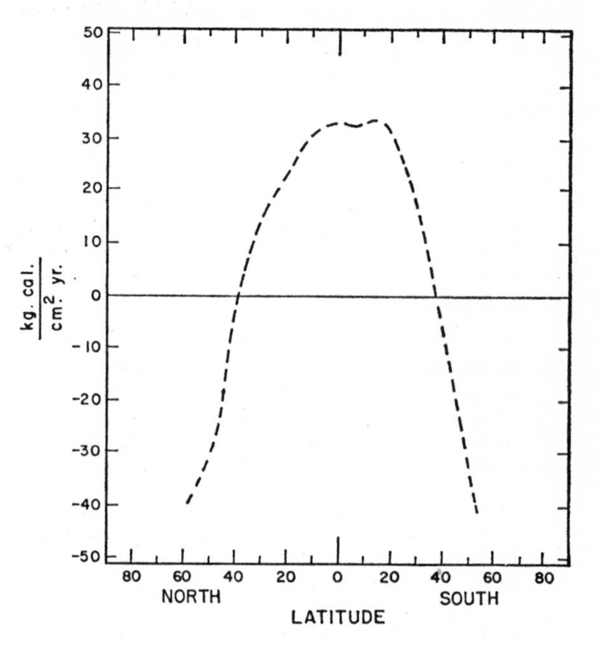

Fig. 18.3 Radiation surplus of earth and atmosphere (after Budyko, 1956).

18.4 Conduction of Sensible Heat

The sea surface will exchange heat with the atmosphere by conduction, heat being lost from the ocean where the air temperature is less than the surface temperature, and gained where the air is at the higher temperature. At the interface temperature will be a continuous function in the vertical and the exchange rate will be governed by molecular processes in the immediately adjacent water and atmosphere. Measurements at the interface are extremely difficult to make and most attempts at evaluating heat conduction have utilized measurements of air temperature over the ocean. The conductive flux of heat from the ocean (Q_h) can be related to air temperature and other variables in the following way:

$$Q_h = C_p A_z \{(\partial\theta_a/\partial z) + \Gamma\}, \qquad (18.7)$$

where C_p is the specific heat at constant pressure for the air (a function of temperature and humidity, but roughly equal to 0.24 cal/g), and θ_a is the air temperature as a function of height z above the surface. Γ is the adiabatic lapse rate for air, i.e. the value of $-\partial\theta_a/\partial z$ for an air column of neutral stability (constant potential temperature).

The exchange coefficient A_z (g/cm sec) is the turbulent vertical mixing coefficient. The nature of turbulent exchange coefficients has been discussed in Chapter 11.

The expression in parenthesis in (18.7) is the effective temperature gradient for inducing heat flow. In the lower layers of the atmosphere (below 60 m) characteristic values for Γ are approximately 0.01°C/m; so that, in cases of moderate or high conductive exchange, the approximation

$$Q_h = C_p A_z \partial\theta_a/\partial z \tag{18.8}$$

may be appropriate.

Because of the difficulty in evaluating A_z, Q_h is seldom evaluated except as a residual term for a large area treated for climatically significant periods.

18.5 Evaporation — The Bowen Ratio

About half of the radiant energy absorbed by the waters of the ocean is returned to the atmosphere by evaporation. Evaporation is particularly active in the tropical regions where there is a large radiation surplus and where approximately 75 per cent of the earth's surface is covered by water (Fig. 1.1).

The evaporation, or flux of water from the sea surface, can be given by

$$E = -A_z \partial q/\partial z, \tag{18.9}$$

where E = grams of water/cm² sec (sometimes expressed in the equivalent cm of water/sec), q is the specific humidity of the air (grams of water/gram of air), and A_z is again the vertical mixing coefficient in the air.

The rate of energy loss per unit area by evaporation Q_E is the product of E and the latent heat of evaporation L.

$$Q_E = LE = -LA_z \partial q/\partial z. \tag{18.10}$$

L is a function of temperature, being 580 cal/g at 30°C and 597 cal/g at 0°C.

Sometimes the water vapor pressure e is a more convenient parameter than q, their relationship being given by

$$q = 0.622\, e/(p - 0.378\, e) \approx 0.622\, e/p, \tag{18.11}$$

where e is in millibars and p is the atmospheric pressure in millibars. Then (18.10) can be written

$$Q_E = -LA_z \frac{0.622}{p} \frac{\partial e}{\partial z}. \tag{18.12}$$

Again the difficulty in evaluating the energy flux arises from the uncertainty in the value of A_z, the vertical exchange coefficient.

For an ocean area ringed by a network of meteorological stations providing good upper air observations, it is possible to evaluate the flux of water vapor from the area on the basis of computed winds and measured humidity as Franceschini (1961) has done for the Gulf of Mexico. This evaluates only the net of evaporation, precipitation and runoff, and, while runoff values may be obtainable, there are very few reliable quantitative observations of precipitation over the ocean.

Although both the heat loss through evaporation and that through conduction are difficult to assess, Bowen (1926) has shown that the ratio Q_h/Q_E can be computed if one assumes that the mixing coefficient A_z has the same value in (18.8) and (18.12). One obtains

$$R = \frac{Q_h}{Q_E} = \frac{C_p p}{0.622\, L} \frac{d\theta_a/dz}{de/dz}. \tag{18.13}$$

The quantity R is generally called the "Bowen ratio". If one further assumes that the gradients of θ_a and e are constant from the sea surface up to the level where both are measured, one can write

$$R = \frac{C_p p}{0.622\, L} \frac{(\theta_w - \theta_a)}{(e_w - e_a)}. \tag{18.14}$$

Here θ_w is the sea surface temperature, and e_w is the vapor pressure over the water surface (equal to 0.98 times the value over pure water at the same temperature).

Introducing representative values of L (585 cal/g) and of C_p (0.240 cal/g) gives the approximate relationship,

$$R \approx 0.66 \frac{p}{1000} \frac{(\theta_w - \theta_a)}{(e_w - e_a)}, \tag{18.15}$$

which can be evaluated from the observations taken routinely by many ships. Jacobs (1951) has computed average seasonal values for R over the North Atlantic and North Pacific between 0° and 60°N latitude. The values generally increase northward, although, as might be expected, larger seasonal variations occur in boreal regions.

In fact, Jacobs shows large negative values occurring seasonally between 45°N and 55°N in each ocean. He also discusses diurnal variations in R and suggests the possibility that this contributed to the generally higher values he obtained for the Pacific Ocean at all latitudes.

Representative values for R lie between 0.1 and 0.2, indicating that the heat loss by evaporation is from 5 to 10 times as great as that by conduction.

For the oceans as a whole, or a suitably large region thereof, the heat budget could be written $Q_s - Q_b = Q_h + Q_E$, so long as annual average values are implied. Thus one could write

$$Q_E = \frac{Q_s - Q_b}{1 + R},$$

or (18.16)

$$E = \frac{Q_s - Q_b}{L(1 + R)}.$$

This provides one means of computing the evaporation from the ocean and the energy loss by conduction can be evaluated as a residual.

Using all available data Wüst (1954) has evaluated mean annual evaporation and precipitation for the entire ocean in five degree latitude zones. His values are presented in Table 18.2. The average evaporation over all ocean areas is about 100 cm/year or a total of 3.5×10^{20} g/year, representing an energy exchange of 2.1×10^{23} cal/year. The excess of evaporation over precipitation is about 10 cm/year or 3.5×10^{19} g/year. If this represents precipitation falling on the land areas of the earth, it would result in an average precipitation of 24 cm/year. The average annual precipitation over land areas is about 70 cm (Riehl, 1954). The additional amount must originate in evaporation and transpiration from the land and its flora.

TABLE 18.2. MEAN VALUES OF PRECIPITATION, EVAPORATION, AND THE DIFFERENCE BETWEEN THEM ($E - P$) FOR THE ENTIRE OCEAN (INCLUDING ADJACENT SEAS). (ACCORDING TO WÜST, 1954)

Zone in degrees	Precipitation cm/year	Evaporation cm/year	$E-P$ cm/year
70–65 N	34	12	−22
65–60 N	65	20	−45
60–55 N	77	34	−43
55–50 N	105	55	−50†
50–45 N	112*	66	−46
45–50 N	102	84	−18
40–35 N	86	108	22
35–30 N	74	125	51
30–25 N	63	132	69
25–20 N	57†	137*	80*
20–15 N	70	135	65
15–10 N	103	132	29
10– 5 N	187*	126	−61†
5– 0 N	146	113†	−33
70– 0 N	101.0	110.6	9.6
0– 5 S	105†	125	20
5–10 S	109*	137	28
10–15 S	94	139*	45
15–20 S	76	137	61
20–25 S	68	133	65*
25–30 S	65†	123	58
30–35 S	70	110	40
35–40 S	90	96	6
40–45 S	110	78	−32
45–50 S	117*	56	−61
50–55 S	109	39	−70
55–60 S	84	12†	−72†
0–60 S	91.45	102.1	10.7

* Maxima
† Minima

18.6 A HEAT BUDGET EQUATION

If we introduce two more energy flux terms, Q_v to indicate the rate at which heat is carried into a region by advective processes, and Q_θ to indicate the rate at which heat is being stored by increase of temperature, we may construct a reasonably complete heat budget equation. We will be concerned with the whole vertical column at a given location and the flux rates will be per unit cross section of the free surface.

Energy Received = Energy Lost + Energy Stored.

$$[Q_s + Q_v] = [Q_b + Q_E + Q_h] + Q_\theta. \quad (18.17)$$

Q_s arises from the radiation from sun and sky; it has the form of electromagnetic radiation in the infrared, visible and ultraviolet. It is absorbed mostly in the top few hundred meters of the ocean.

Q_v arises from advective processes; it has the form of molecular heat and may enter the column at any depth.

Q_b arises from the radiation of the sea surface; it has the form of electromagnetic radiation in the infrared range, and is active only at the very surface.

Q_E arises from evaporation; it has the form of molecular heat associated with the change from

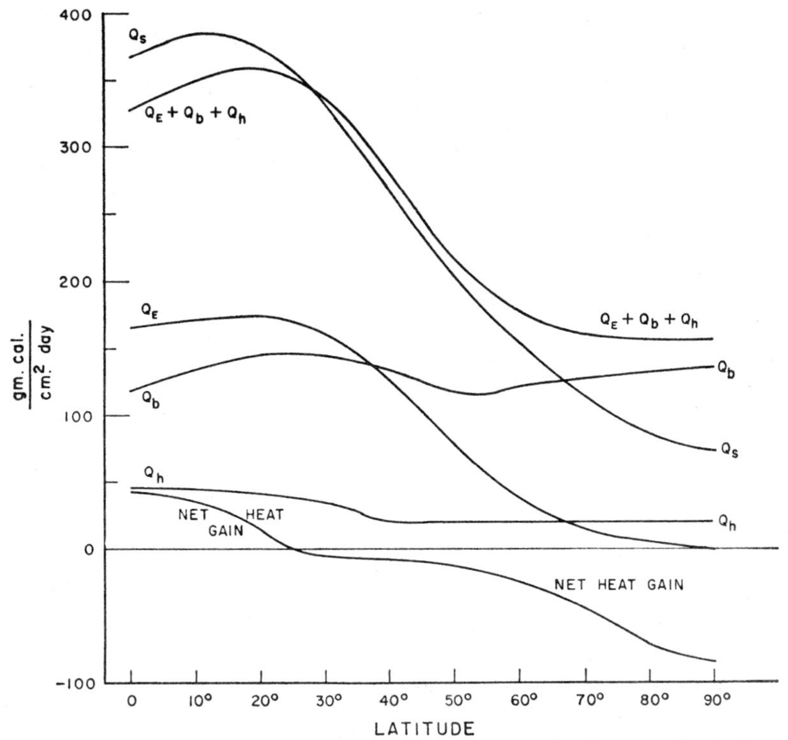

Fig. 18.4 Latitudinal variation in heat budget parameters for Northern Hemisphere oceans (after Defant, 1961).

liquid to gaseous state, and takes place only at the very surface.

Q_h arises from the conduction of sensible heat across the interface; it has the form of molecular heat and takes place only at the surface.

Q_θ arises from the storage of heat associated with the rise in temperature of the water; it is molecular in form and may enter the column at any depth.

For completeness we should mention the heat generated by internal friction. Energy associated with the organized motion of waves and currents which are driven by the winds, and of tides which are driven by the gravitational attraction of the sun and moon, is degraded by friction into molecular heat. Also, in passing, we should recognize the conduction of heat from the earth through the ocean bottom, which at present is thought to have a fairly constant rate over much of the ocean of about 7×10^{-5} cal/cm²/min. Both of these are extremely small in comparison to the fluxes included in (18.17).

18.7 Summary

All of the important mechanisms by which the oceans lose heat (radiation, evaporation, and cooling) operate only at the surface. Since the coefficient of thermal expansion is positive at all temperatures above the freezing point (at least for water with salinity greater than 24‰), cooling produces heavier water and induces vertical mixing which makes heat from below available to the atmosphere. This process brings about the "fall overturn" which renews the nutrients at the surface in coastal waters.

The absorption of heat from the sun and sky, though more efficient at the surface, takes place through the upper few hundred meters. Because of this, the immediate rise in surface temperature is minimized and the rapid loss by radiation, evaporation and conduction is prevented. At the same time, summer heating of the surface layers induces stability in the column which inhibits vertical mixing and thus stores much of the energy in a region where it is comparatively available to the atmosphere when the radiation surplus is negative.

Although the heat budget equation (18.17) may be written, and certain relationships evaluating the different fluxes obtained, there is considerable difficulty involved in the actual evaluation of each term. Very few good quantitative data are available and the exchange of energy between sea and atmosphere remains a fertile field for investigation.

Defant (1961) presented figures for the major energy fluxes on an average annual basis for each ten degrees of latitude in the northern hemisphere oceans. These are plotted in Fig. 18.4. The energy received from sun and sky Q_s decreases poleward from a maximum at 10°N. Latitudinal variations in effective back radiation Q_b and in conductive flux of sensible heat are minor. Evaporative flux Q_E, however, is very high between the equator and 30°N then falls off poleward. Thus a large fraction of the energy where the radiation surplus is high returns to the atmosphere in the form of latent heat of evaporation. From the equator to 25°N, Q_s is greater than $Q_E + Q_b + Q_h$ and the net heat gain in the ocean is positive. North of 25°N, this is reversed. The advective heat flux Q_v and the heat used for temperature change Q_θ have not been evaluated. Since, however, the temperature of the oceans appears to remain constant on a climatological basis, it can be argued that Q_θ is zero at all latitudes and the advective flux Q_v is such as to transport heat northward at rates that will nullify the net heat gain shown. This flux is accomplished by the major currents system. Both the subtropical gyrals and the boreal gyrals carry warmer water towards the north and comparatively cold water to the south.

References

Asklöff, S. (1920) Ueber den Zusammenhang zwischen der nächtlichen Wärmeausstrahlung, der Bewölkung und der Wolkenart. *Geogr. Ann., Heft* **3**.

Ball, F. K. (1954) Sea surface temperatures. *Aust. J. Phys.* **7** (4), 649–652.

Bowen, I. S. (1926) The rates of heat losses by conduction and by evaporation from any water surface. *Phys. Rev.* **27**, 779–787.

Budyko, M. I. *The heat balance of the earth's surface*, 255 pp. Gidrometeorologicheskoe izdatel'stvo, Leningrad. (Translated by Stepanova, Nina A. translation distributed by the U.S. Weather Bureau, Washington, D.C. 1958.)

Defant, A. *Physical Oceanography*, Vol. 1. Pergamon Press, New York. 1961.

Ewing, G. and E. D. McAlister. (1960) On the thermal boundary layer of the ocean. *Science* **131** (3410), 1374–1376.

Franceschini, G. A. *Hydrologic balance of the Gulf of Mexico.* Ph.D. dissertation on file at the A. and M. College of Texas (unpublished). 1961.

Jacobs, W. C. (1951) The energy exchange between sea and atmosphere and some of its consequences. *Bull. Scripps Inst. Oceanog.* **6** (2), 27–122.

Jung, G. H. *Energy transport by air and sea.* U.S. Navy Rept. OPNAV PO 3–8. Washington 1956, 19 pp.

Kimball, H. H. (1928) Amount of solar radiation that reaches the surface of the earth on the land and on the sea, and methods by which it is measured. *Monthly Wea. Rev.* **56**, 393–399.

Malkus, J. S. Interchange of properties between sea and air: Large scale interactions. In *The Sea*, Vol. 1. Hill, M. N. (editor), Chapter 4, pp. 88–294. Interscience, New York. 1962.

Mosby, H. (1936) Verdunstung und Strahlung auf dem Meere. *Ann. d. Hydrogr. u. Mar. Meteor.* **64**, 281–286.

Riehl, H. *Tropical Meteorology*. McGraw-Hill, New York. 1954.

Sverdrup, H. U., M. W. Johnson and R. H. Fleming. *The Oceans*, Chapter IV. Prentice-Hall, New York. 1942.

Wüst, G. (1954) Gestzmässige Wechselbeziehungen zwischen Ozean und Atmosphäre, in der zonalen Verteilung von Oberflächensalzgehalt, Verdungstung und Niederschlag. *Arch. Meteor. Geophys. Bioklim.* **A, 7**, 305–328. Wien. (Defant Festschrift).

Sources of Additional Information

The Sea. Hill, M. N. (editor). Chapters 3 and 4. Interscience, New York. 1962.

Jacobs, W. C. (1951) Large scale aspects of energy transformations over the oceans. *Compendium of Meteorology, Amer. Met. Soc.* 1057–1070.

Montgomery, R. B. (1940) Observations of vertical humidity distribution above the ocean surface and their relation to evaporation. *Papers Phys. Oceanog. and Met.* **7**, 30 pp.

CHAPTER 19

THERMOHALINE CIRCULATION

If, at one location within a fluid, physical processes act to bring about a decrease in density, and, at the same time, density is increased at another location, Archimedian forces will tend to set up a circulation. The fluid of increased density will sink and flow towards the region of lesser density while the lighter fluid will rise and flow on the surface towards the region of density increase. In the ocean density increase may be effected by cooling which is brought about by surface radiation, evaporation or conduction to the atmosphere, or by an increase in salinity which can be the result of evaporation or of ice formation. These processes are restricted to the surface of the sea. Heating, mainly through absorption of solar radiation, can decrease the density as can a decrease in salinity resulting from addition of fresh water through precipitation, run-off, or ice melting. Although solar heating may extend some distance below the immediate surface, it is, in respect to oceanic depths, also a surface phenomenon.

Circulation induced by density differences set up in this way is referred to as thermohaline circulation.

Through much of the nineteenth century it was generally believed that the major oceanic circulations were driven by unequal heating and cooling at low and high latitudes respectively. We now believe the surface layer circulation to be wind driven with intense boundary currents, required for continuity, and controlled in form by internal friction and inertia. Nevertheless, thermohaline circulation must be invoked, at least in part, to explain the deep circulation (Fig. 7.6) as we have done in Section 7.4.

The thermohaline circulation is just one of the many modes of circulation that contribute to the complex motion in the ocean.

19.1 Early Ideas

Humboldt (1814), on the basis of observations of cold water at great depths in the tropics, deduced that cold water sank and flowed away from the polar regions. The implication was that there existed a return surface flow from the tropics and a complete circulation in each hemisphere of each ocean. This notion was prevalent when Maury (1855) wrote his treatise on The Physical Geography of the Sea, and it was widely held that the major ocean circulations were thermaly driven. Although there were those such as Croll (1874) who argued that this was not possible and that the wind must be an important driving force, the idea persisted for some time.

Sandström (1908 and 1919) reported upon laboratory experiments in which he introduced sources of heating and cooling into tanks of sea water at various levels. By introducing dyes into the tanks he could observe the circulation patterns set up. Figure 19.1 shows the strong circulation resulting when the warming was at a greater depth than the cooling (a and b), the weak shallow circulation when they were both at the surface (c), and the absence of a circulation when the cooling was at the greater depth (d).

Sandström (1919) argued that anticyclonic winds in the Sargasso Sea caused a convergence which increased the effective depth of tropical heating in the North Atlantic, and that the Gulf Stream resulted as a pure thermohaline circulation. The winds, he concluded, played an insignificant part as motive power in currents of this nature.

19.2 Vertical Circulation and the Thermocline Problem

The work of Sverdrup, Munk, and others (Chapter 12) has presented convincing arguments that the surface layer circulation of the oceans is clearly wind driven. The intense boundary currents such as the Gulf Stream can be dynamically explained (Chapters 12 and 13) as driven by the wind though not directly coupled to local winds. Nevertheless, a thermohaline circulation must be invoked to explain the waters found in the deep ocean basins

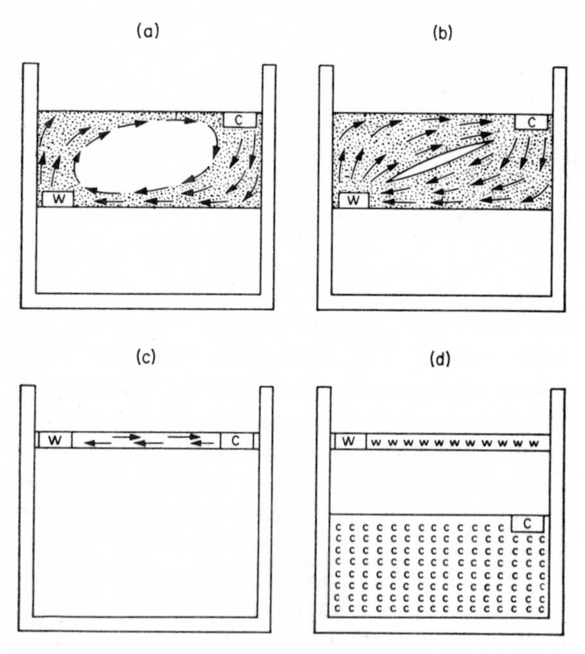

Fig. 19.1 Sandstrom's experiment with circulation induced by warming and cooling.
(a) Warming at greater depth initial circulation.
(b) Same after longer interval.
(c) Warming and cooling at same level.
(d) Cooling at greater depth, no circulation.

and the apparent stability of the permanent thermocline.

The relatively high values of dissolved oxygen content in the deep waters (Figs. 7.5 and 7.8) argue that these waters are being replenished from the surface either continuously or at least frequently. Careful study of the geographic distribution of their physical properties points to two major sources, one in the North Atlantic and one in the Weddell Sea.

Cromwell (1960) described a simple laboratory experiment that sheds some light on the development of sharp density discontinuities or pycnoclines (in the ocean usually observable as the thermocline) in stratified fluid. To a tank with an initially linear density–depth structure turbulent energy was introduced through vertical agitation of a fine mesh screen in the surfa ce layer. A more or less homogeneous surface layer was produced underlain by an abrupt gradient. Although, as Cromwell points out, problems in scaling the turbulence prohibit a direct analogy between tank and ocean, it seems reasonable that wind induced turbulence in the surface layers maintains the thermocline in the ocean. However, as in the experiment, the mechanism provides only for continuous deepening of the thermocline and stability demands a renewal of the deeper waters and an upward flow through the thermocline.

We picture, then, the deep water fed by two fairly localized sources and drained through a distributed sink manifested in upward flow through the thermocline. This classical model of pure thermohaline circulation is illustrated in Fig. 19.2.

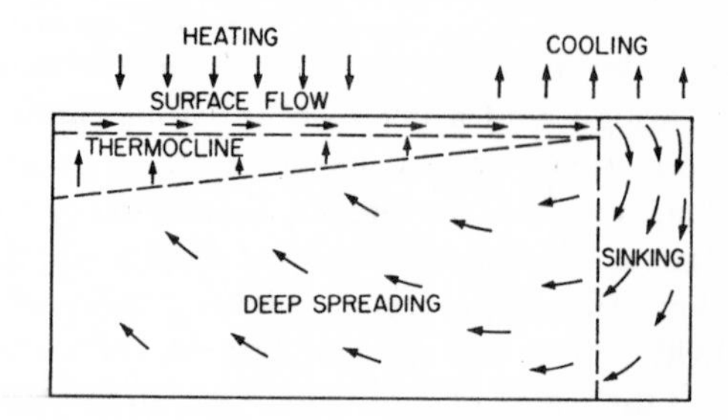

Fig. 19.2 The classical model of a pure thermohaline circulation caused by heating in lower and cooling in higher latitudes (after Wyrtki, 1941).

In the lower latitudes the flow of heat into the ocean warms the deep waters ascending through the thermocline while at high latitude net heat loss produces the colder water which sinks to renew it. Stommel and Arons (1960b) estimate the vertical velocity under a variety of assumptions to range from 0.5 to 3.0 cm per day. Wyrtki (1961) suggests 1.7 cm per day as a likely value and 4.3 cm per day as a maximal value.

Wyrtki (1961) considers the thermohaline circulation, as it must of course be considered, as acting along with the wind-driven circulation. He presents a four-layer circulation (Fig. 19.3) in which he argues that the formation and sinking of Deep and Bottom Waters, and the upward flux through the thermocline are truly thermohaline circulation. The ascending of Deep Water in the South Atlantic, and the sinking of Intermediate Water, he attributes to wind induced divergence and convergence respectively at the bottom of the Ekman layer.

Note that although the net flow in the surface layer may be toward high latitudes as in the classical thermohaline circulation (Fig. 19.2), flow in this direction is concentrated within the western boundary current. Through most of the ocean the surface layer has a modest equatorward motion. Thus the net heat influx goes to raising the temperature of both the surface layer coming from higher latitudes and the deeper water that rises through the thermocline.

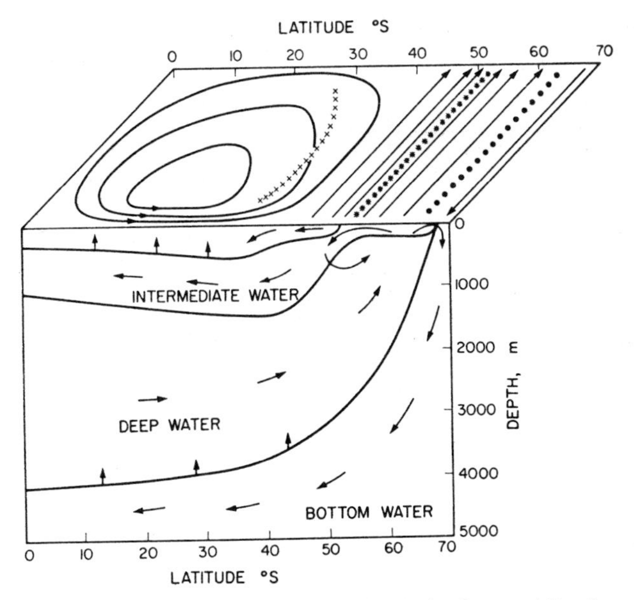

Fig. 19.3 Schematic picture of the circulation in a meridional plane and of the surface circulation in a southern hemisphere ocean (after Wyrtki, 1961). •••• Antarctic Divergence, **** Antarctic Polar Front, XXXX Subtropical Convergence.

19.3 Circulation Patterns in the Deep Water

Stommel (1957), and Stommel and Arons (1960a and b) have given consideration to the patterns of flow that could be expected in the deep waters. They set up a model that has two deep water sources, one in the North Atlantic and one in the Weddell Sea, and a diffuse, ocean-wide, sink. Geostrophic balance is imposed upon the flow regime presented in the 1960b paper. Western boundary currents and an eastward zonal flow in the Southern Ocean are the outstanding features.

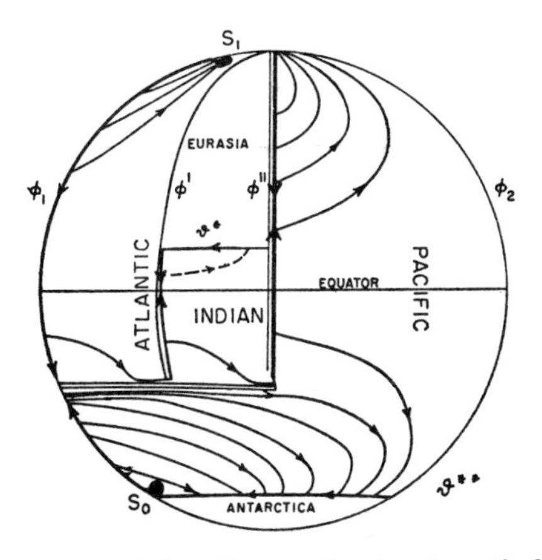

Fig. 19.4 A circulation diagram showing theoretical distribution of abyssal currents proceeding from the two sources S_0 and S_1 and flowing into a diffuse sink uniformly distributed over the whole ocean area (after Stommel and Arons, 1960).

Evidence for the reality of the south flowing boundary current in the North Atlantic has been presented by Swallow and Worthington (1957) from direct measurements.

The model shows deep currents with poleward components throughout most of the ocean area. Again, this is opposite in sense to the prediction of the simple thermohaline model. It should be remembered, however, that Stommel's models are for vertically integrated flow in the deep water regime, that counter flowing Deep and Bottom Waters are not provided for and that the addition of the Intermediate Water to the circulation is not considered.

It is obvious that circulation in the deep water regime must be considerably more complex than used to be generally imagined. Much serious thought is now being devoted to the design of experiments and instrumentation that will allow an increase in available factual data concerning currents at all depths.

References

Croll, J. (1874) On ocean currents, Part III. *Phil. Mag.* **47**, 94.

Cromwell, T. (1960) Pycnoclines created by mixing in an aquarium tank. *J. Mar. Res.* **18** (2) 73–82.

v. Humboldt, A. *Voyage aux regions equinoxiales du Nouveau Continent. Relation historique.* Vol. I. Paris 1814.

MAURY, M. F. *The Physical Geography of the Sea.* Harper, New York. 1855.

SANDSTRÖM, J. W. (1908) Dynamische Versuche mit Meerwassers. *Ann. Hydrog. marit. Meteorol.* **36**, 6.

SANDSTROM, J. W. *The hydrodynamics of Canadian Atlantic waters. Canadian Fisheries Expedition* ***1914–1915***, pp. 221–346. Department of Naval Service, Ottawa. 1919.

STOMMEL, H. (1957) A survey of ocean current theory. *Deep Sea Res.* **4** (3), 149–184.

STOMMEL, H. and A. B. ARONS. (1960a) On the abyssal circulation of the world ocean. I. Stationary planetary flow patterns on a sphere. *Deep Sea Res.* **6** (2), 140–154.

STOMMEL, H. and A. B. ARONS. (1960b) On the abyssal circulation of the world ocean. II. An idealized model of the circulation pattern and amplitude in oceanic basins. *Deep Sea Res.* **6** (3), 217–233.

SWALLOW, J. C. and L. V. WORTHINGTON. (1957) Measurements of deep currents in the western North Atlantic. *Nature* **179**, 1183–1184.

WYRTKI, K. (1961) The thermohaline circulation in relation to the general circulation in the oceans. *Deep Sea Res.* **8** (1), 39–64.

Sources of Additional Information

Dynamical Oceanography. Chapter X. PROUDMAN, J. Methuen, London. 1953.

An Introduction to Physical Oceanography, Chapter 7. VON ARX, W. S. Addison-Wesley. Reading, Mass. 1962.

CHAPTER 20

ESTUARIES

THE fresh water drained from continental areas by rivers first mixes with ocean water within distinctive physiographic features that indent the coast. These regions are of importance to civilization since seaport communities have grown up there. A distinctive community of aquatic plants and animals has also grown up in these regions and these have been intensively exploited by man as a source of food. This is a portion of the environment where there is a need for careful management if man's civilization is to avoid rendering it, by pollution, much less suitable to serve his needs. Hence considerable study has been made of the circulation patterns and mixing processes within estuaries.

These patterns and processes are complex and diverse and it is not intended to here formulate them in any detail. We will attempt merely to provide a generalized descriptive treatment of the phenomena and, by reference to a few significant papers on the subject, direct the reader to the current thinking regarding the dynamics of circulation and mixing.

The salinity distribution within estuaries gives rise to density structure similar to classical models of thermohaline circulation. It should be borne in mind, however, that the circulation is powered by the momentum of river water entering, which in turn has been imparted by the "hydraulic head". Circulation is controlled by friction between outflowing and inflowing waters, by tidal oscillations and the mixing they induce, by winds and by the boundary conditions imposed by the physical shape of the estuary.

20.1 DEFINITIONS AND CLASSIFICATION

The term estuary has been traditionally used by geographers to denote rather loosely the lower reaches of a river where tide and river flow interact. A more precise definition is desirable for the purpose of oceanographic studies where the full range of phenomena related to the mingling of ocean water with waters of different characteristics are under examination.

Probably the most useful definition to accept is that given by Cameron and Pritchard (1963), viz. "An estuary is a semi-enclosed coastal body of water having a free connection with the open sea and within which the sea-water is measurably diluted with fresh water derived from land drainage".

This eliminates from consideration those coastal inlets in which evaporation exceeds the sum precipitation and runoff. In these regions the circulation may be reasonably similar to that in estuaries although in an opposite sense. Several writers such as Pritchard (1952) have classified these as negative or inverse estuaries.

Some workers have chosen to define an estuary simply as a region within which ocean water is measurably diluted by runoff from the land. This, of course, includes large coastal regions where the controls placed upon the circulation by physical boundaries are quite different. The more restrictive definition appears more suitable for circumscribing a range of phenomena for consideration as a unit.

A number of systems for the classification of estuaries have been used. Classification may be based upon:

A. *Geomorphology*

i. *Coastal plain estuaries* are generally shallow with gently sloping bottoms, the depth of which increases more or less uniformly towards the mouth. These have been cut by erosion and, in many cases, are indeed drowned river valleys. They often display a dendritic pattern and may be fed by one or several streams.

ii. *Fjords* are characterized by relatively deep water and steep sides and generally display a minimum controlling depth near the mouth. These occur mainly in regions where glaciation has been a major factor in shaping the land.

iii. *Bar built estuaries* are regions that have been enclosed by the deposition of a sand bar off the coast through which a channel provides exchange with the open sea. These generally service rivers with low volume outflow or in which there is seasonally low volume. Such estuaries are subject to gradual, seasonal, or catastrophic variations in configuration.

B. *Dominant Control of Circulation and Mixing*

i. *River controlled estuaries* exhibit patterns of circulation and stratification that are primarily determined by the rate at which river water is being added at their head. Seasonal variations in response to the cycle of runoff will be observed.

ii. *Tide controlled estuaries* are influenced to a high degree by tide induced circulation and mixing. Variations in concert with the phases of the tide will occur.

iii. *Wind controlled estuaries* are restricted to regions of low tidal amplitude where, within a shallow estuary, wind induced circulation and mixing causes marked variation in the regime.

C. *Degree of Stratification*

i. *Highly stratified estuaries* are generally those in which river flow is the dominant agency producing circulation, and velocity shear is the main source of mixing.

ii. *Moderately stratified estuaries* occur when turbulent mixing induced by tidal motion becomes the dominant factor in determining the salt distribution. River flow may still be important in the circulation pattern.

iii. *Vertically homogeneous estuaries* result from extreme tidal mixing. Tidal motion and the horizontal variations in density control the circulation.

iv. *Fjords* require a separate category under this classification system since they generally contain a deep saline bottom layer regardless of the mixing regime that exists within the upper layers.

The river, by definition, enters the estuary at its "head". The head may be defined as that region where the surface of the river first comes to approximately sea level, or the riverward extremity of detectable admixture of salt water. Ketchum (1951) defines the "inner end" of the estuary as the section above which the volume required to raise the level of the water from low to high water is equal to the volume contributed by the river during a tidal cycle. All these are dynamic rather than geographic definitions, being subject to movement in response to changes in river flow or tidal range.

The "mouth" of the estuary is the downstream extremity where the trend of its banks merge with that of the general coastline.

20.2 Circulation and Salt Balance

If there were no friction involved the fresh water would flow seaward as a shallow layer on top of the sea water. The layer would become more shallow and the velocity less as the estuary widened towards its mouth. Because of Coriolis acceleration the fresh water would tend to hold against the right-hand bank in the Northern Hemisphere. The surface would slope upward to the right of the flow and the interface would have an opposite slope so that geostrophic balance would be maintained (Section 10.2).

Friction between the two waters requires a balancing pressure gradient down estuary. The salt water then occurs as a wedge along the bottom deepening towards the head of the estuary (Fig. 20.1). Mixing of salt and fresh water takes place between the salt wedge and the outflow. The outflow thus carries some of the sea water back towards the sea, and, for continuity in the steady state, water must flow inward in the salt wedge. The outflow from the estuary can thus have a much greater volume than the river discharge. A particularly well-defined salt wedge is observed in the estuary of the Mississippi River.

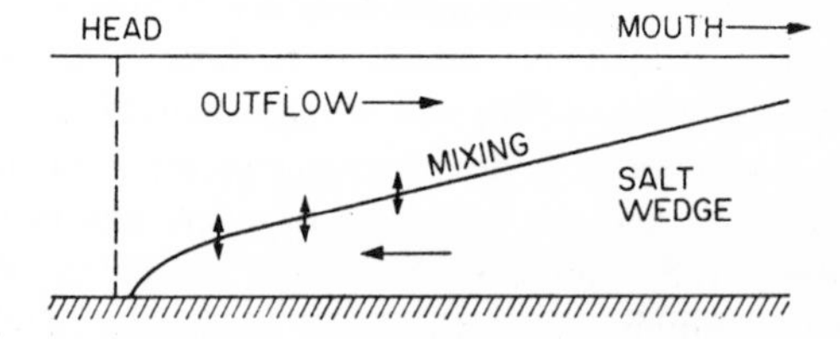

Fig. 20.1 Layered flow in a simple estuary.

In the simplest terms continuity through any cross section of the estuary can be expressed by

$$O = I + R, \tag{20.1}$$

where O is the volume rate of outflow, I the volume rate of inflow and R the discharge rate of the river.

If a salinity S_0 can be assigned to the outflow and a salinity S_i to the inflow, a crude salt balance equation can be written

$$S_0 O = S_i I. \tag{20.2}$$

Combining (20.1) and (20.2) yields

$$O = \frac{S_i}{S_i - S_0} R, \qquad (20.3)$$

from which it can be seen that, as the salinity of the outflow approaches that of the inflow, its volume becomes many times greater than the river discharge.

More precisely we should write

$$O = \oint_{\sigma_1} \int_0^{nT} U \, d\sigma \, dt, \qquad (20.4)$$

where U is the velocity directed down estuary and the surface integral is taken over that cross-sectional area σ_1 where the time-integral over a whole number of tidal cycles T is positive (Fig. 20.2).

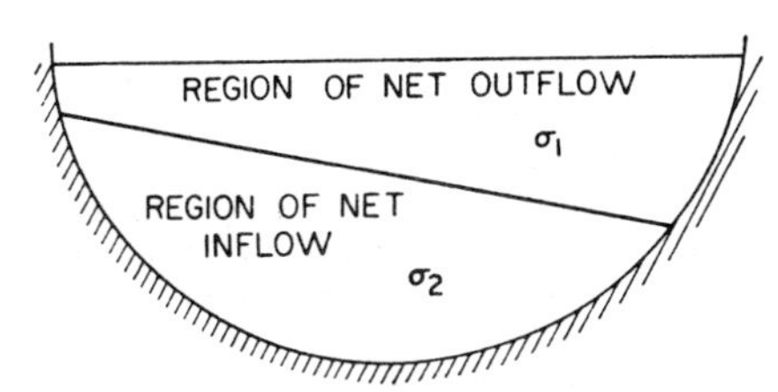

Fig. 20.2 Schematic cross section looking down estuary in the Northern Hemisphere.

Similarly

$$I = - \oint_{\sigma_2} \int_0^{nT} U \, d\sigma \, dt, \qquad (20.5)$$

where σ_2 is that part of the cross section over which the net velocity is negative or up the estuary. Similarly the salt balance could be written

$$\oint_{\sigma_1} \int_0^{nT} U \, S' \, d\sigma \, dt + \oint_{\sigma_2} \int_0^{nT} U \, S' \, d\sigma \, dt = 0, \qquad (20.6)$$

where S' is the mass of salt per unit volume rather than the mass fraction as salinity is usually measured. Pritchard (1954) gives a more rigorous treatment of the salt balance in which the vertical flux of salt (here neglected) is considered.

With certain physical configurations in the estuary, and appropriate flow regimes, the boundary between outflow and inflow (Fig. 20.2) may cut the surface somewhere in the cross section. In the lower reaches of the St. Lawrence estuary, for example, the well-defined Gaspé current holds against the southern shore and counter flow is observed along the northern side. This effect may be augmented by the tidal circulation.

Looking down estuary in the Northern Hemisphere, the back and forth tidal currents tend to be held against the left side on the flood and the right side during ebb as a consequence of Coriolis acceleration. The tidal circulation can be thought of as an in and out motion upon which is superimposed a counter-clockwise rotation. Thus, in tidal estuaries, the outflow is stronger on the right-hand side. This often is apparent from the surface salinity pattern (Fig. 20.3).

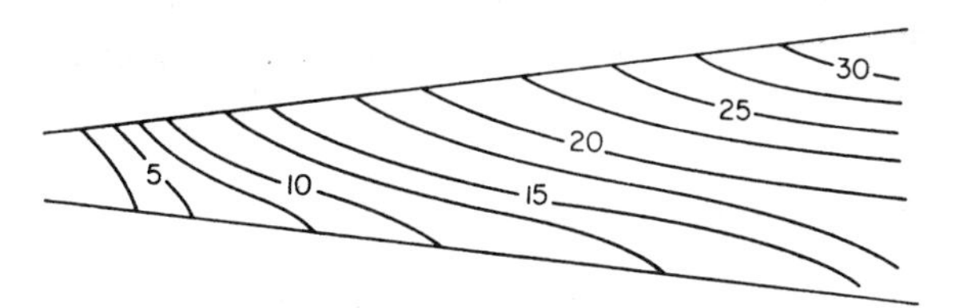

Fig. 20.3 Schematic distribution of surface salinity in a Northern Hemisphere tidal estuary.

20.3 Tidal Mixing

Besides imparting lateral asymetry to the circulation, tidal motion introduces a large amount of turbulence which leads to more effective mixing of inflowing and outflowing water. In an estuary with very little tidal action, the salt wedge proceeds up the estuary with little or no change in salinity. Mixing of salt water up into the surface layer seems to take place without much exchange in the reverse direction. With moderate tides mixing is more vigorous and works both ways, producing a boundary that is far less sharp. The salinity of both layers increases seaward and a far greater flow is required in each layer for balance (20.3). This of course introduces more velocity shear, which promotes mixing but tends to retain vertical gradients.

In the extreme, tidal mixing may produce an estuary in which the waters are homogeneous or nearly so in the vertical. An axial gradient will be observed and, in an estuary of reasonable width, lateral gradients in the sense shown in Fig. 20.3 will exist.

Vertical mixing increases the potential energy of the water column and this may be important in driving the circulation. The Bay of Fundy provides an example of vertical homogenity. McLellan (1958) estimates that of some 3.09×10^6 kW dissipated within the Bay by tidal friction 3×10^4 kW goes into the increase of potential energy by vertical mixing.

Differential flow in the vertical probably always exists though it can no longer account for the salt balance. Some of the exchange can be explained by the cross-estuary gradient coupled with the cyclonic circulation imposed by the tide. Horizontal mixing along the axis of the estuary is probably a more important mechanism, with fresh water diffusing down estuary at a rate controlled by the river flow, and salt diffusing up estuary at the appropriate rate to maintain the steady state. In relatively narrow vertically homogeneous estuaries, where lateral gradients are unobservable, this latter mechanism must completely account for the salt balance.

20.4 Flushing

Considerable study has been made of the problem of predicting the distribution of pollutants introduced into an estuary. One problem is to evaluate the steady state concentration of a pollutant introduced at a fixed rate with the river flow. Another problem is to predict the location and concentration history of a mass of pollutant introduced discontinuously into the system.

Ketchum (1951) developed a theory which attempted to predict flushing on the basis of knowledge of the configuration of the estuary and the tides. He segmented the estuary along its axis such that each segment had a length equal to the average particle excursion during flood tide. Complete mixing within the segment during the tidal cycle was assumed. On this basis the quantity of river water of any age present within a given segment could be calculated. The assumption of complete mixing is surely valid only in exceptional cases and, while a method was suggested for taking incomplete mixing into account, the problem of differential flow was not introduced.

More recent treatments by Arons and Stommel (1951), Stommel (1953), Preddy (1954), etc., are of interest. It is apparent that considerable improvement in our knowledge of the dynamics of estuaries and of the diffusion processes is required for satisfactory prediction of flushing.

References

Arons, A. B. and H. Stommel. (1951) A mixing length theory of tidal flushing. *Trans. Am. Geophys. Union* **32**, 419–421.

Cameron, W. M. and D. W. Pritchard. Estuaries. *In The Sea*, Vol. 2. Hill, M. N. (editor). Wiley, New York. Chapter 15, pp. 306–324. 1963.

Ketchum, B. H. (1951) The exchange of fresh and salt waters in tidal estuaries. *J. Mar. Res.* **10** (1), 18–38.

McLellan, H. J. (1958) Energy considerations in the Bay of Fundy system. *J. Fish. Res. Bd. Can.* **15** (2), 115–134.

Preddy, W. S. (1954) The mixing and movement of water in the estuary of the Thames. *J. Mar. Bio. Assoc. U.K.* **33**, 645–662.

Pritchard, D. W. Estuarine Hydrography. In *Advances in Geophysics*, Vol. 1. Landsberg, H. E. (editor). Academic Press, New York. pp. 243–280. 1952.

Pritchard, D. W. (1954) A study of the salt balance in a coastal plain estuary. *J. Mar. Res.* **13** (1), 133–144.

Stommel, H. (1953) Computation of pollution in a vertically mixed estuary. *Sewage and Industrial Wastes* **25**, 1065–1071.

Sources of Additional Information

Barlow, J. P. (1956) Effect of wind on salinity distribution in an estuary. *J. Mar. Res.* **15** (3), 193–203.

Maximon, L. C. and C. W. Morgan. (1955) A theory of tidal mixing in a "vertically homogeneous" estuary. *J. Mar. Res.* **14** (2), 157–175.

Pickard, G. L. and R. W. Trites. (1957) Fresh water transport determination from the heat budget with application to British Columbia inlets. *J. Fish. Res. Bd. Can.* **16**, 605–616.

Pritchard, D. W. (1955) Estuarine circulation patterns. *Proc. Am. Soc. Civ. Eng.* **81**, 717/1–717/11.

Pritchard, D. W. (1956) The dynamic structure of a coastal plain estuary. *J. Mar. Res.* **15** (1), 33–42.

Pritchard, D. W. (1958) The equations of mass continuity and salt continuity in estuaries. *J. Mar. Res.* **17**, 412–423.

Tully, J. P. (1949) Oceanography and prediction of pulp mill pollution in Alberni Inlet. *Bull. Fish. Res. Bd. Can.* **83**, 169 pp.

INDEX